Front cover
Photograph:
Pandora De Pledge Image Works
www.pandoradepledge.com
Cover Model:
Richard O ' Brien
Make-up, hair & styling:
Pandora De Pledge

Editor: Vicky Lee
Vicky's PA: Marion
DTP: Vicky Lee and Karen
Photo prep:
Rob and Jamie at Image Works
Research & editing: Karen
Advertising sales:
Sue Mills at Planet Advertising
Printing and Binding:
Stones the Printer
Distribution:
DBS & Turnaround & SCB
Published By:

WayOut Publishing Co Ltd
P.O. Box 70,
Enfield
EN1 2AE
United Kingdom

24 hr Info / Message line:
0208 363 0948
Fax:
0208 366 0517
Vicky Lee Direct:
07778 157290 10am - 10pm
E-mail:
vicky@wayout-publishing.com
Web Site:
www.wayout-publishing.com

*This book is dedicated to a brave
young man who is such an
inspiritation to me and my family
Jamie Green we love you VERY
much... Here's to a better year
this year xxx*

WayOut
The WayOut Guide

Intro

**PERSONAL
PROFILES**

Personal
Reports
&
The Listings

Books
and mags
...reviewed

315

Photo Hair & Make-up: Pandora De Pledge Image Works.

1

This book has become the world's most detailed and comprehensive guide to the cross-dressing scene.

It aims to provide newcomers to cross-dressing an overview and regular readers new ideas and inspiration. So that whether you are a participant, or an onlooker, you will have a greater awareness and understanding of the hows, whys and wherefores.

"The Guide is for everyone not just trannies"

A diverse and growing range of people find the subject fascinating. Students of sociology and psychology will find the contents useful. Transgender studies is a frequent subject on the curriculum for a number of courses. The media are continually referring to the Tranny Guide whilst researching articles and programmes.

One particular group of readers who are particularly welcomed to the Guide are the wives and partners of cross-dressers. You may be struggling to understand partner's feelings and desires. Other more experienced partners may be looking for new ways to enjoy the scene.

Vicky Lee

The Pictures

Every year over 1000 pictures are replaced with new ones from a wide range of contributors and every year the pictures just get better and better.

The guide within The Guide

Whether you cross-dress yourself, or want to know more about those that do, this book is packed with tips.

"Newcomers to the Tranny Guide have said the advice is invaluable"

The book covers every aspect, from buying clothes, to stepping out, including the minefield of sexual options within the TG scene. It has evolved through every edition and has been updated and added to every year. Some excellent sections have been dropped to make space for new. These articles are still VERY useful and can be found in the back issues.

If you have read previous editions, there are many new areas of advice and updates and NEW unique personal 'PROFILES', since you last read it. You have changed too, now with new needs, and new experiences to reflect on. You will find advice and general information that you overlooked before. If you find the advice well founded, consider getting the back issues.

The Adverts, Listings and Reports

Through these the Tranny Guide offers a choice of ways to get the best from the scene, whilst at the same time aiming to provide an awareness of the scale, and diversity.

Global Personal Reports

I remember the pain of thinking I was the only person in the world inflicted with the thoughts that I had. When I found there were many more in London I felt better. I then thought that London was the only place with so many people struggling with cross-dressing. When I found that there were people in every area in the world - I was amazed and I thought 'so many people can't be bad ... Can't be 'wrong'.

As I have received reports year by year they have become more positive more confident more full of joy. And there has become many more of them. It is hoped that knowledge of the sheer magnitude of the global cross-dressing community will help YOU feel more at ease with your (or others') feelings, even if you are not able to travel and explore yourselves.

"aiming to provide an awareness of the scale, and diversity"

In early editions we attempted to list every shoe shop, or cabaret bar etc. wherever we could find them world-wide. But now for us to cover every service would lead to a far less glossy book and would inevitably be inaccurate.

Photo Hair & Make-up: Pandora De Pledge Image Works.

It is still possible for us to check the UK listings by phone and email and for the most part they are accurate for the year (April to April)

Edition 9

Edition 10

Edition 11

For the rest of the world the Tranny Guide now features Personal Reports. These reports are great to read and include amazing pictures. In these we try to provide a good contact that we are confident about like a shop, bar, or support group in each area who can give you the latest local news. None of these reports are more than one year old.

Edition 7

Edition 8

Previous editions have featured many reports that have not been repeated (unless they have been updated). Back issues are available to explore if you missed these reports.

"I am now looking for YOUR report containing enough contact details for others to follow in your footsteps plus pictures of you and your subject"

Edition 5

Edition 6

It is my aim, not only to help readers visit areas other than there own, but more importantly, to know that trannies exist in every country and many are having a good time.

Edition 3

Edition 4

Hi, my name is Samantha Foxx, I am a T-girl and live in southern California USA. I just recently finished reading the Tranny Guide it is without doubt one of the best publications I have ever had the pleasure of reading. Without It the world would be a lesser place. Once I started I could not put it down. The part of the guide I enjoy the most is all the fabulous people in the personal profiles, their comments to the various questions is very enriching and like a silk thread, weaves the transgendered community together into one very beautiful family of diversity.
Thank you Vicky Lee for the Tranny Guide, It has already helped me so much, and maybe someday I could be one of the girls featured in the personal profiles that would be a rush :)   Sincerely, Samantha

Edition 1

Edition 2

WayOut w🌐rld

How did it start?

Vicky Lee co-founded 'The Transvestites Guide to London' in 1992 together with Caroline Egerton. This slim volume with no pictures was sold from club to club from our handbags. With a few pictures advertisers and a distributor in 1995 the annual book became 'The Tranny Guide'. During that year Vicky co-founded 'The WayOut Publishing Company' and in 1997 bought the company and re-launched it as 'The WayOut Publishing Company Ltd' becoming director and editor. It was at this same time that Sue Mills of 'Planet Advertising' took on responsibility for advertising in 'The Tranny Guide'. Over the subsequent years we have developed good relationships with a "family" of regular advertisers who's businesses have grown alongside our own.

"You are the Prophet of Trannydom who came down from Stiletto Mountain in a shower of glitter to bring us commandments engraved in eyeliner"

by Benjamina 2002

(an exaggeration maybe ... but beautifully phrased)

Running in tandem from 1987 Vicky Lee met Steffan at the Kensington Roof Gardens in London. After working together on club promotions and performing together they co-founded 'The WayOut Club' which since April 1993 has provided a night out every Saturday for the most diverse mixture of people to be found in one place at one time in the world. Vicky has hardly missed a night at the club where she has enjoyed meeting thousands of trannies and their friends and families. Through the club and increasingly through the internet Vicky has met wonderful people who have become part of 'The Tranny Guide' contributing regularly pictures and reports.

In 1997/98 Vicky co-scripted and was filmed for 'The Tranny Guide for your TV' a video version of The Tranny Guide advice section. This video continues to help spread awareness and understanding, especially between family and partners.

A constant flow of calls are made to WayOut, leading Vicky to provide contacts and help to media researchers who are planning features and programs about the tranny scene. She is a regular advice writer for Forum Magazine and also contributes articles to many other magazines.

Vicky continues to draw strength to achieve what she does from a great team of talented friends especially Marion, Karen, Sue, Steffan, Pan, Rob, Jamie, Fraser, and more than ever from the support of her partner Lesley, friends and family.

Personal 'Profiles' were introduced in the 11th edition of this book after I guessed that there must be many readers that have their own story and advice to offer. I base the questions on the subjects that I have always tried to answer in my 'WayOut of the Closet' advice section. The magic came when I realised that the comparison of answers builds a wonderful understanding of individuality and diversity. I had not imagined the interactive life that these 'profiles' would breath into the book and much more

Monica writes in this edition (page 175)... "In October we were visited by three friends from England. Louise Wood, who had her profile in last year's Tranny Guide, contacted me after having read my profile to see if we could meet (This proves the usefulness of the personal profiles). And so on a dreadfully cold Friday night in October Louise, her friends Zara and Jo, with my friends Jun, Natasha and Renate and myself set out for a night in Amsterdam".

SO you will find MORE of these profiles, contributed from all around the world, throughout this edition.

Of course I would not ask anyone to answer questions that I would not answer myself - so here are my answers to the questions and for the 12th edition I have added a number of new questions.

You are invited, whether past or future profile contributors to answer these questions too. Our answers are building a strong base for future understanding and a record of our times for prosperity.

What is your name and what is your background? My name is Vicky Lee. I have a background in manufacturing engineering and DJing. My life partner and I have been together since 1973. We have always chosen not to have children we have discussed this together often and have taken counselling with 'Relate' on this subject among other things. One of the reasons has been that I am a possible confusion to children. I now have 3 close and 3 estranged nieces and nephews 3 who don't know me and 3 who love me dearly. I have tried to follow a masculine path but during this time descended into workaholic depression. I was a useless partner during this period of my life. Now is the happiest time of my life and my partners too. It has not been easy to get to this point in my life.

Personal Profile  Editor Vicky Lee

Are you happy to be called a tranny and what does this name mean to you?
I am a tranny – Tranny short for transgendered, which I believe embraces transvestites and transsexuals. I also call myself an inbetweeny I believe that if we take ownership of our labels then no one can hurt us by using them against us.

How old are you and how young can you remember thinking about or actually cross-dressing? I am 50 in 2004. From my youngest memories I can never remember NOT dressing whenever I got the opportunity. I first found the London tranny scene, (other than a few closeted Halloween parties), on a Friday afternoon at Transformation in Euston followed by a weekend at The Philbeach Hotel having never talked to a tranny or a gay person ever before.

Where do you buy clothes? I buy clothes wherever I see them. I like to design and make my own clothes. I have just lost a lot of weight and now enjoy the styles that I want to wear.

What leads you to choose the styles you wear? I am influenced by everything around me magazines, films, music videos, women on the street. The hardest thing is finding the look in the shops. Like many I am heavily influenced by fashion (its so hard to feel fashionable in skirts over the last few years). I loved the late 80's opaque tights short skirts and comfy boots look but could never go out in that look now.

Do you have one look or many images? I do have a look. My partner will say of something in a shop or magazine "that's very Vicky Lee". I have tried things that really don't work for me that's for sure. I have played with pvc and leather in my character costumes but can say for sure that I don't have a fetish for any style or material.

Is make-up and hair important to you and if so how do you achieve your look? Madam Jo Jo once told me make sure your face and hair are the best they can be - most people don't look down if they like what they see. My own hair is long I wear a hair-piece bonded to my scalp, all of the time, to fill the gaps. My make up can take an hour but I have done my full stage make-up in 10 minutes. I have been very lucky to be able to watch the best and learn from them.

To what degree do you practice hair removal, and other body feminisation? I shave all my hair from my body every few days (except my back and upper arms, which are waxed monthly). I pluck my eyebrows every day. My ears are pierced. I moisturise and face pack whenever I allow myself time. I have my hair coloured and highlighted. My nails are always groomed and my toes are always painted (this is very important to me).

Who knows that you dress? Everyone I know - knows that I dress fully female. Local neighbours and shop owners accept that I am not male nor female but something inbetween. Many say madam even when I have made no effort - other times sir it does not bother me either

Photo with thanks to Rick & Chrissie

WayOut w🌑rld edition

way. My best male friend was the first to recognise what I was . He approached me and said "*please tell me you are a transvestite because my second option is that you have taken up night fishing*". He has always been most supportive and accepting. His partner has helped as my personal assistant for a number of years and has just had a baby. My partner's family have always treated me as the 4th sister. I am a tomboy as much as they are. My sister and mother have disowned me.

How often do you dress and if you go out where to? I am mostly in cargo pants and tee shirts. But then so are all the girls I know. I often wear something more girly when I am out for a meal with friends, meetings or a party. Saturday at The WayOut Club always fulfils girly dreams and is still after years a thrill.

How much of a sexual turn on is trannying for you? When I was young I would get an erection and masturbate after dressing. But at the same age I would masturbate at ANY time. My partner prefers to wear nothing when we are intimate and took a long time and counselling to accept my feminised body. Clothes can make me feel sexy but happiness is my only aphrodisiac.

What is your definition of feminine? feminine is the ability to embrace a game of paint ball and then to flirt in a cocktail frock and EVERYTHING inbetween. Masculine is to deny any experience, emotion, choice because it might be considered by somebody else as "girly".

To what degree do you feel gender dysphoric (i.e. that your brain is feminine)? I have allowed my brain it's full range of abilities and choices I don't think that I am gender dysphoric but others think I am feminine.

To what degree would you consider permanent hair removal, hormones, surgery? I have endured laser hair removal that proved to me that I am driven to make changes. I have breast envy and would like breast enhancement but only if my partner was happy with this. I have no desire for any other changes. However I know that if I had understood myself and had had the option I would have chosen castration at a young age.

NEW QUESTION Why did you choose your transgender name? When I was first asked for my transgender name (to sign into a hotel) I was scared of being identified and felt I could not use my given name (which IS a genderless name). I panicked for a moment and then out popped Vicky Lee. This name has been good for me and I have many strange

stories relating to it. (I tell these stories in a whole section on choosing names on page 66 in TG 7th edition). However I wish now, that I had used my (genderless) name as it would cause less confusion especially on the phone. Also family and old friends knew me first by my given name and it very hard for anyone to use a different name once programmed into the neural software.

NEW QUESTION What individual has inspired you most in relation to your TG inclinations? I set the question but I can't answer it. I am a product of so many influences I can't choose an individual. I am a tomboy who also enjoys being feminine. I have been inspired by the images and actions of women as diverse as the fluffy stars of the silver screen that I would watch as a kid on a rainy afternoon to practical women who are not restricted by gender barriers tackling all manner of activity - this I admired so immensely, believing then (and now) that most men do not allow themselves diverse freedom. Ok if pushed Katherine Hepburn, and Lara Croft (I wish) !!

NEW QUESTION Do you feel you have any choice in your TG thoughts and actions? Very definitely NOT. All of my life, when I least expect it I find myself seeing a female image or activity that triggers a deep need to share the look or the experience.

NEW QUESTION Have you tried to stop? In my teens I grew a moustache to try to stop myself dressing up. In my late twenty's I submerged myself in long hours of work allowing no time for cross dressing (or anything else including a relationship). On numerous occasions I threw away clothes only to start buying bits over again. My weight has fluctuated between 11stone and 16 stone when I am small my cross-dressing increases and at times I believe I have used my weight to try to stop my inclination. Instead it just make me cross with myself.

NEW QUESTION Are your sexual preferences changed by your TG experiences? I think, like many others, when I was first offered admiration, a drink, a compliment, a hand on the bum (and maybe more) !! by someone who is in fact was the same gender I questioned my own sexuality. I had never experienced this before and as male rarely received the same from females. I don't think my sexuality was changed it was awakened. I believe that if I had been purely hetrosexual I would have reacted differently to these opportunities and by accepting them and enjoying them I accept my bisexuality - though I have had a monogamous relationship with my female partner for over 30 years.

6 The 'portal' to everything tranny on the Internet **www.wayout-publishing.com**

Personal Profile Vicky Lee

NEW QUESTION Have you suffered illness, depression, relationship break ups because of being TG? I have had many days when I have buried myself under the bed sheets in an awful mood often preceding a night when I was expected to present myself next to a partner who would use every feminine trick to build her confidence and make her look great – while I felt lost, not knowing how to present myself and feeling invisible. I would try to overcome these feelings by using my personality to overshadow my inner feelings which resulted in a roller coaster of extreme emotions. While exploring the newly discovered TG world I felt guilt at the hours not spent with my partner who thought I was making up a fantasy world with my stories. After revealing my TG activities to my family my relationship with them spiralled into a disastrous break up. I am accused of being the cause of my father's death and I have been asked to have nothing more to do with my mother, sister and her children since the year 2000. My relationship with my partner has suffered ups and down which can be attributed mostly to my TG feelings in the background, later in the foreground. My partners struggled with the need to not have secrets with friends and family. At a later stage she further needed help to explore her own relationship with what she now fully believed to be a part female person with no turning back. Through all of this, two series of counselling with 'Relate' has been valuable and has helped us focus on our options and make decisions. Furthermore the support of many friends and family has brought both of us through to a stable and very happy period in our lives.

NEW QUESTION If you could relive your life without the TG experience would you choose to? I would never 'choose' to be estranged from my family, yet I have no other regrets at the life I have had. Being TG has not been easy but it has greatly enriched my life. I often think that if I had my life over again knowing what I know now I would have "come out" much younger. But in that case so many other wonderful things and wonderful people probably would not have been part of my life. Understanding my sexuality at a younger age may have made me vulnerable to HIV and AIDS because it was my age group that was caught out with no knowledge of the disease and were wiped out before drugs were formulated to hold the immune deficiency in check and the message of using condoms at all times was learnt.

NEW QUESTION How did you get into performing and what have you done?

With a background of shy performance playing guitar and singing and years DJing - in 1992 I started working with Steffan. When I first took to the stage to perform female mime impersonations. I found to my surprise that in "drag" I had no fear no "butterflys" After two years with 'Dragmania' I went live singing firstly in 'The Vampettes' and then with my own show 'Vicky Lee & Company' with which in one year alone I did over 180 very successful shows. In 1998 on Sky One's 'Little John Live' show, I was particularly thrilled to be able to sing live backed by a fabulous band. On a program for UK Living I sung backed by music that I made on my computer. Pressure of publishing work has not allowed time for making music or performing on the cabaret circuit for far too long - however I enjoy regularly hosting and joining in shows at The WayOut Club.

NEW QUESTION What outstanding TG experiences stand out in your mind?

I am blessed with so many - from simply feeling elated after early infrequent Friday to Sunday weekends of freedom to be me - to meeting Princess Diana at a film premier. I constantly find myself in a situation where I look around and know that I am amongst extraordinary company that I would never have come into contact with if I had not opened my mind and stepped out and then I look at what I am wearing and the feel the confidence they inspire in me and know I am not looking from outside but from within. Standing on stage receiving applause for a performance must be one of my greatest joys followed closely by the joy of seeing many others achieve the same result through our Star Search at the WayOut Club.

FINALLY AS ALWAYS What one piece of advice would you give to someone that has just found they are not the only tranny in the world? Embrace diversity. Realise there is no such thing as normal. You only have one go at life so be true to yourself while maintaining respect for others. Find a balance that is right for you and those that love you. And enjoy.

You may not start at the beginning ...
You may not get to the end ...
You can get off ...
You can get back on ...
You can go forwards ...
You can go backwards ....
But- IF you have a ticket ...
You will always be on the

Tranny Journey.

First written by Vicky Lee in 1996 ...
... Revised in 2004

Without apology I reprint this article once again as I consider it the most important piece of writing I have made. As a new reader the answers are here. As a regular reader you should re-read this, as I do, each year. It always has a new meaning as our lives evolve. Now with the 'profiles', from those that surround this article, you can see how they fit into 'The Tranny Journey'... at least at this point in time.

I strongly believe that there are no two people with the same life story, but based on the books and surveys that I have read, plus hundreds, maybe thousands of casual conversations and other personal experiences, I believe, for most, cross-dressing has a common pattern. (This article is written male to female but please remember that female to male experiences are very similar).

First steps

The first question at the birth of a child - Is it a boy or a girl?. The average tranny has memories that go back deep into childhood, when they first identify themselves as to some degree 'feminine'. At the youngest of ages, boys are encouraged to reject any signs of femininity as being inappropriate for their "gender", with constant reinforcements such as "Boys don't do that". However, at some point a tranny boy will accept the urge to try on female clothes. It is unlikely that the child will understand what he is doing but it will be the first choice given the opportunity. The tranny boy will already know that 'girly-dressing-up' is the biggest taboo, he knows it is sociably unacceptable. It is therefore unlikely that he will talk about his feelings to even the most open of parents. Such feelings become 'secret thoughts' which he will struggle to hide throughout his life. This is SO different to the the young boy that confidently wears a nurses uniform one day and a cowboy outfit the next as - this is play without fear and guilt.

Puberty

With the onset of puberty comes a set of changes. Body hair begins to grow and the voice begins to change. Up to that point, the tranny boy had a soft smooth body, like the females that he secretly identified with. His genitals begin to cry out for attention, and the penis stiffens at the most embarrassing of times. Whilst many boys masturbate with images of others in mind, a tranny boy may have his 'fantasy girl' with him in the mirror. At puberty the tranny boy watches in wonder and envy, as girls of his own age blossom, their bodies become more graceful and they are encouraged to try every feminine beauty product, clothing and accessory. At this time he can feel very confused and mourn the loss of his pre pubescent femininity. At this age it is reinforced to most boys that their role in life is to work and support a family, to compete, win, achieve and prove this with a string of material acquisitions. Meanwhile, the girls seem to be offered an alternative choice of careers and lifestyles. Choice is appears is for women. Typically at this age the adolescent tranny puts his secret thoughts aside and gets on with 'the done thing'. The tranny boy is keen to fit in and prove to himself that he can control his secret thoughts. Often the tranny is very successful in relationships with girls, preferring their company, having more interests in common than most other boys. Many trannies marry young and have children. Many trannies play physical sports, get tattoos grow beards. At this point many have never considered their sexuality as their love for the feminine has always been assumed to be a love of females. In many cases the tranny has no positive male self image, expressing himself rather through possessions, what he does and through his female partner, who he is likely to encourage to make the most of herself.

The pressure pot

Typically by the age of 30 a tranny has accumulated a mortgage, sometimes even a second wife, children, and various material possessions. Typically he works hard, often compensating for the secret thoughts that never go away by proving himself in traditional masculine ways. He may reinforce his masculinity join the army, engage in sport, get tattoos. Many trannies will express their creativity through art, music, or their choice of acquisitions. At this age, work, home and family can become a routine, which on reflection may appear to be an excuse for a life. Years can feel to have slipped by on auto-pilot, with someone else programming the course? Through these years many occasions will arise that frustrate tranny feelings - while his partner chooses an outfit and spends hours getting ready, to then be showered with compliments for her grooming and style, he feels invisible confused, angry. This I call 'the pressure pot'. All of this time the need for cross-dressing is like a beach ball that the tranny is trying to keep under the water while standing in a swimming pool. Have you ever tried to do that? It's impossible isn't it? And if you *can* manage to hold it down for a while it pops right up when you lose concentration right? Keeping it down under that water also wears you out and in the end you just have to let it go. Cross-Dressing is like that beach ball. The tranny is repressing strong feelings, which he has not allowed himself to express. This pressure pot can, I believe, lead to depression, aggression and even violence or suicide.

Relief

Typically over these years a tranny will acquire clothes and spend fleeting moments 'dressed'. He may turn to magazines, books or the internet. He may use specialist services to recreate his version of a special event. During these brief periods of time, everything else in the world is put on hold like 'freeze frame'. The tranny experiences a flood of mixed emotions, adrenaline, excitement , happiness, orgasm - guilt.

Stepping out

It is a giant step for any tranny to present their female image to another in a public situation. Once this step has been taken and acceptance gained, a vast number of opportunities for further experiences arise. Typically the tranny will at this point play a role, affecting mannerisms and conversation, which he feels match his 'femme' image. Extended periods of time in this new role eventually bring racing adrenaline and heart beat under control. Feelings of relaxation and relief can flood the body and mind, indeed exhilaration can follow. However after time and many excursions, the tranny develops a more rounded, less affected alter ego. This can be a very satisfying and happy time for a tranny, but how often can he experience this joy? Once a year? Once a month? Once a week? There is no doubt there are risks in stepping out, none bigger than the fact that the tranny cannot get enough.

TV, TS, Gay

Most of the friendly venues providing opportunities for the tranny to 'step out' in public will bring him into contact with part time TV's, full time TV's, transsexuals as well as men and women with all types of sexuality who enjoy the company of TV's. This may be the first time such a diverse company has been personally encountered. In-bred prejudices may cause confusion until calmed. It can be an exotic and refreshing experience to find that gender and sexuality need not be a factor in accepting each other as good company. However, wearing female clothes and indeed adopting submissive female behaviour can initially put the tranny in a vulnerable position. Many people feel free to make advances to a tranny. This presents the tranny with a situation, which he does not usually meet in his every day role. It is true that some trannies so convince themselves that in their female role, they are another person - a female person - that they consider themselves to be a sexually available female. It is also true that some men prefer their 'girlfriends' to have male genitals, but would not allow themselves to have a gay encounter with another 'man'. It is unusual for any man to be 'chatted up' so this new-found flattery can certainly turn a 'girl's' head. Some trannies in this situation find it hard to handle, not knowing how to say "no" politely. These experiences bring a number of questions into the tranny mind, such as "Am I gay?", and "If I am not gay, am I transsexual?". This can be a very unhappy and confusing time for a tranny. One option at this stage is to set up two lives, two roles and to try to maintain a balance between the two. This can be very hard and stressful. Some accept themselves as 'an inbetweeny', neither totally male nor female, happy to exhibit both feminine and masculine attributes (as many modern women do). This option may take time to develop and means 'coming out' to some degree.

continued over page

Coming out

There are many tell-tale signs of tranny excursions that a typical tranny will be paranoid about, such as traces of nail varnish, hair removal and a carry-over of mannerisms. If the tranny allows this to happen, eventually he is likely to be 'out-ed' if he does not 'come out' of his own accord. Taking time out in the female role sometimes leaves absences that need to be explained to family and friends. This inevitably leads to lies. The more the tranny gets into the role, the more feminisation he wants and the more he wants to take feminine attributes into everyday relationships. The more time spent happily in the female role and the more confident the tranny gets, the more the desire to share this joy becomes, but partners, family and friends may be shattered by such news. Typically they will immediately think that the person is saying he is gay. It may be very hard for others to understand that this is not a 'sudden' and 'disasterous' change. Female partners can sometimes feel that another woman has come into the relationship, a female that she does not like and definitely does not want in her bed. This 'other' woman is taking up her partner's time (and money). If she is initially accepting she may also feel her own sexuality at question. Parents can feel that the tranny is not the son that they 'brought up' or the son that 'they desired'. They may feel. probably wrongly, guilty and responsible. Friends and work colleagues, even if accepting, may worry what their other friends will think of their own reaction. Once 'out' it must be said, relationships can suffer and take years to rebuild, if indeed they can be rebuilt. Also, some trannies who have 'come out' at work have left or lost their jobs as a consequence of their exposure. Many others have maintained successful relationships with family and friends, and these are often positively better for the acceptance of a 'whole person' with (hopefully) the best of masculine and feminine attributes.

Transsexual and Transgender

Those males that feel the presence of femininity to be so overwhelming, or to quote the well worn phrase, "feel like a woman trapped in a man's body", may well be transsexual. If help and recognition is requested from public authorities a course of counselling and medical diagnosis is necessary to confirm this "dysphoria". With the support of health and other authorities many rights can be claimed and surgery and treatments undertaken (given either the patience to wait for health authorities or the funds to pay privately). Ultimately some will take steps including possibly counselling, hormones, voice training, electrolysis, plastic surgery, breast augmentation and genital reassignment surgery to change their bodies to match their own self image. There are others who don't consult authorities - "don't ask permission". It is perfectly possible to live a life as a woman without resorting to hormones or surgery and many people throughout the world choose a full or part time 'transgendered' lifestyle. Some take the steps of electrolysis, and even breast surgery to assist living in this lifestyle. For those exchanging gender role, full or part time, success and happiness depends more than anything on the development of relationships, accomodation and a career that supports this lifestyle. It is a fact, however, that most transgendered people will always be aware of their trans status knowing that they are not a man or woman but something else and will always fear being 'out-ed' as such (if only by an "all seeing" child to a parent or an un-educated youth showing off to friends in public).

Transgendered or Fetish

Cross-dressing has been with us throughout history, but it has become more visible to the public since the 50's. This has caused a confusion that this phenomena is a male escape to an iconic female lifestyle of the 50's and a fetish for the clothes of the era . However over 10 years I have seen trannies leave behind the stereotypical stockings and suspenders and even skirts to follow new generations fashion. The new generation of tranny aspires to look and live as modern women do. Sure some items of clothing, styles, fabrics, are considered sexy, (a turn on) and these clothes have their place in everybody's lives. We just get fewer opportunities to use them and therefore sometimes choose them at inappropriate times.

The New Generation

Increasing openness, better education and the internet is offering the latest generation wider options. Cross-dressing, transvestism, transsexuality and transgenderism are better understood and less of a taboo now, (along with previous taboo's like one-parent families, homosexuality, etc). However there are still those pockets of society, that are so entrenched in nurturing their gender-role stereotypes and images, that even the latest generation will identify with the journey described here, long into the future. Some, long gone, great civilisations revered transgendered people. In the future the world may learn to value again those of us who can feel and use the male and female mix within us. It is through our actions and conduct that we can help make that happen.

Recent years has seen considerable lobbying of government to give rights to transsexuals. These efforts are at last, to a degree, achieving positive change and better lives for Transsexuals. However this greater acceptance must equally be attributed to the growing list of positive transsexual role models. These people deserve, along with the political campaigners, our greatest thanks for this progress.

However at the transvestite end of the transgender spectrum we have very few positive public role models. Until non transsexual transgendered people step forward and find opportunities to gain the empathy of the greater public both transvestites and those transsexuals mistaken for transvestites will in practice, continue to struggle to receive the respect, safety and rights due any human being - and indeed the rights in law accorded to gays and transsexuals.

Transvestite ROLE MODELS

In this edition I feature three "Transvestite Role Models" that insist on acceptance and begin to change public preconceptions. Although all are controversial even within the tranny community they too deserve our support and thanks.

 THE SUN Monday 8th December 2003 Beside a picture titled "Head Turner… Perry with daughter Florence (11), and wife Phillipa last night" The editorial said: A cross-dressing potter, married, 'Grayson Perry,' won art's controversial £20K Turner Prize last night. The paper quoted the winner (under the title "Cross-dresser dad wins the Turner Prize") to have said: "It's about time a transvestite potter won the Turner Prize! … I think the art world had more trouble with the idea of me being a potter than a cross-dresser"

THE INDEPENDENT Monday 8th December 2003 Arts Correspondent Louise Jury wrote: "An artist who turns giant ceramic pots into objects of cutting-edge art was the surprise winner of this year's £20k Turner Prize last night. The most prestigious and controversial honour in British art went to Grayson Perry, 43, a family man who appeared at the award ceremony as his transvestite alter ego, Claire. With the ceremony shown live on Channel 4 he thanked his wife, Philippa, a psychotherapist, for supporting his work. His art on glazed vases explores his personal journey portraying alter ego Claire unhappy in childhood and brings his personal story up to date by featuring his current life as a happily married man. His daughter, Florence, also appears in a series of photographs which form part of his Turner Prize exhibit."

Despite the positive images of winner, family man, wife and daughter - many of my friends and family expressed an unease with the "little girl" outfits confusing the public understanding of what they know as transvestism. This truly is a complicated issue it is evident that being a role model courts many levels of controversy.

EDDIE IZZARD

SEXIE

LIVE

15

DVD

In an interview with Eddie Izzard for 'The Times' Newspaper Sharon Krum reveals the transvestite "Profile" of our hero in a new depth. In answer to questions that you yourself may have answered in our 'Personal Profiles'. Sharon quotes Eddie as saying.....

(Our Profile question - How much of a sexual turn on is trannying for you?)

"My sexuality is straight transvestite or male lesbian," he says, explaining that he has thought carefully about the terminology he uses. "It seems that we are beyond the idea I am gay and hiding it."

He is simply, he insists, a straight man who likes dressing as a woman but is simultaneously wildly attracted to them. "If I had to describe how I feel in my head, I'd say I'm a complete boy plus half a girl.

(Our Profile question - What is your definition of feminine?)

"I don't seem to have the sixth sense that women have or their stronger senses of taste and smell. Gay men can also have it but straight men don't."

(Our Profile question - To what degree do you feel gender dysphoric?)

I have the fun, sexy let's-go-dress-up part of being a woman in me but not the rest.

(Our Profile question - Do you have one look or many images? What leads you to choose the styles you wear?)

"I used to buy off the peg" he says of his stage wardrobe. I had been looking for a designer for some time to really perfect the look I was going for". Which is? "Action transvestite. Somewhat military, somewhat action girl; Lara Croft by way of Marlon Brando in The Wild One. "I don't do drag" he says, emphatically. "Drag is about glamour, pearls, wigs, sequins and that's not where I am. What I'm doing is much more designer"

(Our Profile question - To what degree would you consider permanent hair removal, hormones, surgery?)

"I definitely have beast-envy. When teenage girls were saying, I wish I had breasts, I was thinking the same thing. ...The prospect of securing a permanent pair via sex change once contemplated, has now been abandoned ... I did consider, it but I am not going to do it because I think I would look like a boy who had changed sex. If I looked more girlie I might have already done it. Besides, I fancy women so changing sex would mean becoming lesbian."

(Our Profile question - How often do you dress and if you go out where to?)

"What I want people to understand is this isn't an act. This is an intrinsic part of who I am. I wear girlie stuff on the street, not just on stage.

(Our Profile question - Is make-up and hair important to you and if so how do you achieve your look?)

"I can go from blokey to girlie in 15 minutes and then I'm out the door," he says of his metamorphosis from blue jeans to blue skirt." But that's the fastest I can do.

Becoming a woman takes work."

(Our Profile question -What one piece of advice would you give to someone that has just found they are not the only tranny in the world?)

More than a few women have come on to Eddie and he admits he has thought much about why. "Well, you could say I have fame and maybe they hate all the make-up and clothes are just into the fame thing – but it doesn't add up. I think women are really positive on it because the place that I am trying to come at is the place where girl meets boy."

Watch Eddie's latest video to see him reveal his breast envy and try to explain the falsies. Once again the friends and family cut in ... I "OK with the man in a frock. OK he is a bluddy good bloke (they mean bluddy good entertainer). Clothing rights yea Eddie OK but what's with the falsies if your not being a woman" There they go putting controversially the transvetites greatest ambassador into a very narrow box. I meanwhile re-adjust my bra and wonder despite their love and support what they really think of me.

Quotes from an article first published in The Times Newspaper Body and Soul December 6th by Sharon Krum

A flyer promoting M.A.C. Make-Up

WORKING WITH OUR COVER MODEL

14

MY DAY WITH RICHARD O'BRIEN

by Pandora De Pledge

Richard and I had only met a couple of times socially so I was looking forward to spending a day with the legendary character behind the Rocky Horror Show, host of The Crystal Maze and character actor in too many movies to mention. He has played alongside the likes of Angelica Houston, Susan Sarandon, Timothy Dalton, Max Von Sydow and Drew Barrymore to name only a few and has recently appeared as the child catcher in Chitty Chitty Bang Bang.

Richard arrived wearing this outfit (without the wig and makeup). Many people would have jumped to the conclusion 'dress' - isn't it amazing how hung up people get over the omission of two extra seams!

After refreshments and nibbles we had a chat about what we were going to do with the shoot and both felt anything too 'drag' really wasn't right. Instead we decided that showing the beauty of Richard's feminine side was the way to go. Richard is a person who not only accepts his feminine side but embraces it as a source of strength pointing out that, "If more men were to be allowed by society, their families and partners to dress and express, they would be better, happier, people for all concerned." Richard also made the point that there are many forms of "drag" such as dressing in uniforms, (Police, Military and Nursing for example). Such people are often driven, partly by the garments worn, to express a facet of their personality and to be who they wish to be. I found this fascinating because my dear friend Steffan Whitfield often says, "We are all born naked, everything after that is drag."

"If more men were to be allowed by society, their families and partners to dress and express, they would be better, happier people for all concerned."

We chose a varied selection of clothes and accessories for the shoot and then began the make-up. It's no secret that Richard is 61 years old but he has the skin of a person at least 20 years younger and beautiful clear blue eyes that sparkle like a naughty child.

When I showed Richard his completed make-up and hair I was very flattered to be told, "I think this is the best I've looked.... EVER !"

I couldn't help thinking that 'she' looked rather like Alana Stewart (Rod Stewart's ex-wife) when a moment later Richard exclaimed, "I look a little like a rock star's ex-wife!" Luckily not Courtney Love!

As we began shooting various images it was interesting to note that Richard was only uncomfortable with the image that required padded hips and bottom and rather obvious boobs, (we were going for a kind of Veronica Lake sort of thing - shown here with red background). Richard felt it was too "unnatural", something I could well relate to, because during my own personal journey I have never used fake boobs, etc because they served almost as a reminder of what I didn't have.

Shooting over and safely back at my home we shared a drink and generally chatted about anything and nothing. This part of the day was off the record but ... I was left feeling that here was a person who was a strong individual who had seen and experienced a great deal, some very good, some very bad. An individual who has great empathy for people in the TG community because they too have suffered the prejudice of others, simply for "not quite being the same as everybody else".

Well thank God, because without those differences Richard O'Brien would not be the gentle, cultured and funny person we all know and love. For all the good work you do and our day together, I thank you.

Vive le difference !

Photo Hair & Make-up: Pandora De Pledge Image Works.

TV Role Models continued

Let me sum up this feature by saying that of our three role models - I feel that Richard has possibly done more than any other to inspire a gentle respect for the "sweet transvestite" that resides to a degree in most of us.

Despite years of maintaining an instantly recognisable, highly stylised personal appearance - these pictures are the first pictures of Richard that explore the feminine almost at the risk of losing the person himself behind a facade. This is an aspect that I know Richard was intensely aware of. As Pandora reported, Richard was not comfortable with the curve producing padding as it was "not natural" but enjoyed the make-up and results for a temporary excursion. Richard said "this is the best I have ever looked" indeed I feel he said this in acceptance of the duality. the possibility, the intensity that can be part of the transvestite experience.

What is it that sets Richard as my most acceptable TV Role Model ? How is it that he passes with flying colours my friends and family test ?

I believe it is the fact that he is a "real person", a family man who can inspire true humanity in the consideration of "real" issues like the quality of life of a terminally ill child. But he can do this without diminishing his fierce pride in individualism, his impeccable personal style, his support of trangendered people, his outreach to young people.

He is "the man that put fishnets into halloween". Millions of people have watched and loved his film. To some degree, whether on the Crystal Maze, or a Charity Gig, Richard is Frankenfurter the pied piper that lures us to explore the possibility of androgeny, bisexuality and freedom of thought with a wink, a tongue in cheek smile and a song.

In a sentence Richard is a role model not only for transvestites but to people in general. He tells us " Don't dream it - be it" and reminds us "Time is fleeting".

Richard O'Brien's
Transfandango Charity
Halloween Ball
30th October 2004
London Marriott Hotel,
Grosvenor Square, W1

www.transfandango.co.uk

See pages 190-191 of this Edition for pictures of Transfandango 2003 and details of Transfandango 2004

A picture of Richard as a fairy from this photo-shoot became the iconic picture used for the publicity and event program for the Charity event and the cover of Utterly Fabulous magazine issue 4.

This picture from the shoot is available as a personally autographed 8x10 glossy print and sold with all proceeds going to the charity. To order your copy contact

Wallness Children's Charity
Sorrel Bank House,
25 Bolton Rd,
Pendelton,
Salford
M6 7HL

telephone
0161 737 1203 / 2929
Reg Charity 518086

www.wallnesscare4free.net

Photo Hair & Make-up: Pandora De Pledge Image Works.

WayOut w🌐rld edition

Vicky & Steffan Hi,
I said it at the time but now I am home I have to say it again. Many many thanks for helping make my first night at the club and first night OUT a wonderful occasion. Once I got through the doors and settled down a bit I thoroughly enjoyed my time with you all, 'twas great! Many thanks too to Sarah Lloyd, A-for the great make-over and B-for really helping to put me at my ease with her relaxed and chatty manner. It was really nice to meet you both having seen your articles and pictures in THE guide AND to spend time with and get to know you and so many other friendly and open people a little. Strange too 'cos in some way I felt I had known you all for a lot longer. I look forward to getting back up there again ASAP. Till later Kathy L   xxx

Hiya Vicky, Steffan and Sarah!
Just thought I'd drop you a line to tell you how incredible that night was!
It was totally amazing, Sarah did a wonderful job with my makeup and when I saw it in the mirror, it was like a bright floodlight suddenly turned on in my head, I had never been so happy, EVER. What surprised me more than anything was that I wasn't nervous at all not even a tiny bit :)
However when I had to take the makeup off again - it was like the bright light was turned off again.
Thanks to you all for making my first steps out as Lisa so rewarding!   Lisa XX

Dear Vicky & Steffan,
Thank you for the beautiful time yesterday night in The WayOut Club. The Cabaret show was really one of the highlights. I love the WayOut Club very much but unfortunately I can't be there very often. I'm living in Germany and I'm married, therefore I can only come once a year to stay in London for a weekend.   It was a memorable Weekend for me because first time in my life I took the Underground fully dressed as a Girl. All the previous visits I have used the change facility in WayOut Club.   Half past nine I enter the Club. There was unbelievable moments and I'm happy that the WayOut Club opened me to the new world of experience full of emotions. The night was great full of dancing good to relax except for the feet in high heels.   The best news was your announcement to open a new club for Friday nights. That will double for me the opportunity to be a girl.
In love Gigi

You will find much more detail about The WayOut Club, The WayOut Wine Bar

The Tranny Guide has a symbiotic union with

The WayOut Club

Steffan and myself (Vicky Lee) founded the club with a fusion of creativity and organisational skills, a joint joy in performing, a strong love of diversity and a deep personal friendship.

We have hardly missed a Saturday, in over eleven years since April 93. The club has been at 9 Crosswall (off Minories) London EC3 for over 7 years EVERY SATURDAY.

The publishing company provides the club with a mailing list, and all the publicity services.

The club provides the Tranny Guide with a host of contacts and photo opportunities.

Every week Steffan directs a different show using home grown talent from the clubs, end of the month, 'star search' nights. Alternativly Vicky arranges events like 'The Drag Olympics' and 'Miss Alternative London'. Two Djs mix diva dance remixes with the latest and classic euphoric house. Every week the club sees 200-300 people from all over the planet. This crowd is the most diverse crowd possibly regularly in one place, at one time, in the world. Every race, age, sexuality, gender. Steffan and Vicky encourage a balance of first out and always out. Girls that are part time, full time and (if you've got the time). The club attracts a regular bevy of Londons most beautiful transsexuals and she-males. The WayOut Club has always welcomed tranny admirers and many trannies bring family and close friends. On first glance the club looks like any straight club with an even mix of girls and boys until you start spotting the "inbetweenies". Most report it to be "spirituay uplifting" and "the best of it's kind in the world". Many long term transsexuals say that the club is a relaxing night out a return to their roots. The club has a loyal following of regulars both local and international and a growing 'family' of celebrity friends. All of this is a heady mix and in recent years, the club, though busier than ever, has lost some of the 'girls' who find the night a little awesome. I can understand this I felt the same about the 'Kinky Gerlinky nights' which were amazing (but alas no more). SO NOW to celebrate the 10th year of WayOut the return of ...

The WayOut Wine Bar

This year Steffan and I re-launch our original concept, born in a time when everyone was finding their feet.

We are offering a basement wine bar plus a ground floor restaurant and bar just for trannies and respectful friends. This is a unique NEW opportunity in London EVERY FRIDAY.

This is NOT in Crosswall at The WayOut Club but at a separate much smaller venue (just a few minutes away) in Lovatt Lane (off Eastcheap near Monument tube station) London EC3

The NEW WayOut Wine Bar started in easter 2004. Like the original, the location is in a discreet position with easy parking. There is changing space available and secure cloakroom. This is a slower paced evening with a background of classic commercial pop. Its the perfect place for those that prefer to talk and to chat with other "like minded trannies" without unwanted attention from single males, though invited guests, male and female, are all welcome. The venue has a small basement dance floor but music does not impose on an intimate opportunity to meet and mingle. The ground floor is the "comfort zone" with plenty of seating. An optional menu of snacks and full meals are available. (Three course meals from £18.95).

You will find much more detail about The WayOut Club, The WayOut Wine Bar
& The WayOut Restaurant in the London section at the back of this book ... or ...
www.thewayoutclub.com

All Photos with thanks to Nikki
Top Right - Last years winner Miss Regine with the very popular 2003/2004 winner Miss Rositta
Lower Right - 2003/2004 Miss Gisselle (who won 1st & 2nd best costume winner)

WayOut w🌐rld edition

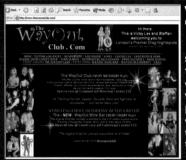

www.thewayoutclub.com

There are many liberal minded people visiting London from the UK and overseas plus regular clubbers who "expect" to see trannies in night-clubs. This is why we started a web site as the clubs glossy brochure.

You will find more help to plan your visit to the club along with unique behind the scenes information about the club at www.wayout-publishing.com

However when you want to show your family and friends where you go on your Saturday nights out, (and to encourage them to join you), this sexy confident site is the one to show them.

www.transfandango.co.uk

We are very pleased, for the third year, to help Richard O'Brien and the Wallness Children's Charity to plan the Transfandango events that have to date raised £60,000 for Manchester Children's Hospital. (Next event 30th October 2004 Transfandango Halloween Ball to be held in London).

We help maintain this independent site as the hub of the events internet network. It is kept up to date with all the details of the next event, venue, places to stay, running order, sponsors. Booking contacts as well as history and pictures of previous events.

www.wayout-publishing.com

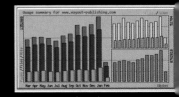

Visits from all over the world to our web site have continued to steadily rise month by month peaking at an all time high in January 2004 with over 1,600,000 hits. That is approximately 70,000 visitors every month. The Links, Shopping Mall and News are some of the most popular pages visited and an amazing number of visitors have been downloading Utterly FABULOUS magazine in PDF format.

1 - WayOut Products - Of course this section introduces new visitors to 'The Tranny Guide'. But I constantly introduce to this section new third party books, videos CDs and CDroms. I now stock a wider range of Girl Talk magazines as all back issues are collectible. These are available direct from WayOut by mail order with a cheque or postal order. But easier still through a secure on line shop run in association with 'Worldpay' who safely take care of the credit card details.

2 - WayOut News - This is NOT just news from the WayOut Club but contains news from a diverse range of sources. This section offers the opportunity to pick up the latest news and also is an opportunity to post your news just send your news in an email and attach some pictures.)

3 - The WayOut Club - This is where you will find unique background stories and all the "inside" tranny help to plan your visit to The WayOut Club. Every question is answered, Where to get help with make-up, what to expect at the club, where to park, how to enter contests, what the gossip is! It also has the weekly diary, plus the history of the club and our events.

4 - Picture Galleries - With over 250 visitors weekly at The WayOut Club and correspondents all around the world there is a constant flow of amazing pictures offered to add to these pages and this is an area that you can expect to watch grow in the future.

5 - WayOut Chat - Now with picture profiles and (for members) video chat rooms this may be the nearest you can get to sharing your feelings with others one to one and face to face.

6 - Articles on line - Early editions of the Tranny Guide have some excellent articles that have not been repeated. In this section of the site some of the best are reproduced. This is the next section to have an overhaul and many extra articles.

7 - Shopping Mall - Our virtual tranny shopping street allows you to 'nip' in and out of a growing number of shops, services and places to go.

8 - Links - Our heaviest hit page is our network of links. We split this into 'Super Resource Sites' which have more great links or good information, 'UK home pages' and 'International home pages' that contain personal pictures, stories and discussion. We even link to a few very sexy sites.

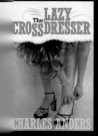

25

Where do you buy clothes?

Retail therapy is my major weakness. I find myself buying far too frequently, typically in Selfridges and Episode but also from High Street outlets where you can get some fabulous stuff. (tip: book a personal shopping appointment at a decent-sized department store - being open with them is a great way to try and buy clothes).

What leads you to choose the styles you wear?

Magazines (I'm addicted to most of the glossies) and what I see on girls of my age group (spend lots of time people watching). I generally look to buy directionally and to fit in with what to wear this season.

Do you have one look or many images?

The look in these shots is the one I've developed. Think high maintenance blonde: all designer labels, full-head highlights, salon manicures and perfect make-up but I do love to experiment with hair and make-up.

Is make-up and hair important to you and if so how do you achieve your look?

It's critical - getting the hair/make-up right will make or break you. My own look has been developed from professional advice/tuition, being open to ideas around what will/won't work - I didn't plan to be a blonde - the right products and lots of practice.

To what degree do you practice hair removal, and other body feminisation?

I'm lucky to have fairly light hair growth and a

What is your name and what is your background?

Kate - not something I gave much thought to: it just seemed right. I grew up in NW England where I still live. Typical grammar school to university education. I have a management position in the public sector. Currently single...but would hope that changes as I do.

How old are you and how young can you remember thinking about or actually cross-dressing?

Early thirties. I've dressed on and off since childhood. Think that when I was a 7 year old, locked in the bathroom whilst grandmother was babysitting, mum's dresses/shoes too big and wishing, even then, that she bought a better quality of lippy!

Photo Hair & Make-up: Pandora De Pledge Image Works. www.pandoradepledge.com

combination of shaving/waxing has meant I've been largely free of body hair for over 6 months. My next step will be to start electrolysis/laser treatment to keep me this way. I also have regular manicures and will nearly always have nail extensions if I'm going out anywhere remotely special. Expensive habit but definitely worth it for the results.

Who knows that you dress?

Mum, dad, sister - they, er, found out - and a couple of (real) girlfriends I told. None of my male friends know, but it's a growing ambition to 'bump into' them in a bar and see the look on their faces.

How often do you dress and if you go out where to?

I've dressed more and more over the last year or so and now go out a couple of times a month. I'll go shopping by myself but will generally go for drinks with girlfriends, either to gay/T-friendly venues or, increasingly, to straight bars. There's a big part of me that feels 'real' for being able to do this.

How much of a sexual turn on is trannying for you?

None - but it does allow me feel like me and I do like attention from good-looking men

What is your definition of feminine?

Gosh, that's not easy as it seems - other than being able to have 50 pairs of shoes, I'll have to resort to that it's what I feel like (and it is).

To what degree do you feel gender dysphoric (i.e that your brain in feminine)?

I've always had TS-leanings but have only recently started to fully accept this. My single biggest regret is that I didn't have the confidence to do this when I was in my late teens/early twenties.

To what degree would you consider permanent hair removal, hormones, surgery?

I'm about to start permanent hair removal and hope to commence hormone treatment within 6 months . Cosmetic surgery is a very likely plan for me in the future.

What one piece of advice would you give to someone that has just found they are not the only tranny in the world?

Have the confidence to act on your feelings

WayOut
of the closet

Feminine Grooming

Shaving Your face

You may think you know how to shave your face but as a 'girl' you want it REALLY smooth and to last for a long time. Start by holding a flannel soaked in hot water firmly to the beard area to soften the hair. Take off excess wetness and apply a good layer of shaving foam and allow it to soften the hair. A blade that has been used too many times will drag and be useless on your face. Shave top to bottom with the growth of the hair first. Re-apply a thin layer of shaving foam and shave up against the growth. For the ultimate, shave one more time after smoothing on a good layer of moisturiser, again against the growth. Feel the skin with your other hand, and learn in which direction the hair grows, especially on the neck, so that final strokes are against the growth. After drying your face, always use moisturiser.

Body Hair

In this day and age a toned, hairless male body is desired by many men and women too. Despite the problem of stubble re-growth much the most popular way of keeping the body smooth is to shave. Once experienced you will never want body hair again.

So - Where do you start First run a bath, not too hot, use some nice bubble bath. Don't touch the skin for at least three minutes after getting in. The skin goose pimples at the change of temperature. After a few minutes it will soften, the pores will open and the soapy water will

soften the hairs. You will need a good triple blade razor. If you are shaving for the first time and the hair is long, the razor will clog up immediately. The secret is to keep the razor against the skin and move back and forth in short movements- under water. The back movement will unclog the blade. For the first few shaves some irritation is bound to occur. This irritation diminishes if you shave regularly. When you get into a routine every 2 - 4 days, the razor only needs to travel in one direction with nice long strokes. The easiest way to do this is by lying on your back in the water and lifting one leg at a time out of the water. Be sure to stretch and position your leg to present as flat an area as possible to the blade. Take care with the back of the ankle and the back of the knees; this is where it easy to cut your skin. On the front of the leg, point the toe to flatten the shinbone and bend the knee to present the knee as a smooth dome to the blade. Keep the leg and blade wet, and wash the blade regularly. Shaving foam is NOT required. A small amount of ordinary shampoo will help the blade cut smoothly and comfortably. Cut against the growth of the hair and use your other hand to feel for any area missed. The prickly feel of re-growth does diminish after a few months. After drying yourself, moisturise all over with a body lotion. This will stop the skin from drying out and will make you feel silky soft. All other areas of the body can be treated in the same way. One area that is much easier to shave than you might imagine, is the least feminine part (the crack and sack), if you know what I mean.

This may all sound tedious, but with practice the total routine for all areas of the body, can take as little as 15 minutes. Many girls shave legs and underarms every day or two. It really is worth it.

Waxing

Everybody has different rates of hair growth but you will probably need to repeat the waxing every four to six weeks. It is true that long term waxing actually makes hair softer. It is possible depending on the amount of hair to wax parts of the face. Epilator machines tend to break hairs off and hurt like hell. (No pain no gain!!)

Eyebrows

Tweezing is a daily chore as eyebrows seem to grow to full length overnight. Never tweeze above the brow always from below. Eyebrows can be waxed into a good shape. this should always be left to an expert. A make-up trick using a theatrical product was shown in detail in edition of the 10th Tranny Guide and is practiced by most make-up artists listed in this book.

Hands & Nails

Soft hands and well-groomed nails are sign of classic femininity. Rule number one when gardening, working on the car, wear gloves. hand cream will rapidly improve your skin and protect your nails too. Filing your nails regularly from the outside into the middle is the way to build strength and shape, Don't cut them. Painting your nails can be a special treat. Everybody's favourite colour is red but after taking it off a tell-tale stain can be hard to remove. without a remover with acetone. You will find browns or pinks don't stain. Another tip is to apply clear varnish first. False nails that use glue or sticky pads, will give you talons of any length, which can be pre-painted. Men's nails are generally wider and wider false nails are available from specialist shops or by mail order. A girly manicure by a supportive therapist can be a special treat. There are many such Beauticians listed in this book.

WayOut
of the closet
Feminine Grooming

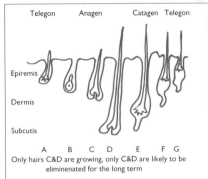

Telegon   Anagen   Catagen   Telegon

Epiremis

Dermis

Subcutis

A   B   C   D   E   F   G
Only hairs C&D are growing, only C&D are likely to be
elimineated for the long term

Long term removal of facial hair is possible using an ever growing choice of processes. Long term hair removal can also be achieved in areas of sparse body hair, but large areas of dense hair really are impractical for most people.

Undertaking ANY of these treatments can not be taken lightly. The treatment will need to be repeated many times before there is no longer significant growth and in our experience it is never totally successful, unless combined with hormone treatment.

In simple terms it must be understood that ALL treatment methods rely on quarterising, (with heat), a hair follicle in the process of growing a hair. Unless the follicle is at this stage it will grow a new hair again. On average only 10% (at best) of the bodies (or faces) hair follicles are in this growing stage at any one time. This growing stage lasts for approximately one to two weeks and then waits for four to five weeks before shedding the hair before entering a new growing stage for a new hair.

To complicate these facts every individual has a different growth length and cycle so hitting the target date for each follicle using ANY method is very much hit and miss.

"The very best expectation for 100% treatment is 10 treatments"
(i.e. 10 x 10% = 100%).

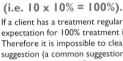

If a client has a treatment regularly every four to six weeks the very best expectation for 100% treatment is 10 treatments (i.e. 10 x 10% = 100%). Therefore it is impossible to clear a beard in five treatments and any such suggestion (a common suggestion), should be treated with suspicion. However a long term "improvement" CAN be expected – but only 50% reduction at very best.

Testosterone is firing up new follicles throughout a lifetime. Therefore without a reduction in testosterone level, even after many treatments these new hair follicles will still become a new problem and need further treatment. Female hormone treatment can (particularly before mid 30s) slow and soften hair growth and this will obviously improve the overall result and appearance.

Many correspondents have spent considerable money to find that various treatments, practitioners and processes are ineffective. My recommendation is to ask any practitioner for testimonials from clients that have at least two years experience of the treatment. A therapist working 8 hours a day will most definitely have more experience and better results than another who does a few hours between manicures and other types of treatments. Treatment prices vary widely. It can cost as much as £10,000 to completely remove the average males facial hair and there are a number of methods of treatments.

Needle Electrolysis is the most widely tried and tested. It is where a needle is put into each individual follicle heated at a precise point whist the hair is also plucked. The benefits of three different variations of this process were discussed in edition 9 of The Tranny Guide. Even a two hour electrolysis session (if you could stand it), will not get all the hairs on an average face. The hair will need to be grown to at least 5mm long for every session.

Tweezering methods have been offered as an alternative to needle electrolysis combined with sound, heat etc. etc. No long term success has been reported by any of these methods.

Light or Laser machines promise much, but the effectiveness of these machines are complicated by the relative short length of experience practitioners and clients have had with them and the fact that there are so many different machines each claimed to be reliable and the best. In general these machines will not treat white or very blonde hair. Though just to confuse things some machines claim not to suffer this limitation. None require more than a days growth before the treatment.

Vicky Lee's monthly laser treatment experience
1 - **Treatment**
2 - **Five to seven days of rough skin that is hard to shave and is hard to cover with make-up**
3 - **My wow day about 10 to 15 days after treatment.**
4 - **About two weeks of ecstasy - days of little make-up and super skin.**
5 - **In the last few days of the month some new follicle growth.**
6 - **After 2 years without treatment most of the face still completely clear of black hairs.**
   (a much larger article on my two year experience in the 10th edition Tranny Guide)

Where do you buy clothes?

Knickers etc from M&S and no one pays attention at all. Bought first pair of high heel boots from Cover Girl as a graduation present! Always shop in person at usual London outlets, Skin Two, Cobblers to the World (as was), Magic Shoe shop, Honour. Charity shops are also are great source for posh frocks, albeit a season behind! I've also had some outfits made for me by Sarah Lloyd, WayOut Door Whore.

What leads you to choose the styles you wear?

I adore glamour, big hair and makeup. This therefore leads to styles that are OTT and glamourous. On a scale of 1 to 10, a Joan Collins look would score 1 and the more make up and hair the bigger the score!

Do you have one look or many images?

Subtle understatement is my calling card! Femininity is very important, but the pure girlie look is not my style. Big face, big hair.......OTT that's Hannah. A drag queen trapped in a transvestite's body. My website has images of almost every style. The obligatory maid and school girl (don't my web fans just love these poses), bunny girl, latex, leather, Patsy from Ab Fab, Disco Diva, in short anything with maximum glamour and glitter.

Is make-up and hair important to you and if so how do you achieve your look?

VERY. I'm a make up junkie and love shopping for it. Strong make up and hair defines an image. Whilst I do my own face and hair when at home, for complete confidence and extra WOW

What is your name and what is your background?

Hannah Mannah, Harbinger of Camp. Married though my wife has no idea and would go mad if she ever discovered Hannah! Living on the outskirts of London.

Are you happy to be called a tranny and what does this name mean to you?

Yes, though I prefer the term GURL or inbetweenie. People seem to view trannys as not normal and it has a slightly seedy connection from the 60's.

How old are you and how young can you remember thinking about or actually cross-dressing?

I'm in my early forties though my website has me in my late thirties!........tsk tsk. At my first pantomime I saw men dressed as girls and it appealed. Also whenever watching Bond films I always wanted to be the girl. She got the better clothes and to wear fantastic makeup. I wore makeup and clothes in anger for the first time when at university at the usual collection of vicars/tarts, doctors/nurse theme parties. Got the biggest thrill when a girlfriend did a superb face and I was not recognised by my fellow undergraduates.

Hannah's Web Site   www.angelfire.com/tv2/hannah.mannah/index.html

Photo Hair & Make-up: Pandora De Pledge Image Works. www.pandoradepledge.com

factor when going out, a face done for me is a must. Perfect hair and makeup also boost confidence even further and get the compliments flowing!

To what degree do you practice hair removal, and other body feminisation?

Chest shaved whenever I have photo shoots but nothing else

Who knows that you dress?

No family and friends know. It would break my Mum's heart and wife would be off.

How often do you dress and if you go out where to?

Dressing goes in phases. I'd love to get out weekly but certain constraints make that impossible. Going out with groups of girls to events such as Rubber Ball or Transfandango always make for a more enjoyable time. Biggest thrill was going out twice en femme when in Australia. I knew no one, but had the confidence of a face form a professional dressing service. I made many great friends on those two nights, though occasionally shudder when I look back at what I actually did. What a buzz of adrenalin.

How much of a sexual turn on is trannying for you?

My en drab job carries a fair amount of stress. Dressing, with a 100% glamour injection (big hair and make up), is wonderful. It relieves an awful lot of stress. Hannah always has a huge smile and purrs inwardly ....unlike her alter ego. We must all be sexually turned on by dressing and equally adore adrenalin. Why else would we dress up and visit clubs or bars.

What is your definition of feminine?

A vision of beauty with perfect makeup and hair

To what degree do you feel gender dysphoric (i.e that your brain in feminine)?

Not at all.

To what degree would you consider permanent hair removal, hormones, surgery?

Never

What one piece of advice would you give to someone that has just found they are not the only tranny in the world?

The internet is a fantastic resource so use it to educate yourself and make many many good friends. DO it don't dream it

Choosing an Image

How to develop a style that suits both you and a critical public?

The very first step must be to critically consider what is possible within the constraints of your body shape and age.

At first, many appear to like to look like a street hooker which maybe ok for your mirror, your camera, the internet and some specialist venues (once you are inside the door). However on most public excursions you need to consider what is appropriate for each occasion.

Do you want to 'pass' in the local supermarket?

Current fashions dictates trousers for women on almost every occasion. To wear a skirt will make you the odd one out. However shopping in the "on the way home from work look" will work.

Do you want to make a sensational entrance at the your favourite night-club?

Trousers rule here too. Think Madonna in her 'Music' video. However this is still the place to show your legs in hot pants or a mini dresses. Larger than life super-heroes can be a star for the night and often get in for free.

Do you want to look as good as the smartest girl in the office?

The office girl look can be so sexy and maybe the image paraded in front of you every day. Nails have to be perfect as they flash across the keyboard in front of you. Skirts to keep the boss happy.

Stockings keep you fresh, (at least that's your excuse). They also drives the boys in the office mad with a flash here and there as you go about your business.

Do you want to hold court at the restaurant?

A meal with the girls is the perfect outing. Match the outfit to the style of eatery and the stage is set. Sitting in comfort in those killer heels. You can flirt from table to table.

Do you want to be the sexiest, most sophisticated, most glamourous girl in the shopping mall?

City malls attract the ladies that lunch. Heavy make-up and skirt suits don't look out of place in the better department stores.

Photo Hair & Make-up: Pandora De Pledge - Graphics by Titch for Image Works. www.pandoradepledge.com

35

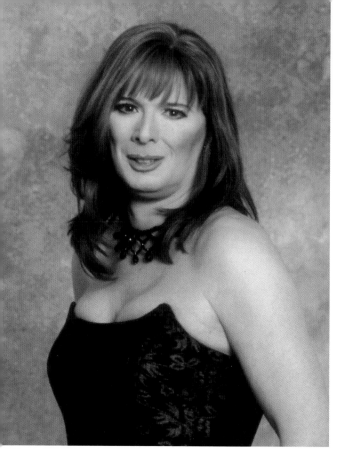

What is your name and what is your background?

My name is Jennifer Simpson.

What's the history of that name?

Jennifer is always a name I have liked and it is one of my initials. As for Simpson surname, that was just an impulse. At my first visit to Pandora's I was asked "do you have a surname". At the time I was looking at a Simpson's video and it seemed to sum up my character. However I do see myself more as Lisa than Homer or Bart. I live on the outskirts of London but do all my dressing in London as it is a secret to my family,

Are you happy to be called a tranny and what does this name mean to you?

I have to admit I do not like labels, what do they mean anyway? I am just me, that is hard enough to figure out most of the time! If people do want to label me, tranny is as good as any other term. I certainly would not take offense.

How old are you and how young can you remember thinking about or actually cross-dressing?

Well what a question to ask a girl. I am in my mid 40's but I have been told that I pass as mid 30's. So that is one good reason to start

dressing it knocks years off you. I have been dressing for nearly two years.

Where do you buy clothes?

Load of places. I love fashion so I like to try out new looks. I do not tend to Internet shop but just wander around the London shops. I have used a personal shopper once or twice and that makes things easier and you can be a bit more adventurous but in the end no one seems to mind.

What leads you to choose the styles you wear?

The source of inspiration is the fashion pages of Magazines and the papers. I have also started to surf the web fashion pages for ideas. The result is a huge number of different looks. I will try most styles and I love to try to get a realistic look for that style. One of the great things is compared to male dress there is so much variety. I have come much more conscious of how to build the total look, for example what lingerie will give the right affect for the dress and what accessories will set the whole thing of.

Is make-up and hair important to you and if so how do you achieve your look?

To me it is critical to the whole look. The right hair and make up makes the look. The eye shadow, foundation and the lipstick are part of the vital accessories to the look. Just look at the pictures you can find on the web. Girls made up to a high standard will pass in male clothes (a bit of reverse logic there) so in a sense the clothes just complete the illusion.

I have tried to do my own makeup but my makeup

Photo Hair & Make-up: Pandora De Pledge - Image Works. www.pandoradepledge.com

skills are not good enough. So I always go to a professional makeup artist I know, (Pandora). This means I get a look I want and it always looks fantastic (well I think so!)

What degree do you practice hair removal, and other body feminisation?

I do not have much body hair so I am lucky. I do not take any hormones. I am happy to create an illusion without changing who I am in the physical sense.

Who knows that you dress?

Of friends and family, no one.

How often do you dress and if you go out where to?

Not enough. I dress four to five times a year. My

domestic constraints are the main reason. I mainly go for dressing days. I try to do one or two nights out per year. For this it is the London clubs. My aim is to try them all over a period of time.

How much of a sexual turn on is trannying for you?

At the start it was a big sexual turn on. However it has become less as Jennifer has come into her own. I now like to get the look that I love and the feedback from the other girls as they appreciate the effort.

What is your definition of feminine?

A gentle illusion.

To what degree do you feel gender dysphoric (i.e that your brain in feminine)?

Not really. I do not feel that my brain is feminine. However when I am Jennifer my persona changes and I do act very different. Why all this happens, I do not know.

To what degree would you consider permanent hair removal, hormones, surgery?

Never

What one piece of advice would you give to someone that has just found they are not the only tranny in the world?

Go at your own pace and seek advice from other girls about some of the feelings and doubts you go through. If is a hobby or a way of life the answer is the same; enjoy it.

WayOut
of the closet

These four pictures are all the same model Firstly she wears a wig brushed smooth and down. Next the same wig is pinned up. The third picture is a different curly wig and the forth is the same curly wig worn over the first wig providing a straight fringe. Instead this could be done with your own fringe if length and colour is suitable.

These four pictures are all the same model Firstly she wears a wig brushed smooth and down. Next the same wig is pinned up at the side. Next the wig is pinned up leaving only tendrils to soften th look. The last picture shows the first wig worn down shoing the straight fringe and the crown blended into a a curlier wig worn on top to provide that "big hair" look.

These four pictures are all the same model This shows an accesory pinned into firstly along style wig and then on a shorter wig. Both look more "dressy" for the evening. The second style needs a graceful neck and shoulders while the first is more fogiving.

With much thanks for all Photos from Pandora De Pledge at image Works
Hair & Make-up by Pandora De Pledge - Wigs by Image Works Shop . www.pandoradepledge.com

H air is probably the most important feature that distinguishes gender difference especially at this time when the fashion for men's hair styles are so very short.

The most obvious way to experiment with your image is to wear wigs.

Wigs

Wigs can totally change your appearance. Many people like this total change. Wigs come in many styles, colours and qualities, you really do need to try them on to get the one(s) to suit and fit you best. Real hair wigs are much more expensive than monofibre and are much harder to look after needing a good understanding of styling techniques.. When choosing a wig, ask yourself whether you want a natural daytime or a big glamourous evening look. Women make the most of their hair for special occasions by styling it, but wigs come ready styled and are

difficult to tame for day wear and a glam wig worn during the day will make you stand out in a crowd. Most longer wigs will look more natural if some hair is pinned, clipped up or tied up. Wigs can be cut and styled to flatter the shape of your face. Lace front wigs appear (at least from a distance) as if the hair is growing from your scalp. These are designed for the stage to allow hair to be swept up off the face. These used to be very expensive but recently a number of manufacturers have brought out reasonably priced ready to wear wigs with lace fronts. So be bold check our listings and have a good chat with the girls in the hair salons and wig shops

All of these eight pictures on this page are the same model. Nothing changes your image more radically than hair colour and style. A full wig can help your confidence as it works well as a "disguise" when you don't want to be recognised. You can also experiment with a wider range of make-up and clothes to match various wigs.

If you are trying to discover a look and image that you feel is the "femme" you, trying many different wigs will help you find that personaity. Many wig shops listed in the book can help you do this but trying different wigs during escorted dressing service trips in public will tell you much more and can save expensive mistakes.

PANDORA DE'PLEDGE IMAGE WORKS

No tranny clones !
Just beautiful individuals

NEW ONLINE Hair and Make-up tutorial
NEW IMAGE WORKS ONLINE SHOP
Luxurious premises (10 mins from central London)
Year-round garden with jacuzzi and summer house
High powered solarium
In-house photography
Incredible Professional Photoshoots
Breathtaking make-overs
Escorted trips both day and evening
Professional make-over tutorials
Hair and Wig services
Comfortable secure customer accommodation
Superb full dressing service with an option of
3hr, 5hr and 8hr appointments

BY APPOINTMENT ONLY
www.pandoradepledge.com
Tel (020) 7682 0340 (9am till 10pm)
www.glamour@pandoradepledge.com

Make-Up

Not every one that cross-dresses will want to go to the extent of wearing make-up.

Few know how to use it - but for those that want to try - what a treat is in store.

Make up is fun, make-up is a disguise, make up can give you confidence. No wonder cosmetics is one of the highest earning businesses in the world.

Meeting, as I do, many trannies as boys and girls, it is constantly amazing how different they can look before and after make-up.

"It is for ever amazing the transformation that make-up can achieve".

I have been lucky to have shared the mirror alongside some of the best make-up artists. But I still say that there is nothing like experiencing and watching an expert work the products on your own face. I have had some excellent lessons myself and would always encourage trannies to have a make-up lesson.

"I always encourage trannies to have a make-up lesson".

There are many people offering make-up lessons listed in this book however I recommend that you talk to them on the phone and look at some of their work (many now have web sites). You need to choose a make-up artist and lesson that is right for you and the look that you want to achieve. You may want a look that is very glamourous to go with your evening clothes or a 'girl next door look' that looks like you have little make up on (which actually takes more skill and different products than a 'full on' look). You might want a look that is suitable for stage or photo shoots which you will find is much heavier than the look you can wear in public. You might want to try a period look to wear on stage or to match a period costume.

I am sure that if you are interested in make-up, that you study the many women's magazines. In these and the many books with step by step guides to make up for women you can obviously gain good tips. However a male skin especially with the need to cover beard shadow needs different techniques and products.

In the Tranny Guide you will find suppliers of specialist make-up for male to female make-up including beard (camouflage) make-up like Dermablend and Dermacover which are just right for a male to female make-up.

It is hard to show makeup technique in a book but in the 8th and 9th Tranny Guide I published a step by step make up feature based on photographs from the shoot for the video 'Trading Faces' featuring the skill of Pandora De Pledge and shot by 'TJP'.

In issue 39 of Repartee magazine Pandora provided a more detailed step by step lesson shown over three A4 pages updated and photographed at Image Works.

When I published the step by step guide in the Tranny Guide I received the feedback "The model had plucked eyebrows...I cant pluck my eyebrows so I can never look that good". This is a fair criticism but it does have a solution. Steffan my partner and co-host at the WayOut Club does not pluck his eyebrows but uses a 'plastic' theatrical technique. So in the 10th Tranny Guide Pandora and Steffan showed us exactly how to perform this theatrical trick to hide and reshape eyebrows.

Watching others, studying the many pictures in this book and other books and magazines plus conversations with others that are experienced is possibly the best way to. improve your results. Nothing beats ...
Practise, Practise, Practise.

Trading Faces step by step make up lesson on Video and CD Rom is available see advert page 330

Tranny Guide back issues are available see page 332
Repartee Magazine back issues are available see advert and listing
Pandora De Pledge and many other make up specialists are listed throughout this book.s

Wigs Continued from page 39

Many well known women, use wigs all the time. UK soap star Barbs Windsor is a real study with the various styles she uses as Peggy at the 'Vic' to a glam look for a celebrity interview. Cher makes it obvious that she uses wigs by changing not only style but also colour all in one show. Wigs can be great fun and can help you create character or period looks whether you want to look like a young pop queen like Britney Spears or historical queen like Marie Antoinette

Wig Care

Most synthetics wigs can be stored tucked away in a bag. Real hair wigs, however, need to be kept on a wig stand to avoid losing the styling. Most wigs are styled during manufacture and will return to shape simply by shaking out prior to putting them on and then gently fingering them into shape. You should avoid over-brushing and combing which quickly damages wigs. Men generally do no more than comb or brush their hair. Watch women - they use their fingers to tease and style. This is also the way to handle your wigs. Some styles will benefit from the use of mousse, spray and leave-in conditioners. Initially ask the advice of a wig shop or hairdresser. Your wigs will need washing and conditioning. Serious mistakes can be made whilst washing wigs. It is recommended to brush the wig through before washing and then submerge in cool water (NEVER hot) with either a special wig shampoo or a fabric detergent, (remember your wig is actually plastic the same as your acrylic clothes). Leave to soak and then rinse first in clean water then soak in clean water with a generous amount of fabric conditioner. Wrap the wig in a towel to absorb the majority of water, give it a good shake holding it at the back of the neck, before putting it on a wig stand to dry completely and before teasing it with a wide toothed comb. Alternatively ask a wig shop or hairdresser to wash and re-style your wig. Then carry it home on the wig stand inside a box.

Your own Hair

For a tranny to 'pass', nothing will look more natural than your own head of hair. Many 'female' styles are very short and most men can wear their own hair reasonably long, therefore you may well be able to wear your hair in a style which suits your lifestyle, whilst looking very feminine when you are dressed. For many people the thought of being able to talk freely to their hairdresser about their dual image seems a mere dream, but we have listed many tranny friendly contacts which can be approached with confidence. They will advise you how to get the best from your hair and will happily cut, colour, or perm. There is hardly a wig shop anywhere that does not welcome male / tranny customers. In this book you will find many that are especially welcoming.

Extensions

The length or thickness of your hair need not hold you back from achieving the head of hair you desire. Victoria Beckham changes the length of her hair from week to week with extensions. Extensions can be attached by a number of methods and some are better than others. Monofibre is cheaper than real hair. None are cheap. Depending on the bonding technique the process can thicken and lengthen your own hair.

With much thanks for all Photos from Pandora De Pledge at image Works
Hair & Make-up by Pandora De Pledge - Wigs by Image Works Shop . www.pandoradepledge.com

Where do you buy clothes?

High street shops, online and catalogues. It's best to be honest with people as that way you get a better service. Besides, they either want our money or not. If I get crap service, I'll leave the shop and spend my money elsewhere.

What leads you to choose the styles you wear?

a) is it in my size b) does it look nice c) does it feel right. I just want to look like I fit in depending on what situation I'm in

Is make-up and hair important to you and if so how do you achieve your look?

Yes it is important as I want to look my best. I don't have many opportunities to practice but I practice when I can to see what works best for me.

What degree do you practice hair removal, and other body feminisation?

I shave everywhere every Friday to keep in a regular routine. I am having electrolysis and have been on hormones for a year.

Who knows that you dress?

Most people know. I told them (I figure it's best to educate rather than keep it a secret). Friends have been brilliant, work take the mickey and my parents whole-heartedly disapprove.

How often do you dress and if you go out where to?

What is your name and what is your background?

Karen O'Connor. Middle class living in Surrey

Are you happy to be called a tranny and what does this name mean to you?

I don't mind, it's one of the nicer names I've been called over the years !

How old are you and how young can you remember thinking about or actually cross-dressing?

34 and dressing since I was a little girl ! (mum needs a consultation about her wardrobe). I can't remember not thinking about dressing, even back to infant school.

Karen O'Connor: Picture gallery:
http://www.pandoradepledge.com/pages/karenoconnor/karenoconnor1.htm

Photo Hair & Make-up: Pandora De Pledge - Image Works. www.pandoradepledge.com

Not too often due to living at home still (lottery tonight though !). When opportunity arises I'll go shopping, clubbing or just chill out at home.

How much of a sexual turn on is trannying for you?

Not really a turn on. I just dress to feel right.

What is your definition of feminine?

A gentler nature. Softer, more defined movements. Less aggressive. An ability to shop till you drop (!)

To what degree do you feel gender dysphoric (i.e that your brain in feminine)?

I am a diagnosed gender dysphoric (licensed to look fabulous!). I've always felt different and now feel as though I am on the right track.

To what degree would you consider permanent hair removal, hormones, surgery?

I currently have electrolysis and have been on hormones for a year. I haven't been ill since I started the hormones which means that my body is now in perfect balance. Surgery ? I'll get there one day but it's going to be a long time (due to debts, current situation). I'll just take each day at a time.

What one piece of advice would you give to someone that has just found they are not the only one

Choose the path of least regret.

KarenOConnor69@aol.com
http://www.theresalotofitabout.co.uk

WayOut
of the closet

Feminine Foundations

Some cross-dressers want to be able to feel soft, feminine clothing against their skin. Others want to see reflected in the mirror, the most feminine shape they can create. Generally women's bodies differ to men's bodies, in terms of fat distribution so to achieve that mirror image may need a little help and some 'tranny tricks'.

You are what you eat

Diet will not only effect your shape but also your skin, hair and energy. You will win support from friends and family if you get to grips with diet.

In truth women's shapes vary greatly. Your icon may be the Gerry Halliwell (on the Atkins diet) or the voluptuous Marilyn Monroe.

If you are honest about the potential of your body and use the correct foundation garments you can make best of what you have got and be who you want to be.

How much you squeeze and pad your body to redistribute your fat (or lack of it) depends on what you want to achieve. If you want to 'pass', you need the right shape, but 'passing' could lead to touching, and you are more likely to feel like an upholstered sofa than a woman.

Hormones

Some trannies may yearn for breasts to fill their bra and generally enhance their femininity by using hormones. Hormones' are available from 'alternative' sources. These fall into the black marketing of prescribed drugs and herbal and cream alternatives.

However It is extremely DANGEROUS to take the hormones originally prescribed for some one else (including HRT and contraceptive pills) adverse medical side-effects can vary from mood swings to dangerous changes in blood pressure and even liver damage.

Each person's will require doses and the type of hormones to be prescribed individually to suit their medical conditions. What may be fine for someone else could be totally wrong for you and may have serious bad side-effects and can kill.

It is recommended that if you really feel driven to see what hormones can do for you, then you should seek the advice of a qualified doctor. In the first instance this will probably be your GP, who may prescribe directly but if he/she is not knowledgeable about specifics then he/she should refer you to a gender identity clinic. You may feel nervous about approaching your doctor and revealing your feelings. If this is the case you are not ready for hormones as they are NOT the beginning of the road of self discovery and acceptance TALKING is.

There is support for the concept that for older Male to Females a course of hormones will flush out the experimenters from the genuine needy transsexual. The drugs will reduce the sex drive and shrivel the testicles, erections will become a thing of the past. Very few gain any degree of breast growth. I assure you that all those super boobs you see in pictures are silicone. In the first year the drugs effects are reversible and many will stop taking them when they realise that their effect is not miraculous.

I know of no long term positive reports of herbal breast enhancement creams or pills - do you?

Boobs

A simple pair of boobs can be made from flesh coloured tights folded into shape and tied into a stocking bag. The knot can be positioned for a nipple. Silicone breast forms are the 'ultimate feel right falsies'. They warm to the body temperature have the weight of natural breast. Attaching them to the body transfers sensation of movement to the wearer. (They also feel very real to others touch). You will find a number of suppliers in the guide. Breast enhancers are available at very reasonable price £20-£30 or so. However a full breast form costs from £100 - £150 but should not cost more. The most important issue with boobs is to get the right size to suit you but also balance the proportions of your body. Wearing a low cut bra that exposes the breast form can ruin this expensive enhancement, it is best to choose a pretty bra that covers the breast form completely.

Alternatively a corset or one piece 'body' could provide bra cups which could hold the beast forms, however, the breast forms, corset and maybe hip pads too can look like a Michelin man (Even through your outer clothes). A firm one piece 'body' will helps to bring the whole look together, smoothing out the joins and giving you the appearance of wearing just one piece of underwear.

For a strapless outfit you should consider having breast forms built into a Basque or corset

A 'Wonderbra' can also do quite amazing things by creating a cleavage from almost nothing.

A favourite trick, to enhance cleavage, is to use tape from armpit to armpit pulling loose flesh together to create that all important decoltage. This needs experimentation, beware some tapes will stick so firmly that it will tear your skin on removal, avoid this with a small test for a few hours.

Photo - with thanks to Francis - read about her experience of breast implants in the 10th Tranny Guide

Your secret is safe with...

Suzi ®

THE FASHION WIG CENTRE

506 BROMPTON WALK, LAKESIDE SHOPPING CENTRE
WEST THURROCK, ESSEX RM20 2ZL
Telephone: 01708 865515
Website: www.suziwigs.co.uk
E-mail: sales@suziwigs.co.uk

- **All Leading brands of ladies fashion wigs**:
  Hairaisers - Trendco - Natural Image
  Dimples - Piere Pasgal - Revlon
  Jon Renau - Gisela Mayer - Pony Express
  Noriko - Ginchy - Renee of Paris - t'co,
  etc.
- **VERY LARGE SELECTION**
- **PRIVATE FITTING ROOMS**
- **FRIENDLY TO ALL TVs/TSs**
- **FUN WIGS AVAILABLE**

Vanity

PLUS!
our own exclusive imports

**Mention the "Tranny Guide"
for a 5% cash discount**

Legs

It is easy to get passionate about tights and stockings but - if it is not possible to wax or shave hairy legs the look and the feel is ruined. Dance tights sheer to the waist and with a great deal of lycra in them, are the perfect foundation for the lower half. These tights will smooth out imperfections and are thick enough to hide, with just one layer, hairs and blemishes. Flesh coloured dance tights worn over a flesh coloured dance belt, (the corset can also be worn underneath), to gives the perfect nude image below the waist. Sexy lacy undies, sheer tights or stockings can be worn over this foundation. Now you know the secrets of all the showgirls.

Genital area

The first question every one asks
"Where is the three-piece suite?"

With your legs wide apart, you can gently ease your testicles into the cavities from which they descended they will disappear leaving only the loose scrotum sack. OOH, it doesn't hurt - really! If you then put your penis back and down between your legs and put your legs together you have... **as we say, in the trade 'tucked' !**

The more you do it the more natural it will feel until as you push back your penis the testicles will find their way into the cavities on their own. When you take your knickers off and spread your legs the testicles should drop out into their normal position in the scrotum sack. If they don't it is because the testicles are a little large for the cavities openings. Gentle pressure on the groin (where the pubic hair grows) will pop them back out. With a bit of practice you will create a flat girly genital area. But please - at your own risk.

(N.B. We know of no evidence to suggest that this practice has any long term detrimental effect from, for example, prostrate cancer. However raising the testes to full body temperature, as they will be in the body cavity, for any length of time will inevitably reduce fertility temporarily. After a period back at the natural body temperature normal levels of fertility will return. There should be no detrimental effect on your ability to get an erection or to orgasm).

Suitable panties with a wide gusset hold everything in place. Ordinary knickers generally are not strong enough. A strong panty girdle will hold everything in place. But this will also squeeze the femininity out of your bum. Specialist tranny shops sell a device called a 'cache sex' or 'gaff'. A girls dance belt from a dance wear shop, (not the boys as they are padded), is perfect as it holds all the bits securely, whist leaving the buttocks soft and full.

A flesh coloured dance thong under flesh coloured dance tights is perfect. Then the fishnets, nylons, and fancy knickers can be worn on top. Now you know !!!.

Hips Rear and Waist

Fashions have differed in this area over thousands of years. However most women have wider hips and more amply rears than men. You will find specialist pads and padded underwear for the purpose of shaping these areas in this book. Foam shoulder pads, carefully positioned beneath dance tights can also achieve the desired shape. It is rare to find any woman who believes her waist to be small enough and stomach flat enough.

If you are not already aware that you "are what you eat" you will be if you aim to feminize your body. Most of us still need help to create a feminine waist, so a good lace up corset may be a necessity. The choice of corset depends on the shape of you and how much bare flesh you are going to leave exposed. You will find many corset suppliers in this book.

Photo with thanks to Renee

The clothes I wear exactly fit my mood, not too provocative but not too classical.

Is make-up and hair important to you and if so how do you achieve your look?

Both wigs and make up are very important for me. I can't imagine going out without having done them perfectly. I don't want to look like a drag queen

To what degree do you practice hair removal, and other body feminisation?

I shave my legs and the hair under my arms

Who knows that you dress?

Some girls I met on-line in a chat room know it. They accepted it very well when I told them.

How often do you dress and if you go out where to?

I can't dress as often as I would like. If I could find the right man, I surely would do the "big jump". Yes, I have gone out en femme in some restaurants and a discotheque in London.

How much of a sexual turn on is trannying for you?

Going out en femme was a real challenge for me at the beginning but I realized that it was also the discovery of a second self I had and did not want to assume.

What is your definition of feminine?

I know that I am so.

To what degree do you feel gender dysphoric (i.e that your brain in feminine)?

I like to be admired, to be appreciated as a pretty woman.

What is your name and what is your background?

My name is Anna. I am living in Strasbourg, France. I am a tax councellor and am single.

Are you happy to be called a tranny and what does this name mean to you?

I am not happy with the name tranny. I would like to be called with something else but I don't know what.

How old are you and how young can you remember thinking about or actually cross-dressing?

I am 36 and I began at 8 ;

Where do you buy clothes?

I usually buy clothes on line but I also have bought in a shop before.

What leads you to choose the styles you wear?

Photo Hair & Make-up: Pandora De Pledge - Image Works. www.pandoradepledge.com

To what degree would you consider permanent hair removal, hormones, surgery?

I would always consider having sex reassignment surgery if I could be sure of the love of a man for me. I don't want to prostitute myself so I want a man who can secure me, love me and make me feel as a lady everyday.

What one piece of advice would you give to someone that has just found they are not the only tranny in the world?

Look around you; you are not alone...

WayOut
of the closet

Buying Clothes
Mail order

Fundamentally cross-dressing is all about wearing clothes. So how does a guy go about getting women's clothes for himself?

If you have a female partner there is an enormous temptation to try everything she owns (whatever size it is).

Even if she is supportive she is likely to be upset about her new size 8 'La Perla' lingerie being stretched onto your size 18 body. However she might designate safe-to-borrow items. If she doesn't know, she is very likely to notice the change of position, the smell, the make-up mark.
You are playing with fire.

It is common practice for cross-dressers to go to a shop, and ask an assistant for help with a special present for a wife or girlfriend. In most cases, however, the shop assistants can tell if you are buying the 'present' for yourself. Carry a good photo (just one or two) too flash as explanation and most with increasing awareness and and the need to take money will be grateful for your custom. In this guide we list shops throughout the world, many of which specifically encourage cross-dressers to shop with them.

Your positive and polite attitude will be your ticket to success. When you have spotted your potential purchase, approach the senior assistant who will have had the most training and experience, and will know or be able to decide on the shop's policy. If you are uncertain about the size or style and want to try something on, state that you would like to buy this for yourself but that you are worried about the size/style. The assistant will generally help you with alternative sizes, styles, return policy and MAY offer you the chance to try it on. This will be based on what facilities the shop has available and how busy the shop is and . If the shop has individual changing cubicles will usually help. Many shops have individual changing cubicles but however convincing you may think you are, please NEVER use a 'communal' changing room to try things on. You not only risk arrest under breach of the peace law - you risk negative publicity that lets down cross-dressers everywhere.

Accessories

Most girls do not feel complete until they have the earrings, necklace and handbag to match their outfit. Not to mention the hat, gloves, rings, scarves etc. etc.. Think Ascot Ladies day ... Think accessories. Buying these items is probably the easiest of all for cross-dressers. After all men are expected to buy accessories as presents for the 'girl' in their life Right?!? So do so for extra brownie points.

Lingerie

No other piece of clothing is as feminine as lingerie. It is designed for a woman's body. However to buy it can be most embarrassing. If you shop in regular shops, forget about trying things on. Even real girls rarely try before they buy. To work out your sizes the mail order catalogues show you how to measure yourself and have useful size charts. Specialist shops for TV's can be most helpful, as it is their business to put you at ease. They are also likely to stock sizes that will fit you. Their prices may be a bit higher but they provide a service to save you embarrassment. Our best recommendation, however, is to buy via mail order if you can. At the very least you can use these catalogues to sort out sizes, brands and styles, so that you can then go into a department store and confidently ask for exactly what you want. In our listings we include some of the best suppliers and specialists. Many catalogues will have a bra sizing guide this can be used to check the measurement under your 'bust' and work out what bra and cup size you should choose.

Mail order has many major bonuses for cross-dressers. You can apply for any catalogue to any company in your femme name. You can in most cases pay the bill for your 'girlfriend', as the name of the customer does not have to be the same as the person who pays the bill.

The explosion of internet shops with good on line purchasing systems has brought high street names and specialists alike to the world of mail order.

One advantage of mail order is that unlike an actual shop they do not have to pay to display stock. Therefore they can offer a wider range of sizes. The internet is also a great place to find wild designs and specialist products which may have too small a market to support a shop.

Catalogues generally have good sizing information that is accurate. Almost every mail order company offers a good returns policy (but check before ordering). Companies that only sell by mail order expect returns simply because the item isn't as expected or didn't look good on. Many regular girls will send back two thirds of what they order for these reasons. However you will gain a black name if you do this and never buy anything.

Whether specialist products or regular main stream products everything is available by mail order. Whether using the Internet or fax buying from other countries using a credit card has never been easier.

On the down side it can take a long time to get your deliveries and you need an address that is available to receive your delivery. There can also be hidden costs in p&p and duty .

Mail order is highly recommended for trannies and you may get a free carriage clock or kettle just for taking on a mail order book - well!!

Photos with thanks to The Bullring shopping centre Birmingham and photographer Juli Edwards. and with thanks to Stacey and Kitty from Birmingham UK - Read all about their shopping trips in the UK section

WayOut
of the closet

Buying Clothes

The Internet

Footwear

It hardly needs saying here that the internet is an amazing resource for EVERYTHING with 24 hour browsing at your leisure, price comparison, anonymous online shopping. However it IS worth saying that the web has special significance benefits for trannies.

High street shops such as Next (for example) offer their high street styles in much larger size ranges on the web. The web has many specialist sites offering almost anything that you might need in a wide range of sizes and styles. Sites for large and tall provide a service for the manly framed 'girls' compared with regular shops and indeed regular online shops.

Next to a wig, footwear is definitely your most important purchase and potentially the most difficult. Most shops only stock up to UK size 8 (Euro 41) and then only in some styles. Your evening can be ruined by shoes that hurt your feet after standing for a few hours, never mind dancing. Therefore unless you are just doing a quick pose in front of the mirror it is advisable to try before you buy, To add to the problem it is very difficult to judge women's footwear by size alone because of the variety of styles and shapes. If you are not fully dressed, at least wear tights as the difference in fit between wearing tights/stockings and men's socks is enormous. For those who are not able or do not wish to go into a high street ladies' shoe shop, we have listed a number of shops where cross-dressers have been made welcome. For those who have large feet we mention the size range.

Finally there are the specialist services that aim directly at serving the tranny market (sometimes it has to be said - at premium rates).

All of these sites can be found by Google searches but this can be hit and miss when you don't know that a particular site exists.

There are however many tranny resource sites and personal home sites that link to these specialist services and many of the better useful regular sites. In short if you have not got your head round computers yet – get on with it and here are some sites to start with - you will find many more throughout this book.

We also recommend looking at the fetish clothing shops which often cater for larger sizes and are very friendly and discreet. If you do buy without trying ask if you can bring them back to change them for another size or obtain a refund - many shops will be most helpful.

Photos with thanks to The Bullring shopping centre Birmingham and photographer Juli Edwards.
and with thanks to Stacey and Kitty from Birmingham UK -
Read all about their shopping trips in the UK section

www.plussizeclothing.co.uk large specialist
www.outsizeclothes.com large specialist
www.tallandall.com tall specialist
www.tallgirls.co.uk tall specialist
www.reelclothes.com clothes from the movies
www.ianardo.com/shoes.html home site with good links to large size shoes
www.cherylbrenda.co.uk/clothes.html home sites with excellent links
www.crissywild.com A tranny resource web site
www.wayout-publishing.com/shoppingmall.htm A virtual tranny shopping street on the web

A Post Office P.O.Box at your local depot costs just £50 per year.

Many new parcel receiving services are beginning set up to cope with the explosion in internet mail order sales - look out for them arriving near you.

Many dressing services offer a parcel receiving service.

Toni being fitted by Nan for Harem suit in Cambodia

Toni in leather from Buenos Aires

As a tranny I love dressing, I like to create my own compositions of loveliness. I want to look attractive, nice, stunning, sensuous, feminine, interesting, ambiguous, androgynous or various combination. And occasionally I want heads to turn and say "Wow"! Because I am a tall man with big feet I have to go that extra mile and sometimes I have things specially made for me. I suppose one way to describe some of my clothes is that they follow the classic iconic looks ensuring that they never go out of date and I can enjoy them over and over again. But here's the big problem, it can be expensive unless you can make your own. As I travel to New Zealand every 2 or 3 years my own solution is to arrange stopovers in places which offer advantageous skills and rates. You have to be clear in your own mind what you are after. Good communication is essential to ensure that the artisan understands what you want. Diagrams, drawings, models or samples are ideal. Look at what they do, the quality and the price as these vary wildly..

HONG KONG

Hong Kong has excellent shopping, wonderful materials and highly skilled dressmakers, tailors and craftsmen. Reasonable accommodation and food are readily available. English is widely spoken and armed with a suitable map, (free from the airport), it is easy to get around.

VOGUE SHOES

Shop B-23, Basement, Hyatt Regency Hotel, 35-79 Nathan Road, Kowloon Phone: 23668150 Email: vogueshoes@hotmail.com

I made the mistake of finding them last, so although I ordered 4 lovely pairs of shoes they could not make them in time so they had to post them to me. Consequently I had to pay UK import duty. So stay in Hong Kong 6 days and get your shoes measured up as soon as you arrive.

Vogue shoes are not cheap but they are well made to your own requirements and fit comfortably which is always a bonus for big uneven feet.

Hong Kong is famous for tailors and dressmakers. You can order clothes in the UK that can be made for you in Hong Kong, For example

WEAR NICE FASHIONS

3 Well Close, Camberley Surrey GU15 3NL UK Tel: 0127 6682815 had (for example) an offer of one suit, blouse, slacks and scarf for £370. The same firm in Hong Kong at Shop 20, Ground Floor, Tsim Sha Tsui Mansion, 83-97 Nathan Road, Kowloon had the same package for £159.

I made contact with an agent

MR MIKE HO

Tel: 6285 9220 and he guided me to a tailors workshop in my own building where I was fitted for some clothes of my own design. I wanted an exotic ladies style 3 piece suit with a high collared Chinese cut jacket, waistcoat and trousers. I also wanted a traditional pink Cheong Sam ("Suzy Wong") style dress. The cost of tailoring was £200 and the high quality silk brocade was £85. It is certainly not 'dirt' cheap, but I'm sure something of this nature would be considerably more expensive in London. The quality of the tailoring is truly excellent. The material came from

Full circle skirt above made to measure by Jennie Davis Tel: 01372 450687 Surrey, UK.
Lindy-Hop Shoes by Colin Johnson Tel: 020 8647 6948 Surrey, UK

Made to Measure  by Toni Vain

YUE HWA CHINESE PRODUCTS

301 Nathan Road, Kowloon. Buying through a tailor or an agent such as Mike Ho can result in a discount.

I had another excellent suit and shirts made at

UNION TAILOR LTD,

G31, Ground Floor, Hyatt Regency Hotel, 35-79 Nathan Road, Kowloon, Phone 2368 5582 Mr Tom Tong.

There are also many Indian tailors in Hong Kong. I had some cheaper shirts made at one of these, however from my limited experience Chinese tailors generally do better quality work.

STANLEY MARKET ON HONG KONG ISLAND

One day I took a bus out to the market where I bought a very nice red silk tie for just £1.00

CAMBODIA

During a visit to Cambodia for a couple of weeks I found a market with some cheap materials. I found a dressmaker, who did not speak English but who was willing to help me. Her name was

KEO-NAN

She lives and works opposite the Angkor Reach Hotel, next to the War Museum on Route 6, a few kilometres out of Siem Reap. With the aid of many drawings, sign language, smiles and laughter I conveyed my plans for 5 mix and match pieces. I politely tried to ask the cost and was told it would not be very much. I went back three times for fittings. Then I asked her how much again, sheepishly she asked for only £4. She and her assistant had spent 6 days on the project, so I gave her £16. She was very pleased.

Some types of fastenings including zips that can be undone and separated were not available, so I had to settle for low tech solutions. So try things out, take your own, explore, experiment and don't worry if it is not perfect.

SOUTH AMERICA

If you fancy a high class jacket and skirt made with the finest Alpaca fibres in the world, - they are smooth, silky, lightweight and very warm. Then try Arequipa in Peru. If leather or furs appeal to you try Buenos Aires, Argentina.

A three piece Chinese silk suit, white cotton shirt, and gold shoes. Tailor made in Hong Kong. Red silk tie, Hong Kong. Earrings made by Toni, ribbons and blank earring clips from John Lewis, Oxford Street, London

Toni contributed in the 6th and 7th edition of The Tranny Guide which included the 'hair raising' tale of a New Zealand Bungee Jump. This was alongside much more local tranny knowledge of the major NZ cities.

The feel of silk stockings and blouses to the hand or on the body, benefit the garment wearer and those lucky enough to feel the sensation from the outside. The texture of velvet, the caress of stretch wear, the slickness of a freshly lubed latex cat suit, just topically describe fashion and the sense of touch.

The earthy smell of a leather skirt or jacket, sweet white chocolate and vanilla of a clingy rubber dress, aromas from vintage nylon girdles and stockings to freshly washed cotton t-shirts, all play part in a sensual grand scheme of fashion.

A personal favourite of mine is how the sense of hearing comes into play. I love to hear the strong rhythmic sounds of a pair of high heels walking down a hard floor hallway, reverberating with each step. Perhaps if one is lucky enough; the sounds of vintage fully fashioned stockings gliding together or the crunching of a crisp leather jacket may be heard as that person walks nearer. The snap, crackle, pop, rubber garments make, is with out a doubt musical percussion to my ears.

I won't go into the sense of taste aspects of fashion, giggles… You can use your own imagination.

The whole composition then, comes together visually. For both the wearer and the viewer, the symphony of style, colour, texture, light and

I call myself a multi-media artist. What I really mean is; I am a multi-sensual artist. Composition in the arts is a constant. It is how any given aspect of media is consumed by the senses we stimulate and how it is interpreted by the brain. Therefore if one understands composition, only the tools change when one sets out to stimulate the senses.

I feel fashion is one of the most well rounded mediums capable of stimulating multiple sensory arousals that I have had the pleasure to work with.

If you think about the different garments in your wardrobe; it's easy to see how important fashion is for yourself and those around you. It could be easily said, that fashion is important because, thank God, it covers up the neighbours derriere. However the sensuality of fashion is the direction that most of us enjoy.

shadow, take form in four dimensions. From the top of the head to the soles of your shoes, you become an interactive kinetic sculpture, stimulating from within and without.

I got my first sewing machine after watching the carpenters sew scrim together at the Playhouse, Opera and other theatres where I was a scenic painter. This machine was used at first to sew backdrops for various bands I was in at the time. I then started experimenting with stretch wear. It was off to the races from there.

After designing garments and patterns I began a body wear company. We manufactured swim and body wear, made in our home and sold worldwide. Still a huge body wear fan, long after we shut the company down, I kept all the machines, tools, cutting table and fabrics. It was shortly thereafter that I discovered the "lil Ms. Emma M." that you see here. With much evolution, determination and dumb luck, I developed my interests in fetish wear first, then an elegant but edgy day and evening look. All this predicted on the do-it-yourself mindset.

For years I have been telling folks to buy a sewing machine. Not just one but two! If you have a sewing machine it sets you free of the designers and manufactures who are making garments for girls that have figures constructed differently than yours. Sewing machines offer you the ability to alter garments and make them fit perfectly. When a garment fits perfectly; it is noticeable!

Sewing machines offer you the independence to make your own garments from scratch. You can pick colours, fabric, and styles in any combination. It is a wonderful freedom of sensual expression. Most fabrics that I use are cut then constructed on sewing machines. Latex rubber on the other hand is cut with a roller then glued with (what else…?) rubber cement. It is an arduous process that helps explain the retail pricing of that product.

What inspires me to design? Fabrics; vintage, classic and experimental fashion; my physical attributes and limitations, mood, seasons, colour, shoes, textures, aroma, music, plays, history, the list is endless… Humour and whimsy play a large role in my design as well. Being able to poke fun at yourself adds a bit of dimension and off balance harmony. The key is to learn as much as you can, then grab different parts of your life, mix them up with the utmost confidence and throw it out there to be scanned. If you trust yourself, you will be ok.

by Emma from Ohio

61

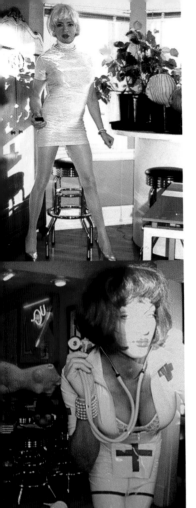

Made to Measure

I use lots of basic design elements to fix body flaws. High neck garments are worn frequently to visually slim a neck that I perceive to be bigger than I would prefer. I developed waist nipping thong panties (a gaff) that solves three issues for me; slimming my waist, keeping my tuck and leaving no visible panty line. These trunks come in a variety of sizes and colours. They work well to tuck and nip for most body types. They sell for $12 U.S. and can be ordered by e-mailing me. I make skirts that nip the waist even further while creating the illusion of hips with extra fabric on the sides. The only padding I use is breast forms. Shoes, hosiery, foundations to outerwear are always adjusted to maximize a look.

90 – 95% of the things that I wear; I make or have altered. Unfortunately I live in a small market town that does not market for the trends and tastes that I have developed from seeing the world market. This creates the drive to develop new looks for myself.

Most of us use the senses of sight and touch when considering what to wear. When picking fabrics to make a garment or finding a treasure on a clearance rack, I use the same combination of sensation. My thought process is that of a graphic designer. I try to choose garments for lines and statements that they will make when juxtaposed in as many combinations that I can derive. I absolutely love dresses but find they don't offer the versatility that separates do. It's the "once worn, its been seen" rule. So the garments I design have to be versatile, sensual, make a statement and fit perfectly. Lordy!

Examples of some versatile garments are the leotards I designed for the body wear company I had. I love these garments because they can be used for working out, dancing, swim wear and if you put a skirt and jacket over it; they can be worn to a five star restaurant. By the way, many of these garments are currently being blown out at fabulous prices on E Bay auctions. Use 'leotard' as the search word.

I have to mention that there is quite a buzz and a bit of humour involved, pretending to be a GG model in all my E Bay auction site ads. If the public at large knew, they might never be the same. (Laughs) It's our lil secret... See the leotard photo in this article.

Once all the garments are made, shoes and hosiery collected, I enjoy archiving the efforts and zeitgeist. Photography is a vital part of my sensual artistic path. It is also a huge part of the learning process. By doing photos of the image I have created, I am able to study the flaws and the achievements. Flaws can then be adjusted and achievements can be reused for future ensembles.

Photography is also then, a means to an art of its own. Chiaroscuro the study of light to shadow, drama, body language and of course the multi-sensual ensemble combine to take the art to another level.

But perhaps we can discuss photography and image in another issue.

Contact Emma M. at: emmamdd@aol.com

http://groups.yahoo.com/group/emmamsfetishtgirls/

E-Bay auctions: key word 'leotard'

E-Bay seller name: mcdmcx0

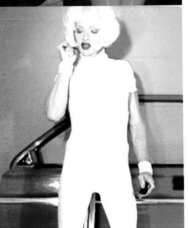

by Emma from Ohio

63

Where do you buy clothes?

I buy my stuff in normal shops, sometimes with the help of my sister. Mail order can be handy as well.

What leads you to choose the styles you wear?

The feeling of the day has a big influence on my style, but most of the times I try to look sophisticated sexy. Everything has to look perfect.

Do you have one look or many images?

As many images as possible, especially in the beginning. I try to explore which of the looks fancy me and therefore I try many looks. After three years I have now more feeling which suits me better. The images vary more in hair colour and use of make-up than in styles, most of the time I have the same style.

Is make-up and hair important to you and if so how do you achieve your look?

Very important. For me the make-up and the wig make the big difference, especially the wig. The same make-up, but another wig can make you look completely different.

To what degree do you practice hair removal, and other body feminisation?

I do not practice hair removal or any other body feminisation at all. When I go out I shave a little bit more than usual but that is it.

What is your name and what is your background?

Hi, my name is Natasha form Utrecht in the Netherlands. I'm a single living 30 years Old Dutch 'girl', who likes her work as a civil engineer and playing her volleyball in the weekend.

Are you happy to be called a tranny and what does this name mean to you?

The word tranny doesn't give any special emotions to me. I am who I am and I do what I do and I don't bother how other people call me, but the word tranny has a nice sound.

How old are you and how young can you remember thinking about or actually cross-dressing?

The thought of cross-dressing was always there, but only in the back of my mind. When I was 27 years old it really came out. This happened when I went to Miss Cassandra in Amsterdam, she showed me what kind of girl I could be. From then on Natasha was born.

Photo Hair & Make-up: Pandora De Pledge - Image Works. www.pandoradepledge.com

Who knows that you dress?

Most people who are close to me know what I'm doing and have seen the pictures. They know because I told them about my feelings. It makes everything a lot easier, because I can now speak with them about my feelings and I can do it out in the open.

How often do you dress and if you go out where to?

In a year I would say I dress once every month and go out every two months. Most of the time I go out with friends in Amsterdam. I don't go out alone.

How much of a sexual turn on is trannying for you?

When I look at other beautiful trannies it can turn me on. When I'm doing it myself it gives me very nice feeling inside me, which has nothing to do with a sexual turn on. It makes me relaxed and amazed how a person can be changed.

What is your definition of feminine?

To look beautiful and be able to show what you have got.

To what degree do you feel gender dysphoric (i.e that your brain in feminine)?

I have no problem what-so-ever to be a man. I like to dress-up every now and then to see how a man as me can be turned over in a beautiful woman. The change from male to female is for me every time again a wonderful experience.

To what degree would you consider perma-nent hair removal, hormones, surgery?

I won't do anything per-manent, because as I said before I like to be a man and I don't want to be a woman.

What one piece of advice would you give to someone that has just found they are not the only tranny in the world?

If possible try not to hide it from your close-by family or relatives. It will make every-thing much more compli-cated. But don't tell every-one you know, only the people you need for finding your way in the tranny world.

Many transgendered people have a strong desire to be seen 'dressed' and 'accepted' in the company of others.

For some the concept of mixing 'dressed' in public will always remain a fantasy.

However there **IS** a steady growth in crossdressers getting 'out' and about.

Of course there are many doubts and fears to overcome.

"A phone call and a casual chat before taking any step is the secret to getting the most from any experience".

The help of a specialist, club, service, support group or network of friends is invaluable. You will find many contacts in this book.

All should give you time on the phone to calm your fears. But do minimise the call by reading their web sites and brochures first

"Who ever you contact be honest both of you should be in no doubt about what you expect and wish to achieve"

Read this section then make that call..."

Photo with thanks to Lorraine of Hide & Sleek models at the Hide & Sleek Fashion Show see UK section for more details

Keep a Grip on Reality

When out and about I always recommend that, (despite your outer image and your inner joy,) you retain a firm grip on reality. You are a tranny, you have every right to be a tranny. When you walk down the street, go into a shop or stand at the bar, you are a tranny. You may be addressed as "madam" in the shop, whistled at by workmen and offered a drink at the bar by an admirer, but equally you may be addressed as "sir" in the shop, the workman may call out "all right mate". You may accept the drink at the bar, but the admirer may do an embarrassed about-turn. You are a tranny and you can expect both reactions. If you expect them you can feel comfortable with them. Be proud of what you are.

Be Street Wise

No woman would take the risk of walking alone in a quiet un-lit place, walk through crowds of rowdy young people or go alone into certain establishments (come on you know what I mean). Furthermore ... No woman would put her self at even more risk by doing any of the above in six inch heels and a micro mini. Dress appropriately .. OK Enough said !

Dressing appropriately

Meal, Club, Shopping, Holiday - There are no end of opportunities to fulfil your fantasy throughout the world. We list places which are crossdresser friendly but you will not be welcomed in tarty or fetishy outfits. Wear something similar to the other female clients and you will be appreciated as a customer at almost any venue.

Mannerisms and Deportment

However good you look, if your body language is still clumsy and masculine, or worse nervous and intimidated, you are likely to give yourself away attracting unfavourable attention and be subject to ridicule from other people including other trannies and especially uninhibited children, groups of teenagers and some over critical gay guys.

CONTINUED PAGE 68

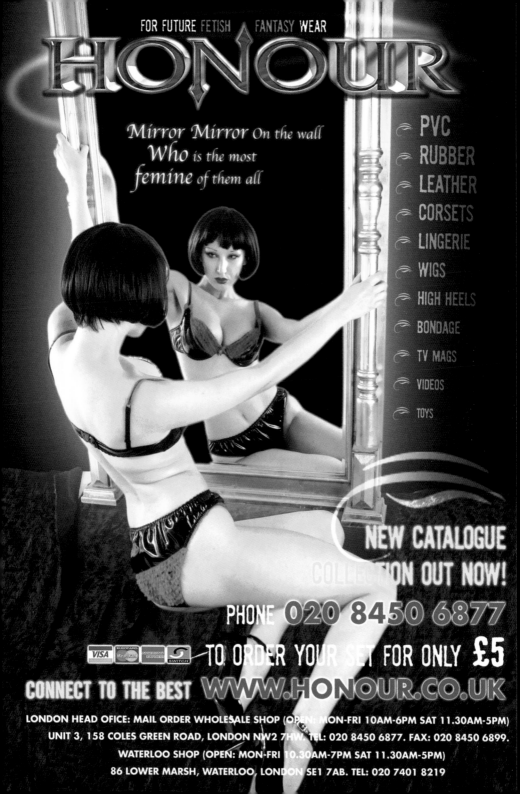

WayOut
of the closet

Stepping 'OUT'

Coping with Admirers

For those that mix with others, there will come a time to respond to a compliment, or indeed a proposition. Of course a simple honest, polite 'No thanks' always proves to be the best answer to a proposition, if 'No' is the answer you want to give.

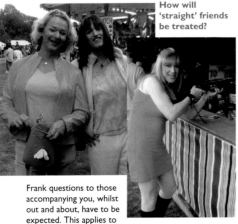

How will 'straight' friends be treated?

Frank questions to those accompanying you, whilst out and about, have to be expected. This applies to "real girls" or male friends. In places where some trannies have breasts or are in every way "passable" only a frank question gets you past first assumptions. A born female friend CAN feel insulted if caught off guard while feeling a bit ill at ease. if asked "when did you have your surgery" or similar. Similarly if your male friend is asked "how long have you been attracted to trannies" or simi-

lar. However let's face it - your friend will now know how transgendered people feel when questioned WHEREVER we go.

Network of Internet friends

Many trannies meet each other on the internet, through personal email conversations after reading home pages, or in chat rooms. (Do I really have to say DON'T give out your home phone number or address?). It is a good idea to arrange a chat on the phone before committing to a meeting. Most people will give a mobile phone number at first to maintain privacy. There is a lot to be learnt about a person by talking to them on the phone that emails mask. Many now go on to meet physically with a network of friends. Strength in numbers, going out with 'big' sisters can be a wonderful experience and just getting ready together is half the fun.

Formal Support Groups

All around the world there are support groups. Many of these groups suffer an outdated image but this is generally unfounded. Join them, support them, contribute to planning and communication within and outside the group and the image will change and the tranny community will be stronger.

Many of the smaller self-help groups, are organised by an over-worked, non-funded, un-trained person, often with the help of a long suffering partner, who may also give help, advice, and a friendly shoulder to you or your partner. These groups can be excellent for local tips on shops, services and places to go. Some groups organise parties and outings. Some may have a contact network and may be able to introduce you to like-minded friends to visit or to go out with.

Beware that some of these groups can be narrow minded and judgmental. Some may have a limited view of self expression, sexuality and other issues. Some may lead a newcomer to think that gender reassignment is the goal and less is worthless. Others consider that only straight transvestites are acceptable.

However in most groups you will find trannies from EVERY background and it is this diversity that can be even more life enriching than the opportunity to dress as you wish together.

I strongly advise telephoning the "contact" of the group to discuss the group, before visiting in person. Ask open questions like - what is the typical mixture like at a meeting? What do most members wear? What activities does the group enjoy? When you have a picture of what the group is about - go along with an open mind and make the most of the opportunity to meet others.

Dressing Services

These services are up front about the fact that they charge for their services. In the past poor service and high prices have led to a bad reputation for dressing services by trannies who are notoriously stingy - and that is very understandable as for many, it is hard to justify (or to explain) why they are spending what they spend.

However over the last ten years in a more open, more informed market - those dressing services that do not provide a good service soon disappear. Furthermore it would be true to say that in recent years more trannies have also "progressed" to the point where they have

CONTINUED PAGE 70

With thanks for photos to Jodi at The Boudoir and her Boudettes

Photo with thanks to Lorraine (centre) of Hide & Sleek on a trip to London for Bella Joy's (Roses network & Repartee magazine) Boat trip

reorganised their lives and their relationships to make the most of their cross-dressing and openly budget time and money for their "hobby" as others do with their interests.

Those dressing services that get it "right" gain loyal clients and often expand their service to safe accommodation, transport, shopping trips, and outings to shows, events, safe bars, restaurant or a club, individually or in small groups.

There are a host of facilities that you can ask for - sinks and showers, wardrobe, make-up, hair styling, beauty treatments, videos, books, internet surfing, conversation, others to meet, storage, mail order receiving photo or video shoots, Some may offer more specialist role-play and even sexual experiences. But it should not be assumed that ALL dressing services offer these "extras". Most services now have comprehensive web site - Do thouroughly read the site BEFORE making a phone call. A casual chat before your visit is the secret to getting the most from your experience. After this call the service should be in no doubt about what you wish to achieve.

With thanks for photos to Jodie at The Boudoir and her Boudettes

Counselling

It has to be said that some people 'inflicted' with any degree of gender dysphoria or desire to cross-dress (especially in public) may feel that they are a medical case that needs to be made "normal"

In the UK for most immediate support there is none better than **THE SAMARITANS**. You don't have to be suicidal and you can visit a centre in person after initial contact by phone. Relationship problems can be addressed by **RELATE** you don't have to be married. Same sex couples or family relatives are also counselled.

If you feel you need 'help' for yourself, or you and your partner, it is best to check qualifications and approach an accredited service.

But - Let me save you hundreds of pounds and many years of discussion. YOU CAN'T BE CURED - YOU WILL ALWAYS BE A TRANNY

Where can I change to go out on my own?

Dressing services are all about providing a place to change (and of course charge a fee). However if you are braving the outdoors alone, to go to a support group meeting, or to meet up with a network of friends, and getting ready and leaving from home is not possible - where do you get changed and made-up?

As part of a network you may be able to find a friend who can accommodate. A gift of a bottle of wine or a box of chocolates would not go amiss in this case, especially if there is a partner in the house.

It may be easier to take your first steps well away from your local area. It is possible to 'dress' in the privacy of any hotel room but it may not be a good idea to go down to the bar in your cocktail dress.

We have listed TG friendly places to stay where you can dress freely and anonymous hotels that give you a pass key or card. This may be costly on your own but with a small group it becomes a viable option.

Gay venues

The gay community can offer a wealth of opportunities, to trannies. But you may have your own misconceptions and prejudice to overcome before you can feel comfortable in a gay venue. Many gay bars have regular drag entertainment that can vary from vulgar panto to USA style impersonation both live and mime. Many of these bars run talent contests and karaoke but I recommend you watch what choice of material and costume gets the audience's support before taking the challenge yourself.

The gay community is very diverse, assumptions are rarely valid. In general, gays have sympathy for other minorities, however even some gay drag queens find it difficult to understand why a man would want to dress like a woman unless it is to attract a straight man. Most see their own dressing up as just part of their culture, To some gay guys trannies and drag queens are seen as a glamourous appendage to the gay community, whilst to others we are too obvious, too camp, in short, indiscreet. Generally, most gays are friendly, fun, kind and affectionate, but they can also be bitchy.

CONTINUED PAGE 72

Throwing Shade

Giving Attitude - Gay trannies and drag queens have the phrases, 'throwing shade' or 'giving attitude' which in essence is ensuring your confidence is (or appears to be) bigger than any others. This is done by body language and how you talk, (e.g. 'I am more of a woman than you'll ever have and more of a man than you'll ever be' and other phrases that simply mean 'don't even think of messing with me'). However this attitude (while fun among friends) can be the cause of verbal or physical aggression in return. What is more it is never likely to help you 'pass' but for those that "throw shade" this is the last thought on their mind.

Straight venues

You may be surprised at how easy it is to enjoy straight clubs if you are confident and especially if you are with girlfriends.

However, as most real girls will tell you, men appear to go to straight clubs for one thing. If you really 'pass' easily, you will have to deal with men who try to pick you up, usually rudely, persistently and aggressively.

These guys are often quite drunk and are probably showing-off to their friends. It is best to explain politely, (humour helps), what you are and what you are into. To 'tease' can lead to a nasty incident and an unnecessary brush with the management. Often these guys will still be quite happy to chat you up - remember the last line in the film 'Some like it Hot', "No one's perfect".

If (can we talk frankly?) you don't 'pass' easily, then you must be prepared to face the occasional hurtful remark. Again, a big confident smile and a comic return is much the best attitude, in this situation.

Mixed venues

In many magazine listings, you will see the clubs and bars that are described as "mixed/gay".

The customers of these promotions are, on the whole, a liberal crowd without bigotry and who are out to have a good time. Many of these are the clubs where the record companies introduce new acts and where pop celebs. and the fashion scene 'party'.

Straight 'real girls' often enjoy these clubs more than the straight clubs as there is not the constant pressure from men trying to pick them up, and they therefore have more of an opportunity just to have fun. These girls are usually intrigued and very friendly to trannies.

You will be particularly welcomed at these venues if you 'add to the night', by being friendly, extrovert and dressing to 'fit in' with the style of the club, (rule one is smile at everyone). However, the management of some clubs may be concerned if you are too loud, trashy, or dowdy.

Fetish venues

Designers flirt with fetish fashion. Pop videos draw on fetish images. The fetish scene is generally welcoming to cross-dressers.

Fetish events are attended by friendly, broad-minded people from all walks of life. Some enjoy their clothes as an expression of their sexuality. For others the clothes are simply exciting to wear. A certain conformity to the fetish dress codes scene must be adopted. For example denim or daywear is not acceptable. Trannies should wear what a woman would wear to these events.

Some people use their time in these club to escape reality. Some people, who are into S & M roleplay, seek inspiration from the sights around them whilst others get into mild fun and games. These events tend to be either monthly or less frequent, and some are annual events. Many of these events are by ticket only. Tickets can be purchased from many of the fetish clothes shops listed in this guide.

Dressing & Driving

Driving yourself or sharing a car is by far the safest way to travel but there are things that we take for granted that get suddenly complicated if 'dressed'.

What if I break down? With a change of clothing, (tracksuit, trainers and face wipes in the wheel well) it is fairly easy to sort yourself out. Alternatively, join a rescue service and always carry enough money and a friendly reliable taxi companies number.

What if I get a wheel clamp? Parking is a growing nightmare everywhere. It is important to check the latest parking rules. To take a risk could leave you ticketed, clamped or worse still, towed away. If in doubt, park in an easy area then call a cab for the last part of your journey. An attended car park is a good alternative.

What if I loose my keys? If you are unfamiliar with using a handbag it is all to easy to lose it (or have it 'lifted'), and every girl does done this once (rarely twice!). It is a good idea to leave a spare car key hidden on the car

CONTINUED PAGE 74

With thanks for photos to Jodie at The Boudoir and her Boudettes

WayOut
of the closet
Stepping 'OUT'

(you can get a magnet box for just that purpose), along with a spare house key hidden inside the car.

What if the police stop me ?

Again prevention. Make sure you car is in good condition and all the lights are working properly.

Drive carefully. Don't drink and drive. If you are signalled to stop, stop in a safe place, switch off, open the window and wait in the car.

The officer is most likely to say "would you step out of the car" which is normal procedure and is not done to embarrass you. If the officer says "Miss" correct him immediately and politely by saying, "its Mr, actually officer" (unless TS in transition or post). The officer is unlikely to ask why you are 'dressed'. In the UK the police are encouraged to politely address you in the gender you prefer. Always give correct details to match your paperwork.

My Credit Cards say 'Mr'
How do I pay to fill my tank?

If you are thought to look female with a male card or are 'read' as a tranny with a female card you may be asked "Is this your card". There is a much simpler solution (other than carrying cash or planning ahead and filling up before setting off), and that is to tell your credit card company to issue your card with initials only and no gender designation. It would be embossed (for example) just ... V. LEE. When I contacted my credit card company and requested that Mr be removed they said they could not do this for security reasons... "gender recognition is our first line of defence against card fraud".

I said "exactly I am being suspected of card fraud because I frequently don't look like my given gender"... I followed this with "if you can't oblige me, I will cancel my account and take out one with a company that can". The card was immediately re-issued without my gender.

With thanks for photos to Jodie at The Boudoir and her Boudettes

What is your name and what is your background?

My name is Marie Tyler. I live in the Manchester area. I'm single, 30 years old (sob), university educated (at least my male ego is) and let's just say I work in the public sector – health, education etc. Take your pick! (Oh and I'm the archetypal paranoid tranny...)

Are you happy to be called a tranny and what does this name mean to you?

I suppose I don't have much of a choice as that is what I am if you take the term in its broadest possible sense. I've always hated being 'read' and being told by people that I'm a really good-looking tranny doesn't help! So, in short, I wouldn't exactly say I was happy to be called a tranny but accepting...

How old are you and how young can you remember thinking about or actually cross-dressing?

I think I was about 6 years old when I first cross-dressed into my sister's clothes but I've only really been out of the house in the last 2 years or so.

Where do you buy clothes?

I buy all my clothes online now. I've become pretty good at picking the correct sizes (after a few mistakes) and have amassed a fair wardrobe. I try not to stick to the online catalogues and buy from all over but its normally just women's stuff – I've never bought from a place that caters solely for trannies since I've been shopping online.

What leads you to choose the styles you wear?

I usually just look at what women wear and work from there. I prefer just to blend in if possible and favour 'smart'.

Do you have one look or many images?

I only have one look, although this does tend to change every six months of so (usually just the hair). The style of clothing I choose is pretty much constant. However a visit to Pandora's was fun exception – a lot more glam than I usually am and doing a lot more with the hair. The red bob was my usual look though.

Photo Hair & Make-up: Pandora De Pledge - Image Works. www.pandoradepledge.com

s make-up and hair important to you and if so how do you achieve your look?

Very. I achieved my look through lots of practice. It took me a long time to realise that 'less is more' and I've gained useful hints through using various dressing services and talking to other girls like myself.

To what degree do you practice hair removal, and other body feminisation?

If I'm going out I'll make sure I'm completely 'shaved'. I often used depilatory creams as well, although these can be expensive. I do suffer from hairy arms (a trannies curse in the summer) but have learnt how to thin the hair out so as to be adequate in either male or female mode. I'm also lucky being naturally fair. I do pluck my eyebrows but more to tidy them up rather than to completely feminise them. I'll use an eye pencil to do that.

Who knows that you dress?

Only other TG girls know that I dress and a few people online. To say my extended family (and it is a large one) aren't tolerant would be understating it a little! I suspect my mum knows as she nearly caught me once in my teenage years still living at home and will still make a point a point of telling me EXACTLY how long she is going out for if I ever go to visit….

How often do you dress and if you go out where to?

It's tempting to say that I never dress at home alone as this is only the case every 3 months or so. I used to get out regularly once a week with friends to clubs in Manchester and the occasional visit to London but I'm taking a break from it all at the moment and concentrating on my career although I'll probably drift back again when I have the time.

How much of a sexual turn on is trannying for you?

I would say very much so when I first started – particularly adolescence when the hormones were raging… Now though it's merely a case of projecting my true self even if that does sound a little clichéd!

What is your definition of feminine?

OOOhhhh…tough question! Feminine is many of the things I try to hide about myself (or at least temper) when in male mode. I can't describe it any better – sorry!

To what degree do you feel gender dysphoric ?

I believe my brain is feminine – certainly more so than masculine anyway – in comparison to what I regard as feminine anyway.

To what degree would you consider permanent hair removal, hormones, surgery?

In an ideal world there would be no question of me settling for what I have at the moment and so my answer would be yes to all of the above. However, I am pretty much resigned to my life as it is now and think I'm pretty successful all things considered!

What one piece of advice would you give to someone that has just found they are not the only tranny in the world?

A little hypocritical of me to say this but – be yourself, enjoy it, try and meet people like yourself but above all don't forget there are other things in life too.

What is your name and what is your background?

My name is Miss Bambi and my residence is located in Hasselt, capitol of Limburg, Belgium. My age is classified information but I can tell you I'm in the business since 8 years now. I was never married and I always worked in nightlife, more particularly in the (straight) clubscene.

Where do you perform?

I perform on all kinds of parties. I worked as official host for the biggest clubs in Belgium but also on corporate events, press parties and of course on the clubnights I organise myself. These days I work every saturday night in different clubs and every first friday of the month in 'Le Cabardouche', my own party at 'Transit East'. On regular occasions I organise show dinners in fancy restaurants. I won some awards (Personality of the year www.move-x.be) and I already had two singles who were quite succesful in Bel-

gian clubs. Everybody can read and follow my career as a showgirl on www.miss bambi.com.

What is your style of performance and do you see yourself as a female impersonator or a character actor or maybe just you?

I see myself as a female impersonator. My shows are provocatively sexy. I'm not really a Drag Queen or a transvestite. I see myself more as a showgirl.

How did you get into performing?

About 8 years ago I started to organise my own parties called "Disco Fever". We wanted to hype the brand and came up the idea to put a face on Disco Fever. So on my next party I got dressed like a woman. The reactions were so good and I received so much male attention I decided to go on with it. A new star was born, Miss Bambi...

Are you happy to be called a tranny and what does this name mean to you?

"Tranny" is an unknown term to me in Belgium. We never use it. By profiling myself as a showgirl nobody can figure out I'm actually a male.

Where do you buy clothes?

I buy my clothes in all kind of shops. Alternative shops, designer shops and specialised shops. Never on the net. In the beginning I tried them on in the shop itself. I was never ashamed to do so. Through time I learned a

lot and since years now, I know what fits and what doesn't without trying them on first. Sometimes i work together with a designer who is specialised in show clothing and who makes my dresses for special occasions so I can be sure nobody will wear the same dress that night.

What leads you to choose the styles you wear?

I always try to look as sexy as possible and I have the luck, my legs are very long and beautiful. So why not show them? The clothes I wear are often inspired by the latest trends in the club-scene.

Do you have one look or many images?

I have one image but many looks. That depends on the occasion or the club where I have to perform. For example, my wig is always pink but I have different haircuts for corporate parties, cocktail parties, television, clubs and so on... With clothes, exactly the same.

Is make-up and hair important to you and if so how do you achieve your look?

Make up, hair and clothes are the key to success. The three most important features to look good. I achieved my look by experience. I've been doing this since 8 years now, so I became really good in it. I often do the make up for other nightlife performers and they really love my work.

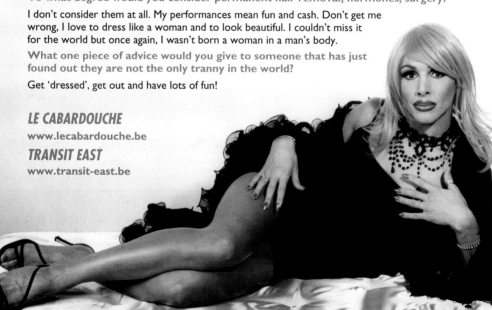

To what degree do you practice hair removal, and other body feminisation?

I remove all possible hair except on the head. That's the only body feminisation I admit to. My nails are a little longer and I also do my eyebrows, but that's it.

Who knows that you dress?

That's a very good question. Only club managers, some journalists, some friends and family and of course the crew I work with, know the real person behind Miss Bambi. I think a lot of people would be surprised if they would find out who really is Miss Bambi. I decided not to mix those two different worlds so i can do my business in peace and keep a distance between me and my fans.

How often do you dress and if you go out, where to?

That depends on the number of bookings. Let's say at least 2 times a week. I often work in clubs so going out is what I do to pay my bills. I get payed for being somewhere, entertaining the crowd and having fun. So I often go out, always as Miss Bambi but it's also doing business.

How much of a sexual turn on is trannying for you?

Wearing woman clothes is not really a sexual turn on to me but do believe me when i tell you i get a kick out of this. A lot of hetero sexual men want me. They often don't know i'm not a real woman and actually they don't care when they found out. They want me anyway. I'm having a fantastic sexlife and I'm very grateful for that.

What is your definition of feminine?

I guess "feminine" is a perfect mix of beauty, sex appeal, elegance, class, fashion, emotional intelligence and charm, flavoured with some arrogance and attitude.

To what degree do you feel gender dysphoric?

Like I said before, hair removal is the only body feminisation I allow. I'm gay so I'm more feminine by definition so I wasn't born in the wrong body.

To what degree would you consider permanent hair removal, hormones, surgery?

I don't consider them at all. My performances mean fun and cash. Don't get me wrong, I love to dress like a woman and to look beautiful. I couldn't miss it for the world but once again, I wasn't born a woman in a man's body.

What one piece of advice would you give to someone that has just found out they are not the only tranny in the world?

Get 'dressed', get out and have lots of fun!

LE CABARDOUCHE
www.lecabardouche.be
TRANSIT EAST
www.transit-east.be

WayOut
of the closet

Stepping 'OUT'

Gender in the work place?

We have all heard of the female football manager and the male beautician. However these are still extremes in terms of gender in the workplace. In many comapanies gender stereotypes (and worse trans/homophobia) are strong if not institutionalised. This being the case, in practice, for those intent on gaining acceptance as trans-gendered may prove impossible.

I know we should have rights! But lets get real - why push a boulder up hill (and be called an idiot for doing so). When you can choose to roll the boulder down the hill instead.

There are ever growing home working opportunities. There are paid and voluntary work environments that have strong equal ops policies and some are even insti-tutionally tolerant. Obtaining a new job from the start as transgendered means that there is a principle of sup-port, though of course each new person you contact is a test. To make the move is a big step requiring a search through your latent skills and possibly retraining - but it is possible.

How can a transgendered person try out the female role in the work place?

Most local civic centres will be able to introduce you to a choice of voluntary work. What's the point if I don't get paid? The answer is experience and training, and the network of contacts that you will gain which can lead to, and prepare you for, a surprising and rewarding change of paid career. Voluntary work opportunities vary from photo copying and coffee making through computer and office skills such as accountancy, through shop keeping, to specially trained work. I worked, for example, for community transport, driving various disadvantaged people in a bus to therapy and day trips.

Introductions

It really is best to be straightforward and honest don't expect others to know what transgendered means so explain (very briefly) in your introduction what it means to you.

He/She or your name?

The biggest problem is getting round he/she and him/her which people do get embarrassed about. However good you look some people will still 'see' you as male and struggle with the descriptor. Why complicate this embarrassment by asking them to use a very girlie name when you can use a name that suits either gender like Chris, Frances, Lesley or Toni.

What will you wear to work?

If you want to win friends and influence people - look around at the others in your group and let their style of dress influence you. If most of the girls wear trousers and flats it really is best to do the same, at least until you find your place in the group.

Finally Toilets

Use the easiest option, which should be available in most of the places we have been talking about. Find the toilets for disabled people, which is always unisex.

You may think that I might advise you about government legislation and transgender rights. But OH NO

I don't believe that a militant employee with a string of tribunal cases is ever going to be happy or welcome in any business.

It is YOUR responsibility to be employable

The fact is that employers struggle to recruit employees that fulfil just the fundamentals never mind questions of gender.

What are these fundamentals that many employers are struggling to find ?

1. Do you live within easy commuting distance and will travelling costs dampen your motiva-tion.

2. Can you be trusted. Not only with property and belongings but also with confidentiality and a whole host of other 'trust' considerations (like staying sober).

3. Will you be flexible enough and self motivat-ed enough to find useful productive ways to work without constant supervision.

4. What is your attitude and personality like. Will others that you might work with, get on with you without constantly falling out.

5. Are you reliable i.e. will you remember arrangements and instructions, turn up on time and keep in good communication.

6. Are you skilled enough to do the task in hand but even more important will you apply good common sense while they are doing it.

7. The last thing would be what you want to wear and then it would depend on how much the job involved the public and how what you wear represents the business.

As you read through that list, were there any areas that you might fall short on? Be honest ! I think we all have!

So before worrying about what people will think about your gender portrayal - it is worth bearing these points in mind and working on being your very best in these areas.

If you match up - you will be very employable that no one will be thinking about your gender status.

The 'portal' to everything tranny on the Internet **www.wayout-publishing.com**

Miss Tiffany's Universe

Tiffany's Show in Pattaya is the first and biggest transvestite cabaret show in Asia with 1,000 seats and offering 3 shows daily. For the past 30 years Tiffany's Show has entertained millions of guests and received accolades as the best transvestite cabaret show in Asia. Tiffany's is no stranger to organising beauty pageant contests, as they have successfully held the popular Miss Tiffany's Universe yearly since 1997. This contest is receiving more and more attention especially since it is broadcast live on National Thai television with an average 10 million viewers. This program is also shown internationally.

Tiffany's Show has always been proud to promote Pattaya City and improve the transvestite performers and the cities image abroad.

This year Tiffany's Show Co., Ltd. is celebrating its 30 years anniversary with a unique and exciting NEW event.

The Miss International Queen Contest 2004

October 23th, 2004 at Tiffany's Show Theatre.

The Miss International Queen expects to welcome contestants from over 30 different countries. Revenue generated from the contest will be used for donation to HIV infected children and create awareness of the disease.

The Miss International Queen prizes

Winner Miss International Queen: 5,000 US$ + diamond crown + trophy + sponsor's gifts + domestic airplane ticket

First runner up: 3,000 US$ + trophy + sponsor's gifts + domestic airplane ticket

Second runner up: 2,000 US$ + trophy + sponsor's gifts + domestic airplane ticket

Best national costume: 1,000 US$ + trophy + sponsor's gifts

Best evening gown: 1,000 US$ + trophy + sponsor's gifts

Best swimming suit: 1,000 US$ + trophy + sponsor's gifts

Miss friendship: 1,000 US$ + trophy + sponsor's gifts

Tiffany's Show Pattaya,
464 Moo 9, Pattaya 2nd Rd., Nongprue, Banglamung, Chonburi.
Tel : (6638) 429642, (6638) 421700 to 5
Fax : (6638) 421711 to 2
e-mail : tiffany@tiffany-show.co.th
website: www.tiffany-show.co.th,
For Miss International Queen 2004
www.missinternationalqueen.com

What is your name and what is your background?

Ok my name is Sasha. 26years old, and I was born in Penang island, Malaysia. I work as stage performer in Kuala Lumpur, as a dancer and part time model. Yes, I am single.

Are you happy to be called a tranny and what does this name mean to you?

Yes I am happy to be tranny!!! I don't care about others people thinking. As long I know who am I and I do the right things to survive!!!

How old are you and how young can you remember thinking about or actually cross-dressing?

I dress up when I was 14years old. I can't remember since then that I use the gents toilet.

Where do you buy clothes?

I like fashion, coz I do modelling. Mostly I like simple and glamour styles. I like to buy my clothes at MNG (mango)

What leads you to choose the styles you wear?

I like up to date styles and my choice depends on what function I go to.

Do you have one look or many images?

My dear, I only have one look.

Is make-up and hair important to you and if so how do you achieve your look?

Make-up? Yes very important to everyone - not only trannies even for man and women too.

To what degree do you practice hair removal, and other body feminisation?

I can say hair removal is very important for trannies as you know no body perfect!!! As a tranny we want to look good!!!

Who knows that you dress?

Every one in my family knows that I like to dress up like a gal since my childhood. All I can say I am a very happy and very lucky person on this earth.

How often do you dress and if you go out where to?

Actually, hormones do help for trannies and its goes with hair removal too.

How much of a sexual turn on is trannying for you?

Polite no comment.

To what degree would you consider permanent hair removal, hormones, surgery?

Surgery? For me, I am happy the way I am. For me it is too personal to talk about surgery. Coz we have to think what we want in life!!!

What one piece of advice would you give to someone that has just found they are not the only tranny in the world?

My advice to all trannies in this world. Be kind and be honest to each other, coz without honesty we won't go far. Make lots of friends and make no enemy!!!

**Sasha won
Miss TG Malaysia 2003
and subsequently won
Miss Tiffany's Universe 2003**
She visited London in 2004 and proved to be a delight to meet, very grounded and very lovely.

"Ladies and Gentleman welcome to the gay parade Sao Paulo Brazil 2003 - Come and discover Brazil

Travel with us in this unique moment of luxury, glamour, glory and the joy of a social class, that although repressed, are still happy".

The San Paulo event each year marks our presence throughout the world, with achievements and victories leaves us feeling proud of ourselves. Every day that goes by we keep conquering our universal territory and of course our place in the sun.

Miss Gay Brazil 2002

"Ladies and Gentleman, I, Alekssandra Ceciliato, have come directly from London. I bring our bible 'The Tranny Guide' and I will take back for you a little bit of the gay parade in Sao Paulo for the 12th 'Tranny Guide' with wonderful photos full of beauty, of a gay population that can express their feelings and frustrations without losing the humour and the happiness of living".

Another annual Gay parade in Sao Paulo has ended, and we are already missing it and full of hope for the year to come so we can have another wonderful day like we did in 2003. We hope that 2004 will be even more than perfect.

The gay parade has a different theme every year and this year the theme was..... *Building up Homosexual Politics*

In Brazil the first gay protests started at the end of the 70's in Rio de Janeiro and Sao Paulo with the support of the newspaper 'Lampiao D'Esquina' and the group 'Somos'. From then on in the 80's and 90's there were support groups for gays and transgender people all over the country. Happily we see that every year we advance the work of educating the public to have respect for diversity. It has had positive results in irradicating prejudice.

The first Brazilian Gay Parade was in 1996 and in 1997 over 2,000 people turned up. From 1999 it started to be organised by the association of the proud parade LGBT. (Lesbians Gays Bisexuals Transgender). The movement gets bigger every year in shocking numbers and this year, 2003, we reached one million people.

Michelle X – Organiser Miss Gay Sau Paulo

82

Alekssandra with the 'girls'

Alexia Twister

Thalia

Pietra, Kimberley & Cuka Maxy

Pietra, Mirella & Laleska

Apollo

One million people together ! It was a beautiful sunny Sunday. The march started half an hour late but finally our seventh gay parade was on the streets. This is the biggest event of its kind in Latin America and in second place in the world, losing the first place to San Francisco or maybe Toronto.

The 'Prefect' of Sao Paulo marked her presence in one of the floats and she did not complain for a minute, she danced to the sound of the beautifully decorated floats during the whole march. Although she is the Prefect of the biggest Brazilian town, she also sets a good example of being gay and proud because she has a son who she supports and who is a respected artist and assumed gay nationally.

Anyway the Gay Parade was a big success. We hope that our protests will be heard about our decent and respectable society, and that our lives can be seen as normal. We hope that we can be accepted as human beings, capable and responsible, otherwise we will always be the free show to the eyes of the societies spectators....

With the distribution of the prizes for Miss Gay Sao Paulo 2003 the show came to the end. There were two second places. With the most votes the winner was the publics favourite but, believe it or not, she won only by 3 points, it had to be like this! Of course Miss Gay Sao Paulo will now represent her area in Miss Gay Brazil 2003 in Juiz de Fora and our Miss Sao Paulo will be there with us. Me and 'The Tranny Guide' will be at that marvellous party, because I, Alekssandra Ceciliato am Brazilian and also a Tranny.

Miss Gay Brazil

Be it for lack of curiosity or lack of information most people have no idea about the history and grandiosity of the Miss Gay Brazil competition. The birth of this event, in fact like lots of things, happened by coincidence and like the majority of coincidences, we can now call it a great success!!!

The history of Miss Gay Brazil, started in 1977 from a joke, kidding about the contest Miss Brazil for for women. Chiquinho Mota was one of these jokers. He was also an organiser at that time of the samba school 'Juventude Imperial,' ("Imperial youth"), which was situated in a small town in the interior of Minas Gerais. The school was having a financial crisis and to help raise funds he decided to have a party where the principal attraction was an "alternative" Miss Brazil contest.

The event was an enormous success and started to happen every year always in the month of August. The first three contests in 1977, 1978 and 1979 connected to a samba school had carnival mixed with transformation.

84

People would not want a particular area to win even if they were not from the same area; they wanted all areas of Brazil to be represented.. However their favourite samba schools all from Juiz de Fora, the town where Miss Gay Brazil was born!!

In the eighties the rules for the contest were created - Transgender people with implants could not participate, any participant who had breast implants and won would lose the title from the contest, that's if someone could prove it!!

After the prestige of Miss Gay Brazil was recognised, through the years the contest started to happen in other areas. Originally the contestants after winning in their own area would go onto the main contest to try to win.

In 1999 for example Miss Rondona, sent in her application which was free of charge, in accordance with the organisers of Miss Gay Brazil contest. (They do not charge any extras because all contestants have to pay high costs for travelling, clothes, accessories and staying, etc).

As the years went by the contest became so respected that big celebrities from the music business, politics and TV agreed to form the jury.

The event now takes place every year in August and is now as well respected as the original Miss Brazil contest for gender born women. For one week in August the little tranquil town called Juiz de Fora is turned into a real carnival, with all the hotels fully booked for that week, (the more experienced usually book their hotels 3 – 4 months in advance). The little town stops, with thousands of people in the streets all together to enjoy the event of the year.

As soon as the contestants enter the finals all of their efforts are doubled or tripled. Their efforts are noticed by the organisers and other contestants. They have to make sure that everything is correct at the rehearsal to make sure that on the day of the big contest things will be as perfect as possible...

The Miss Gay Brazil contest is always on a Saturday, followed by an invitation for a social lunch on Sunday. A wonderful Feijoada "Bean Stew" is served with great music. It doesn't matter if it is Axe music, Pagode music or any type of Brazilian music, because what Brazilians really like is a good Feijoada, samba and then drinking the traditional drink known by the name of Caipirinha. It is made with Cachaca, "Fire Water" lemon, sugar and lots of ice.

The event has become very competitive and very expensive; probably the most expensive event of it's kind because of all the fantasy clothes, accessories, travelling and accommodation and everything. but it is all SO worth it to be part of such a great event.

Alekssandra & Miss Gay Sao Paulo 2003

85

WayOut world

Miss Gay Sao Paulo

eronica

Victor

Morgan

Rodrig

Pietra & Kimberly

Alex & Kimberly

ernan

Morgana

Cibelly Star

Pietra

Cibelly

Rasha & Thalia

Miss Gay Sao Paulo as other contests of the same kind makes the heart of the candidates race a bit faster every time the contest is about to start. They will get recognition for the final and one of them will become Miss Gay Brazil 2003.

The house where the event took place is called 'Planet G', and is situated in rua 'Rego Freitas' one of the most well known streets on the old centre of Sao Paulo. One hour before the big party started the venue was already very full.

As soon as I could get in I went straight to the changing rooms to talk to the contestants and take some photos for 'The Tranny Guide'. When I got there I saw three beautiful candidates and when I looked around I realised that choosing the candidate would be a hard job for the judges thoroughly selected by the organisers Bruno and Michelle X, (Miss Gay Brazil 2000).. Amongst this years judges were Miss Gay Brazil 2002, and Miss Gay Sao Paulo 2002, celebrities, and organisers of the Paulistan Night. Two of the judges was none other than the actual mainstream contest winners Miss Sao Paulo 2003 (born gender woman), and Miss Acre 2003 (also born gender woman).

I could see that the audience were very impatient, and of course the contest was a few minutes late to start. As soon as the contest started and the stairs on the big stage came down and nobody else apart from the most qualified and remarkable presenters for this wonderful night appeared. Silvetty Montilla (who has performed in London at our beloved WayOut Club, on her journey to Europe in 2002). Silvetty was joined by the other big star for the night, Greta Star. With her long black hair and her remarkable glamourous, presence on stage, we could not stop the wonderful millions of remarks to her. Her personality shows us her internal light, beauty and love, which she has shared with us for the last 20 years on Brazilian stages.

The night was full of different emotions, celebrations and special presentations. The most remarkable celebration was for an ex colleague of mine who had a big personality, who unfortunately is not with us anymore, but will always be remembered by all of the people who loved her.

The evening dress show started, it was the event most waited for. The enjoyment was enhanced by the wonderful lighting work that follows in detail each step that the candidates takes. The perfection of each dress, looking like they had been designed by God. With every single detail perfect to the millimetre.

At the end of the wonderful, luxurious and feminine, 'evening dress' show, started the big final where the public were already screaming and totally divided supporting their candidates. The judges could not be indifferent in the presence of so much beauty, and as each candidate passed by, the more difficult it became for the judges to make a decision. Even the (gender born woman) Miss Sao Paulo 2003 said that she had never seen to a show like this - the glitter, love and competition and especially the detailed organisation by the organisers Bruno and Michelle X.

Miss Acre 2003 (real woman), Miss Gay Brazil 2002, Miss Sao Paulo 2003 (real woman

Michelle X - Organiser Miss Gay Sau Paulo

Morgana

Morgana

Humiliation House
Where There Is A Fine Line Between Pleasure 'n' Pain!!

09080 191 239
OR 4 MOBILE ACCESS DIAL: 020 8791 0519

Corsets and Stilettoes For These Kinky TV Tarts
09080 191 240

Madam Mandrakes' Castle of Humiliation & Degradation
09080 191 241

I'll Lick it as it Slides In and Out Of Her Forbidden Hole
09080 191 242

Penis Punishment as Administered by Madam Stella
09080 191 243

Worm, Drink My Liquid, Don't Spill A Drop
09080 191 244

The Castle of Feminized Sex Slaves
09080 191 245

Enforced Feminism (The TV Maid)
09080 191 246

Madams' Dungeon of Discipline
09080 191 247

The Governess of Superior Domination
09080 191 248

The Confessions of a She Male Secretary
09080 191 249

Enema Relief Performed By Matron
09080 191 250

Enforced Cross Dressing with Sindy
09080 191 251

Bottom Worship for the Connoisseur
09080 191 252

Janet and Her Whipping Boys
09080 191 253

Gay Sex Initiation
09080 191 254

Miss Vickies' Nursery!!!
09080 191 255

30 Second LIVE Instant Relief
09080 824 097

What is your name and what is your background?

Rani...Indian name for princess a [part] anagram from Dorian..my real name. I'm a DJ. I work in fashion and am a 5th dan black-belt in tae kwondo!

Are you happy to be called a tranny and what does this name mean to you?

Well I get called a lot of things so tranny is the least of my worries but I prefer madame!

How old are you and how young can you remember thinking about or actually cross-dressing?

I'm 33 in tranny years and have been dressing since the age of 4.

Where do you buy clothes?

Karen Millen is my fave, followed by top shop...I invest in a lot of designer clothes and accessories but you can't beat having them bought for you....any offers?

What leads you to choose the styles you wear?

Fashionable in public is THE only way to present yourself...one must keep up to date with Vogue, Cosmo and Footballer's Wives!

Do you have one look or many images?

Never seen twice in the same top is a must ... well not in the same country anyway. It's very difficult to keep up with trends so making good accessory buys is a must along with purchasing designer items that will last and last. You can never go wrong with black! I LOVE leather...jeans skirts jackets and coats...all a must.

Is make-up and hair important to you and if so how do you achieve your look?

Make up and hair...well MAC is the only cosmetic I buy now. It really is brilliant, my hair is taken care of by Hair InXs in Maidenhead. Debbie who owns the salon is an expert at extensions and superb at getting the colours and styles just right!

To what degree do you practice hair removal, and other body feminisation?

I have had 2000 hours of electrolysis, which I wouldn't recommend to anyone any more. I had lazer for one year and am finishing off with IPL which also treats the skin. The lazer is effective as is the IPL. My advice if you're going on hormones...get the hair sorted first, it's less painful!

Photo Hair & Make-up: Pandora De Pledge - Image Works. www.pandoradepledge.com

Who knows that you dress?

Everyone knows i don't [can't] hide it...life really is TOO short.

How often do you dress and if you go out where to?

I've made my life as 'tranny friendly' as possible. I can work, shop, party, eat and sleep as a woman if I wish but this involves being a little ruthless with those who are not inclined to your way of thinking. If you are a confident person and above all honest with yourself and those you love, you will have support, if you don't get support from those around you, you have to look at your relationship and see if they are really people whom you want in your life!

How much of a sexual turn on is trannying for you?

Sex....UGHH

What is your definition of feminine?

Feminine for me is style, sophistication, glamour, intrigue, mystery and conviction!

To what degree do you feel gender dysphoric (i.e that your brain is feminine)?

Who you asking me or her??

What one piece of advice would you give to someone that has just found they are not the only tranny in the world?

If you look at the process of transgenderism as a bus travelling... we all get on and off at different stops some go all the way others get off at the first stop. I like to hop on and off especially when a shiny new bus comes along but I suppose I'll get off when the journey gets a little lonely!!

Finally a piece of advice.....if you are going out dressed try to keep to the basics...even Bet Lynch has a day off!

More Pictures of Rani at
www.pandoradepledge.com/pages/rani/rani1.htm

WayOut
of the closet

A t this point I hope you have found the Personal Profiles in this edition as interesting as we have.

Of course reading the profile while looking at a picture of the individual puts the writing into a totally different context.

This has been my only problem. Some of the most interesting 'profiles' were sent with the most awful pictures. Not that the person looked awful but the PICTURE was awful.

They were sent by email at very low resolution, they were out of focus, they were too dark, they were too small. They were taken in a lonely uninspiring bedroom. The background was horrific. The pose was very unflattering. The picture was more background than subject. AND a mixture of ALL of the above.

"A picture says more than words can"

When you tell someone that you cross-dress, his or her mind paints a picture. His or her mental picture is very unlikely to be flattering. That is the most important reason to have a few good pictures to show of yourself at your best.

"A simple snap can be OK but many do no justice at all. In fact they LET YOU DOWN just when you need all the help you can get".

This article has been edited specifically to help you get a good picture for publication or for your tranny portfolio. Finally if in doubt go to a professional they are worth every penny as none of us are getting any younger and the moment to capture your image is now.

PLEASE PLEASE let me know what you think of the profiles and if you have a set of answers to contribute PLEASE send them to me with YOUR pictures to vicky@wayout-publishing.com or post to
WayOut P.O.Box 70
Enfield EN1 1DA UK

Your Pictures

Whether you are visiting a photographer, or taking the pictures at home ... A photographic session should be a fun experience. To ensure it is - you need to prepare well before hand.
Here are my tried and trusted suggestions:-

1 Collect cuttings of poses and outfits from magazines that take your eye and study them to see if the image would suit you.

2 Practice your favourite poses and images in a mirror.

3 Most people in front of a camera tighten up. So practice smiling into a mirror and when you have it right remember how your face muscles gums etc feel so that you can do it again without the mirror.

4 Set digital cameras to the highest possible resolution and read the article opposite or stick to 35mm if you want to get into print .

You can use a good set of pictures in many ways. A good set of pictures allows you to see more clearly what you look like, which makes it easier to make improvements. If you work with a dressing service or an experienced make-up artist you can vastly improve your appearance. Pictures record the moment for future nostalgia. You may look better but you will never look younger than your last picture.

When shopping in male attire for female clothes etc., again a good photograph slipped out of the wallet will often win an assistants support, help advice and interest.

After pressing the shutter your photographs will be developed without any questions by any film processing lab whether local or mail order service. However, most processing labs will not return pictures that breach any of the obscenity laws. So keep your knickers on or use digital.

If you are worried about being recognised in your pictures remember most cross-dressers are unrecognisable in full make-up, wig etc. However, Aunt Maud's favourite Ming vase in the background may give the game away.

Once you have your pictures you should perhaps consider where you intend to keep them, particularly if there are people that you wish to keep them from.

As for pictures on your computer - I have two words for you ... Gary Glitter.

Continued on page 94 ...

WayOut
of the closet

Your Pictures - continued from page 92

Digital cameras

Are immensely popular with trannies. One reason is that like every one else we like the instant gratification of seeing the picture on the little screen. Of course there are also financial savings in film and developing costs, but more importantly for trannies there are no worries about strangers looking at the pictures.

These cameras have come down in price now and the technology has matured. It is worth buying a camera with a minimum of 3 mega pixels and a good size memory card. This will allow you to shoot many pictures using high resolution ensuring all your pictures will be capable of producing good quality hard prints (and the files will be suitable to a published).

Preparing pictures on the computer

There are many things that can be done with pictures when you get them into a computer. You can send a picture with an email. You can put pictures on a web site or give them to others to put on their web sites. You can print glossy prints to show your friends or to put into a frame. You can offer your pictures to publications without sending prints in the post. You can also manipulate pictures to get rid of wrinkles scratches and red eye (or even add features that do not actually exist - OK - like tits).

The process of downloading to a computer varies and instructions software and hardware will come with the camera. When the picture is in the computer you will need a photo manipulating program to prepare it for any use. This software may come with the camera. The 'free' software may be a limited version of Adobe Photoshop which is the industry standard for working with pictures for publishing or the web. The fully featured Adobe Photoshop cost £449. The second most popular software is Jasc Paintshop Pro. This is often favoured by professional web designers and is slightly easier to find your way around and is cheaper at £60. These programs allow you to rotate the picture, (as any pictures taken sideways will appear on screen on their side), crop the picture leaving the central part of the picture plus more remove red eye, smooth wrinkles save various versions in various folders.

Image Size, Resolution and File Type

Now the tricky technical bit. about resolution, image size and file type. Your digital camera will have a setting for resolution. Typically a resolution setting of 1280 is available on most cameras now. On a 32mb (mega bytes) card you will be able to hold about 60 pictures at this resolution.

Continued on page 96 ...

We all have at one time wanted to do a Photoshoot – But does the thought of an expensive and sometimes sterile photographic studio put you off? Well what about an alternative location – providing interaction with daily life, atmosphere and much more fun! Finding somewhere to undertake an interesting and fun photoshoot is not difficult – it's all about getting the right elements to come together – just follow this simple guide.

Photographer : You may have a talented friend but there is nothing better than working with a professional - be honest - be bold.

Location : You just need to step outside the box and view what's around you from a different perspective. Start by looking at the practicalities - Where do we get changed, or do we change at home? How practicable to access as your 'girl' self, take a walk around, a step back, and look for opportunity.

Outside – This can be the easiest to find – but the most difficult to control. Finding a venue is not about just architecture – which is a good starter, but about finding a vision of colour, texture and style. Street furniture, fencing, doorways, corners of buildings start to take on a new significance. Think about what outfit/look you wish to convey in your location. You need to be streetwise, and to remember its still a public place. There will be interruptions of passers by and cars plus all the obvious comments from White Van Man [love'em]. Above all you should not attract the "authorities" insofar as "causing an obstruction" or a danger to "your" safety. (You know what I mean - read elsewhere in this Tranny Guide – in You and the Law). There are many places that you may think are "public" which in fact are privately owned or managed. Go and see the people responsible and arrange permission (if possible in writing). Take with you a photo of your "girl" self, or better still also bring along your photographer, (it shows you mean business). Outdoor markets and precincts are good examples of this type of location, (you may also need to sign a simple indemnity as well).

There are some disadvantages however in choosing an outside location – weather being the main factor, including most importantly light levels, (I usually try to set up a few dates with my photographer and agree the day before if the shoot is a "goer"). The other limitation is the number of outfits you can use. This can be overcome a little, by changes of accessories and the use of jackets and coats on and off.

Inside – An inside (private) venue – has the advantage of being a more controlled surrounding, with more opportunity to change your outfits. The disadvantage is finding them and getting permission. A good source of ideas are the fashion shoots in mainstream magazines. Getting permission can be more tricky than an outside location as it is far more intrusive to the day to day activities of the venue, expect to work around times that are convenient to them. One really big incentive, is if you intend to try to get your photos published and that their venue will be getting some free publicity.

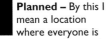

Planned – By this I mean a location where everyone is taking photos (in London you could associate this with Trafalgar Square) – also more usefully indoor events such as the Car Show or Erotica exhibition. – where you have the opportunity to combine writing an article with a shoot. In this circumstance arrange prior permission with the organisers (and get a press pass), but otherwise there aren't many restrictions.

Technical Stuff - Wherever you shoot, lighting is the key. Your photographer

WayOut
of the closet

Your Pictures - continued from page 94

When transferred to the computer the picture will typically be stored at 72dpi (dots per inch) and the size will be 45cm (centimetres) x 33cm (about 18 inches wide).

If you were to send this picture by email it would not fit on the recipient screen (though they 'could' put it into their software and change it themselves if they know how to).

To prepare a picture to send in an email

Save a copy of your picture by renaming it (keep your original file). Working with the copy file - keep the resolution at 72dpi but change the width to 12cm and save as a JPG file type. Some software will offer an optimised setting - choose medium. If not offered this feature look for it in help and optimise your picture. This reduces the size of the file to speed it through the internet and on to the screen.

To prepare a picture for a web site –

Do exactly the same as for an email but change the width to suit the layout of your web page. This will ensure that the pictures pop up as quickly as possible on the web site.

To prepare a picture for a glossy print. -

Save a copy of your picture by renaming it (keep your original file). Working with the copy file – this time change the resolution to 300dpi. The width will automatically change to the maximum size at this resolution.

Any lower resolution will degrade the quality of the picture substantially, (any higher will not make an appreciable difference). Save this file as a TIF file type. Printing the picture will depend on your software and printer – but most will have a straightforward print feature in a drop down menu. Don't forget to load some glossy paper and set the printer options to glossy paper.

To prepare a picture to send to a magazine

Prepare your picture as you would for a glossy print (above). send on a CD or by broadband internet these files will be quite large.

Scanning pictures –

Modern computers have large hard drives so storing a large portfolio of pictures at good quality is unlikely to be a problem. So when you scan select a good target size -select a resolution of 300dpi. Now scan. Save as a TIF file. From this original file you will be able to prepare the picture for glossy print, web site, email or to send to a magazine as above always retaining your original file in your portfolio at optimum quality for further projects.

End

P.S I look forward to seeing your pictures

will be your guide here, as to whether there is enough natural light or flash/portable lighting is required. When my photographer uses his large professional camera people seemed to take our presence far more seriously and are often more considerate . A professional photographer can also make you work for each shot to make them special and not just an endless series of "holiday snap" poses.

The Results - The pictures here were shot at *LOUNGELOVER*, A fabulous cocktail bar in London. Using the principles above I arranged a meeting with their manager and Don Allen (my photographer). I showed them our previous shoots and the ideas that we were looking for in this shoot. It transpired that they were regularly approached for such shoots (so much so that they are able to charge a considerable fee to TV companies and fashion/style magazines). However as this was for hopeful inclusion into this Tranny Guide and Utterly FABULOUS magazine and we were also using a local neighbourhood dressing agency (Adam & Eve) they kindly agreed to waive their fees. (Sorry girls I may have burnt this venue out as a freebie). We arranged for our shoot the following week, and with numerous outfits and the girls from Adam and Eve kindly assisting - Don soon had me working hard. With just enough natural light, Don opted not to use Flash Lighting, which could "bleach" away some of the atmosphere of the unusual surroundings. Unfortunately our stay there was to undertake a shoot so we never had the time to sample the Loungelovers sublime cocktails, Champagne or fine wines (maybe a return visit one evening on a girls night out perhaps!) Well the results of our shoot at this delightful setting are here for you all to see – and hopefully will inspire you to attempt something similar – maybe it will be your pictures in next years Guide!

Andrea - Has had published by WayOut Publishing : - Her profile, A report on a day working as a shop girl, A review of Erotica Show, A review of a fashion Fair, Plus other articles in other magazines and on the Net. These have been based on her communication skills, writing, good subjects and of course the pictures. Thank you Andrea
Andrea's Acknowledgments::
Don Allen Photographic – Tele. 07708 668886
Web site – www.donallen.me.uk
Adam & Eve Dressing Service – Tele. 020 7729 7447
Web site – www.adamandeve121.co.uk
Loungelover (Special thanks to Craig) – Tele. 020 7012 1234
Web ste - www.loungelover.co.uk

WayOut
of the closet

Stepping 'OUT'

Chat Lines

Judging by the number of busy tranny chat phone lines services, it is obvious that trannies and tranny admirers do get their kicks from these services.

For those driven by their sexual desires, these services are a safe option for sexual relief.

Sex on the Net

By the very nature of the internet gender can be disguised. Alias names re-touched pictures and a fantasy life as far from the truth as you wish.

A conversation by email in a chat room or 'one to one' requires only your imagination to take your reader on a gender trip controlled only by your understanding of what the other gender thinks like and writes like.

I know girly girls (real girls) who lead on other girls by talking "like a man" - even girls who join chat rooms as gay guys.

The internet has thousands of sexy personal pages and sites exhibiting every kind of image (Obviously the more explicit are usually commercial and charge a pay per view)

Fetish Fantasy

Some people enjoy fantasy scenarios and fantasy clothes, for example Tarts, Maids, Schoolgirls or Dominatrix.
Some like to enact roles which may be submisive or dominant.

Some like to exhibit themselves in public in there extreme outfits.

However there is no reason to believe that trannies are any more interested in these extremes than the average person.

"It is very important to understand, and at all times to remember that any sex ... MUST be SAFE sex."

What EVER you do play safe. Always use a condom.

Guys have been heard to say to a tranny "why do I need a condom ... you can't get pregnant".

Get real boys and girls, the HIV & AIDS virus has no respect for gender or sexuality. It is possible for sexually transmitted diseases to be passed during any kind of liaison, and it is not only yourself that may be put at risk but also your regular partners.

It is all too easy to get carried away with the fantasy and the excitement and forget the simplest of precautions.

Use a condom WHATEVER you do.

Many dictionaries define a 'Transvestite' as:-
"A person seeking sexual pleasure from clothes normally worn by the opposite sex".
It may be true that trannies get sexual excitement from the feel of ultra feminine clothes on themselves, after all we are led to believe that the majority of men and women get turned on by the same on women..

For example marketing companies use a pair of legs in stockings to sell just about anything, to any one, anywhere. They obviously know they turn people on. So is it any surprise that we find them a turn on when we see them on ourselves.

It is a fact that statistically most TVs are heterosexual.

It is not surprising that a hetro tranny is turned on by frillys on their female partners. This however will often be untrue in reverse. Even female partners who are happy for their partner to cross-dress, may draw the line at love making, dressed this way. In this case it is best that both partners discuss this openly and make a mutual agreement.

When you socialise dressed as a girl in any environment you must expect that you send signals that can be confusing.

Many guys and some girls (and some trannies) like a 'girl' with that little bit extra.

Pre-op TS 'girls' are often more sought after on this scene than their full change sisters. The guys generally see this attraction as 'heterosexual' as they are attracted to a girl; however, what they may be after is a body that they are familiar with, rather than one which can be a total mystery.

Some girls are attracted to trannies for their feminine nature and feminine feel, while still having that all important masculine attribute tucked in your knickers.

Gay guys are generally less likely to hit on a tranny and lesbian girls may come out with the line "If you were a girl I could fancy you", but that really is as far as it goes. Gays are generally less pushy when picking people up than straights, they know that there is a rainbow of people and preferences. They having much more subtle means of communication in these matters knowing that they may be reading the signs incorrectly. You need to know that by your appearance you may be giving a signal that you may also be gay, or bisexual. You may be subtly checked out, but you are very unlikely to need to put off advances from a gay or lesbian. If you do, it will be accepted with respect and without a fuss.

Although, if asked, most trannies would say they were heterosexual most trannies also like to be treated 'like a lady'.

It is now generally recognised that trannies are enjoying a growing level of role play and that includes adopting the sexuality of the borrowed gender (therefore frankly speaking - gay when 'dressed'). In this case the tranny may initially prefer to keep 'wee willy' tucked well out of the way. In fact if willy joins in the games the whole illusion, (and the attraction) may be destroyed. This situation however may be very confusing for the

admirer who may not understand this piece of logic as in his mind he is playing with a chick with a dick and it is the dick that he is interested in. This situation is potentially dangerous and could become violent.

There is only ONE way to avoid 'potential difficult situations' ...

Before retiring to a private place together with anyone, talk about each of your likes and dislikes, don't assume you know what each other are 'into', you will inevitably be wrong. You may even find that talking about it can be as exciting as doing it and is much safer.

Photo Hair & Make-up: Pandora De Pledge Image Works.

WayOut
of the closet
Transgender & the Law

The police in most countries in the world are now taking strides to better understand and serve the LGBT (Lesbian Gay Bisexual and Transgendered) community. and that DOES mean you and me.

Many governments have set targets, guidelines and time scales for these improvements. In the UK the Stephen Lawrence and Copeland nail bombing enquiries branded the police as institutionally racist and homophobic. The government is determined that this situation must be reversed.

We can't expect an instant improvement at street level. But I can assure you that from the highest ranks there is a will to achieve a much better service for trans people.

What does this mean to us? It means that you should feel confident to present yourself 'dressed' in front of a police officer, to give witness details, or to help in an enquiry. You should feel confident to step out of your car and give your details when needed. You should feel confident to report crimes or abuse performed against you. If for some reason, you are taken into a police station under suspicion, for search or questioning. you need to know that you are going to be given equal rights and will not be subjected to distress just because you are a tranny.

Protect & Respect
How is this improvement in the level of service being achieved?

Step 1 During training and retraining at Hendon officers work through sections of their handbook which now has a section relating to transgendered people..

Step 2 - The police now have a trans policy to refer to. It is part of their job description to keep up to date with new and changes of policy. The policy is available in written form and on their (internal) web site, and this policy is under review for further improvement by LGBT advisors working with the police.

Step 3 - In every borough and county a designated LGBT liaison officer is being recruited. This officer is responsible for learning about the transgender community and has responsibility to consider local training issues and all incidents that have LGBT implications. If you feel that the police are not responding to your needs with enough discretion or understanding you need to know that you can ask to bring your situation to the attention of the LGBT-LO. These officers will be working with local LGBT forums (discussion groups), I encourage you to find and attend these forums and add your voice and experience to the efforts in your area.

A review of how well these efforts are working can be found in this edition on page 192 - 194

• In the UK there is no law which states that a male can not dress in "female" clothes

• In the UK there is no law, per-se, which states that a male cannot go into a female lavatory.

Kathy DeVine, our TS lawyer, reminds us however that we can inadvertently put ourselves in the position where we may be accused of an offense

IMPORTUNING: No matter where you are - a bar, a club, a public lavatory or on the street - it is an offense for a man (even for a post-op TS) to approach others persistently, for immoral purposes, i.e. to suggest having sex. This offense is called 'importuning'. You can be fined or even sent to prison. So be careful about using suggestive remarks ... even if joking

BREACH OF THE PEACE : Unless you are completely convincing (lets face it, few of us are) avoid places where you might be received with hostility, eg , straight pubs. If you get into trouble, the police may consider it easier to remove you from the incident (although not necessarily charge you for the potential charge of 'breach of the peace'). Try not to use public lavatories while cross-dressed as If you are 'read' while using the 'Ladies', the police might be called and if you use the 'Gents' you might be assaulted. So avoid places (including gender designated toilets) and groups of people who may feel they can provoke a reaction and then blame you .

INDECENT EXPOSURE: To expose male genitals to a woman without her consent is an offense called 'indecent exposure'. To expose any part of your body to anyone in a way that transgresses the bounds of accepted decency is also 'indecent exposure'. So you might think a mico mini skirt looks fab but others might call it indecent exposure. Simply dress appropriately for the occasion.

AT WORST YOU MUST:

1 - Be polite, even if others are not.
2 - Remain calm and composed.
3 - Reveal to the police your true identity and gender openly and as soon as possible.
4 - Say as little as possible, except for asking what offense you may be considered to have committed.
5 - If taken into custody, ask for immediate legal representation.
6 - Do not make a statement until you have taken proper legal advice.

Disclaimer: The Tranny Guide cannot accept responsibility for the information contained in this article. Or the actions taken upon it's advice.

(International circumstances may differ in detail)

How old are you and how young can you remember thinking about or actually cross-dressing?

My age is rather more than I would like at 50+, the problem is that the plus is 13. I knew of men dressing when I was 9 years old but did not try dressing until I was 54. So I have been dressing now for nearly 9 years. As I was a late starter I have spent a lot of effort on trying to catch up for lost time. I have been to lots of dressing services and now have a large collection of my own outfits. Pandora's has been the highlight of my dressing service experiences.

Where do you buy clothes?

I am a size 14 and shoe size 5 1/2 so I can find good items in charity shops and these come cheap. I do have some items specially made for me. I shop for new items and I have tried items on in a shop, but this is not too usual. I am not at all embarrassed to say that items are for me and I do find this creates great interest from assistants. I buy make-up from market stalls. Following the article in the last Tranny Guide I had a make-over at the MAC counter in Leeds and found this very good recovering the make-over cost in MAC products.

What leads you to choose the styles you wear?

The styles I wear are purely the result of what I have been able to find and where I am to be seen. I like to match with whoever I may be with.

Do you have one look or many images?

The joy of dressing to me is the opportunity to have many looks and images. I delight in fooling people who know me by looking so different that they do not recognise me in person or in my photos. The styles I play with include bridal (I have 12 dresses), maids, PVC, evening wear, period outfits e.g. 50's and 20's (but these are difficult to find).

Is make-up and hair important to you and if so how do you achieve your look?

Make-up and hair is essential to me and I think the most important part of being a transvestite. Pandora's make-up on me was immaculate and I nearly cried when I had to remove it. My eyesight is the biggest handicap to doing a good job. I have quite a few wigs some good favourites and some not so good. I have had great fun from some of the cheapest wigs I have bought.

To what degree do you practice hair removal, and other body feminisation?

I do shave fully even though I am blessed with very little body hair. I have no chest hair at all. I love the smooth legs after shaving, but it grows so quickly. I also pluck my eyebrows which also improves my male appearance. Other body feminisation is only a monthly manicure and hand wax treatment plus clear nail varnish to strengthen the nails (it still does not cure my split nails).

What is your name and what is your background?

My name is Sara Yorke, and I live in a beautiful area of North Yorkshire outside York. Professionally I call myself a physicist and my proper job was in textiles, but not in frocks. Currently I run our family business and this gives me freedom and time to more or less do as I please. I am married and have three children all of whom have left home.

Are you happy to be called a tranny and what does this name mean to you?

I am happy to be called a transvestite. I use the full word rather than any euphemisms as I think one has to come to terms with what one is. To me it means the proper definition of one who dresses in the clothes of the opposite sex.

Photo Hair & Make-up: Pandora De Pledge - Image Works. www.pandoradepledge.com

Who knows that you dress?

My wife knows I dress but we discuss it very little. Originally I asked to visit a dressing service after we had been to see Danny La Rue and I said I would like to get dressed up in the same way. It was much later that she actually saw me dressed, and she then required me to perform as part of the entertainment at one of her Women's Institute do's. My daughter has seen me dressed twice and was most impressed when we went to the Rocky Horror show and the Sing A Long to the Sound of Music (I won a prize there).

How often do you dress and if you go out where to?

I dress a couple of times a week in private. With friends as and when they can come to see me, probably once a month on average. I like to go away for the various weekends, especially the Bridal ones. The places I visit are Bournemouth, Scarborough, Rotherham, Manchester and Blackpool. In practice I aim to be seen by other trannies fully femininely dressed I prefer not to be seen in male garb by others who are dressed.

How much of a sexual turn on is trannying for you?

I think it would be silly for anyone to say that dressing is not a sexual turn on, it has to be. The trick is controlling it as it is most unfeminine to display what is clearly male excitement. The turn on can take many forms including no turn on at all and just enjoying being dressed in something very nice.

What is your definition of feminine?

My definition of feminine is that it is the feeling for an individual rather than the achievement of being a passable woman. What is important to TV's is how they perceive themselves and what they have been able to achieve. A young tranny may be able to throw on a frock and a bit of make-up and wig and look good, but that may not necessarily be feminine to themselves. A tranny who is the wrong size can work very hard at all the details and be feminine to themselves. Beauty is in the eye of the beholder.

To what degree do you feel gender dysphoric?

I personally have no feelings of gender dysphoria. I have considered these issues many times and I conclude that I am a man, but not a macho one, and I am happy with that.

To what degree would you consider permanent hair removal, hormones, surgery?

I have considered hair removal. I have had a consultation with Chris Hart at Cristianos Clinic, having seen the results of one of her clients,. She was very patient with me, explaining all about the procedure. However she said she could not even do a test patch as I was too sunburnt. So I have abandoned the idea.

What one piece of advice would you give to someone that has just found they are not the only tranny in the world?

When I started to dress the objective I set myself, and would commend to someone else, was "Through my dressing I will be a better person ". I have since produced a dedication which sets out my code of life as a tranny, and it works for normal life too. Finally I say to myself "I proclaim myself as Sara a transvestite with pride and confidence, without guilt or self doubt."

Where do you buy clothes?

I am quite shy and easily embarrassed (hence the name) so I tend to shop online. It's cheap, and totally discrete. Some things like wigs need to be bought where you can try them on, but such stores are totally used to trannies so there is no problem. The obvious problem with shopping on line is buying things that you find don't suit you when you get them, but I have learned from my mistakes and get things right most of the time now.

What leads you to choose the styles you wear?

It's easy for trannies to get things wrong. We can't all look like some of the gorgeous tranny babes you see in pictures, so by trial and error you find out what works for you. I see pictures and also women in the street and sometimes try to work out the look they have. Though for me it can be as much about feel as look, what I might wear at home on my own is not always what I would actually be prepared to be seen in. Going to an expert is a huge help, as her experience and skill counts for a lot in helping you find looks that work for you. But like any silly girl I still make ludicrous impulse buys, that are expensive mistakes.

Do you have one look or many images?

I tend these days to stick at one or two looks, that work. The older you get the more you understand. And I go for something that is generally elegant and fairly sophisticated, as I cannot carry off really young styles or ultra skimpy clothes (though I wish I could).

Is make-up and hair important to you and if so how do you achieve your look?

Hair and make up is crucial. I learned an awful lot from having Pandora de Pledge work on me. Hair especially needs expert advice, because a badly chosen wig is a very expensive disaster. Make up is something you can learn by advice and trial and error. But once I have worked out how to achieve something I like, I tend to stick with it.

To what degree do you practice hair removal, and other body feminisation?

I remove what body hair I can, without it being conspicuous in my "normal" life. I shave my legs regularly and keep them

What is your name and what is your background?

My name is Melanie Blush. I am 36 years old, gay and single. I am university educated and work in the academic sector. I currently live in Essex and work mainly in London

Are you happy to be called a tranny and what does this name mean to you?

The name Tranny is a good as any, and though for a long time I didn't like to admit that I was one, I have come to love the term. The first time I openly used the term to describe myself was totally liberating, it meant I had come to terms with what I am. To me now it means excitement, glamour and sex.

How old are you and how young can you remember thinking about or actually cross-dressing?

I am 36 years old, and though I can't be certain, I guess my first urges to cross dress were around the age of six.

more pictures on gallery:
www.pandoradepledge.com/pages/melanieblush/melanieblush1.htm

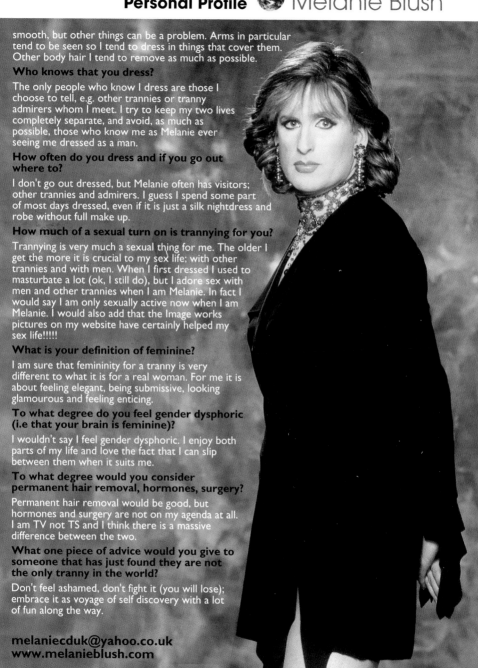

smooth, but other things can be a problem. Arms in particular tend to be seen so I tend to dress in things that cover them. Other body hair I tend to remove as much as possible.

Who knows that you dress?

The only people who know I dress are those I choose to tell, e.g. other trannies or tranny admirers whom I meet. I try to keep my two lives completely separate, and avoid, as much as possible, those who know me as Melanie ever seeing me dressed as a man.

How often do you dress and if you go out where to?

I don't go out dressed, but Melanie often has visitors; other trannies and admirers. I guess I spend some part of most days dressed, even if it is just a silk nightdress and robe without full make up.

How much of a sexual turn on is trannying for you?

Trannying is very much a sexual thing for me. The older I get the more it is crucial to my sex life; with other trannies and with men. When I first dressed I used to masturbate a lot (ok, I still do), but I adore sex with men and other trannies when I am Melanie. In fact I would say I am only sexually active now when I am Melanie. I would also add that the Image works pictures on my website have certainly helped my sex life!!!!!

What is your definition of feminine?

I am sure that femininity for a tranny is very different to what it is for a real woman. For me it is about feeling elegant, being submissive, looking glamourous and feeling enticing.

To what degree do you feel gender dysphoric (i.e that your brain is feminine)?

I wouldn't say I feel gender dysphoric. I enjoy both parts of my life and love the fact that I can slip between them when it suits me.

To what degree would you consider permanent hair removal, hormones, surgery?

Permanent hair removal would be good, but hormones and surgery are not on my agenda at all. I am TV not TS and I think there is a massive difference between the two.

What one piece of advice would you give to someone that has just found they are not the only tranny in the world?

Don't feel ashamed, don't fight it (you will lose); embrace it as voyage of self discovery with a lot of fun along the way.

melaniecduk@yahoo.co.uk
www.melanieblush.com

LIVE CHAT with

Lady Jay

My niché is the training of TV maids & She-Males. Dare You Call!!

09080 824 092

Fetish 4 Mobiles
020 8791 0504

Subservient Transvestites
09080 824 093

𝕱em 𝕯om 𝕺n 𝔜our 𝕸obile
020 8791 0505

Tranny GUIDE
International Listings
.... PLUS

This edition has received a very comprehensive update.

The UK section listings have been fully checked and include many new entries. The International section however concentrates on new reports which include enough contact details for you to follow in the footsteps of our intrepid reporters.

It is always best to telephone or email before visiting. We apologise in advance for any disappointments. We apologise for any omissions from these reports and listings and do not imply any criticism by omission.

On behalf of my readers I am immensely grateful for these contributions. I believe that these reports & listings not only help us to find shops, services and places to go, but **MUCH** more importantly help us all put into perspective, the level of cross-dressing opportunities on a global scale.

I hope that YOU are inspired to send me your pictures and reports. Techno e-mail or a note on a napkin just send it.

Vicky Lee

Profiles

Photo by ullirichter.com (URP London) Tel: +44 (0) 7980 920580
Makeup & Styling by Lorraine@annodom.com
Model Jo@annodom.com

International ■ *Personal* Reports

M Lo

Miss Monica Russo

Katrice

Monica

Marlayna

THE TRANNY GUIDE
ON THE SCENE IN LA
WITH MARLAYNA LACIE

To say that the closing of the LA legend, The Queen Mary Show Lounge, in 2002, left a huge void in the lives of many, would be a gross understatement! Then again, when I met the late rapper/actor Tupac Shakur (RIP), he spoke about how changes are part of life, and we all have them coming to us.

'QUEEN MARY REUNION TOO'

Yes, our beloved Queen is gone. However, her spirit lives on, and that is more than enough to transform people who were always there behind the scenes to step up. Ever since I can remember, Kristina Johnson was a pillar in the Queen Mary family. After the initial shock of the club closing, Kristina decided to ensure that the proverbial Phoenix would rise from the ashes. Her next step was to put together a dedicated group that would put their egos aside to see to it that the legend would continue. Kristina (bless her heart) contacted the ever popular Butch Ellis who was our Front Room Show lounge Mistress of Ceremonies for the last century! (only kidding. Butch!!).

Meetings were held by the trio, and eventually the result was a Friday and Saturday night extravaganza. The show was held at the ever-tranny-friendly Beverly Garland Hotel on Vineland Avenue in North Hollywood. Needless to say I was on cloud nine, when I received a VIP press pass to the first Annual QUEEN MARY TOO REUNION. As expected both shows sold out, and the buzz is that we can look forward to another event next year. When I arrived at the Saturday night show, my limousine driver Larry S. took one look at the crowd waiting to get in. "Look at all those hotties!" Larry salivated. "If I wouldn't lose my job, I would park this tank and join you!" After I informed him that most of these 'hotties' were trannies. Larry just smiled and indicated that he was just fine with that revelation!

It was as if the Karma of the Universe had said, "Lets' do the Queen Mary Time Warp again!" The show started with MC Butch thanking all for attending and then she mentioned that we should thank Kristina for all her efforts. It was pandemonium in the room, when Kristina took the microphone to

It's a WRAP with Vogue

Miss Simone

welcome and thank all in attendance for making this very special night a reality. Then, it was Showtime! The magic of the Queen was back in full force, as the lovely ladies hit the stage with a sizzling rendition of "Lady Marmalade". The next two hours were a high- energy, non-stop drag revue which featured some of the premier acts presented over the years at the club. Leading the troupe was veteran stage diva Miss Monica Russo, who stole the show with her sexciting number "Devotion"!

This reporter was seated with Kristina and her 'Girls' however, I spent most of my evening scampering around taking photos for you to see.

'ANNUAL WEST HOLLYWOOD DRAG RACE'

This event is the first of the official "tranny season" in West Hollywood and is a prelude to the huge costume contest to be held on the following

Momma with Dragsters

weekend (but this year rained out)! However, the sun was shining this day and the cameras were rolling at this high-heeled drag race.

The rules for this 50-yard dash requires that all the contestants run in three inch heels or stiletto pumps, and all must be in DRAG. This event is a media favourite, with numerous video crews from local television stations and hundreds of people in attendance. The party, (excuse me! The DRAG race) was staged on the sidewalk in front of *MICKYS*, which is located in the notorious gay jungle known as "Boys Town" on Santa Monica (S & M to the locals) Boulevard. The drag races was a sight to behold, as the ladies (and Pete Penn from the Sharon Osbourne Show) ran the gauntlet. By the way, Pete was resplendent at race time, in a pair of whorehouse-red hooker heels! Later, the Master of Ceremonies David Logan began to announce the winners and present the prizes. During the ceremony David announced that he had a very special presentation to make. MOMMA West Hollywood's most celebrated drag diva was awarded the Key to the City of West Hollywood! Yours truly had a memorable afternoon, taking photos and recommend you time your LA visit to join the fun and zany antics of the West Hollywood Drag Races.

Sister

Rhor

Loret

111

Miss Coco Peru

Judy

Winner of Miss Red Dress

'THE RED DRESS PARTY'

The Tranny Guide was on the scene at the 'Aid for Aids' benefit: The Red Dress Party on Sunday, October 26th at The Factory in West Hollywood. The nightclub was transformed into a Hall of Candy Apple Red: Asian Style specifically for this incredible revival event. Red dresses, Red Costumes, Red lingerie, even Red chaps. Guests from glamourous to gaudy and creative to curious, dragged the red out of their closets and flaunted it during this fabulous evening of dancing, divas, and dazzle. Billed as "the highlight and must-do event of the Halloween season" this gala had everything from a first class VIP room with complimentary Smirnoff bar, neck and hand masseurs and make-overs by Too-Faced cosmetics) to an outrageous costume contest hosted by "The Goddess of Comedy" Judy Tenuta and "The Drag Queen of Comedy" Bridgett of Madison County.

Jazzmun, Marlayna & Yolanda

Jasmine & Momma

Participants were judged by celebrities Jean Smart (Designing Women), Joan Van Ark (Knots Landing) and Patrlka Darbo (Days Of Our Lives) for the titles of Miss Red Dress, Miss Red "Guess" and Miss Red MESS.

For 20 years. 'Aid For AIDS' has provided direct financial assistance to persons living with HIV/AIDS that are disabled and living below the poverty line. AFA's mission is simple: keep a roof over their clients heads and the lights on by paying for the necessities of life-including housing, health insurance premiums, and medications. THE RED DRESS PARTY is the 'benefit' to help raise awareness and the much needed funds. Make sure you globe trekking trannies attend the NEXT year and the Halloween Costume Parade and Carnival as they are both held the same week!

'DRAG *N* YOU OUT PARTY'

"Drag N You Out" is the brainchild of Hollywood's favourite drag diva, Jazmine, who can be seen as a guest star on "The Anna Nicole Show" as Anna's lookalike "gal pal." Committed to taking the art of drag transformation to a new level. Jazmine's mission is to inform educate and promote tolerance for people of all creeds, colours and sexual preferences. On Thursday June 19, www.jazmine.com (www.jasminesworld.com) presented a dazzling evening of drag at 'The

Jackie Beat & Marlayna

Claire Voyant
& Marlayna

Andy Warhols superstar Holly Woodlawn
also subject from Lou Reeds song
"Take a Walk on the Wildside"

Chad
Michaels

Jazzmu[n]

Chi Chi La Rue

Momma

Dee Dee Divine

Factory' in West Hollywood. The event was in memory of renowned make-up artist Kevyn Aucoin, and 100% of the proceeds benefited the Elizabeth Glaser Paediatric AIDS Foundation. "Drag N You Out" kicked off Gay Pride weekend with MC Boy Mike, and was directed and choreographed by critically acclaimed choreographer Brian ("BP") Paul Mendoza. (Grease! 42nd Street, A Chorus Line, and Bye, Bye, Birdie. Xanadu Live. Coop's |As It Is In Heaven and Matrix's Anyone Can Whistle). The glamourous divas included Adrenalin, Bel Aire, Bridgette of Madison County, Cassandra Fever, Chad Michaels, The Chanell Twins. Cherie. Chi-Chi La Rue. Chris Green. Clare Voyant, CoCo Peru, The Confused, Constance, The D.D. Divine. Desiree La Fernme, Diva, Dixie Longate, Electra Lox, Ethylina Canna, The Fabulous Phyliss, Fontasia LaMore, Glamour, Holly Woodlawn, Honey Suckle, Honey West, Jackie Beat, Jazmine, Jazzmun, John Price, Julie Shepard, Karen Dior, Kelly / Mantle, Lady Dante. Lucky Charm, Milienium. Momma, Mr Dan, Nomi Moore, Niki Starr, Scott Kaske, Sister Roma! Seven, Shante Bouvier, Tera Nova, Vida de Ville and Viva Sex.

'CLUB 7969 TRANSFORMATION RELEASE PARTY'

Every Friday and Monday evenings the CLUB 7969 is T-girl central with a non-stop parade of trannies of every type and persuasion. They say LA'S the place and in many ways this true! The hottest drag shows and concrete catwalk on the West Coast and maybe even on this drag loving planet IS the CLUB 7969 .

Yours truly along with Viva Sex are presenting release parties every time a new copy of 'Transformation' magazine is published.. It's a perfect Friday night in Southern California at the infamous T-Girl palace the 'CLUB 7969' (formerly known as Peanuts) is packed with a standing room only audience. LA'S premier Madonna-style clone Viva Sex has once more claimed the club's stage for her own and was just finishing, thanking her audience

113

for all their love and support. I assumed (WRONG!) the show was over, so I began to sashay over to the back bar for a quick libation. To my surprise I heard the siren call from Viva onstage... "WHERE'S MARLAYNA?? She was just here a moment ago, snapping pics for The Tranny Guide from England. Twas like someone hit the "ON" switch and yours truly was up on stage with Viva doing a major show and tell for The Tranny Guide. **www.vivsexmadona.com**

'LYDIA'S TV FASHIONS'

13837 Ventura Blvd. Suite 2 Sherman oaks. Open Tuesday through Saturday 12 pm to 7 pm. Email: lydiastv@sbcglobal.net. Tel: 818 995-7195 toll free Tel: 866-995-7195.
Yours truly has been shopping at Lydia's TV Fashions from evening number one! On a recent visit I overheard a globe trekking gal from Scotland exclaim, "YOU folks have it all! I think I'm in Tranny Heaven"! Lydia's TV Fashions has been a local and International resource for TGs and cross-dressers of every persuasion since 1991. They stock wigs, breast forms, foundation garments, panties, maid outfits and shoes and heels up to size 17,

dresses, skirts, sexy top, unique fashions, stockings, magazines, books, feminising supplements and a full line of makeup. Discretion and privacy are always a priority so parking and the store entrance is off the boulevard. A unique service exclusive to Lydia's is their 24/7 access to a discreet private dressing space with personal lockers for a monthly fee. Lydia's has complete make-over and transformation services as well as makeup lessons; everything to transform you into the inner woman you wish to express. One can rent complete outfits for a few hours in the store or for an evening out on the town. Lydia's also has a 'Personal Guide' service available to make your trip out shopping or to famous tranny palaces like the 7969 CLUB, memorable, safe and secure.

Lydia's has been under the new management of Jerry and Kelly Nakahara since 2000 and they roll out the royal red carpet when they welcome out-of-towners and first-timers. If you are new to the tranny scene, curious, or just ready for your first night out 'en-femme, the owners and staff at Lydia's are there to help you. By the way, I have to mention that Lydia's always has the latest issues of most magazines including Transformation and of course the Tranny Guide. A more substantial report with many pictures on this exceptional service by Vicky Lee is available in issue 9 of the Tranny Guide.

'CLASSIC CURVES INTL'

P.O. Box 115, Wilmington, CA 90748 USA tel/fax: 562-595-9148, Outside California call 888-898-8787, or e-mail: cci@fws.net
Ms. Espy Lopez and her team at Classic Curves are celebrating their 10th year serving the transgender community. They offer custom-made body prosthetics for the TG woman who demands the very best. Classic Curves outfitted three movies this year along with orders from various costume houses and theatres. 2003 saw the introduction of 'Veronica 3' with innovative polymer jell prosthetic pads for the derriere and hips, a development of their best selling product . They are now working on 'Veronica 4' a pull on garment with bra cups that are strong enough to hold the weighty jell pads. **www.clcrv.com**

Ter

'THE JIM BRIDGES BOUTIQUE'

12457 Ventura Blvd, Suite 103, Studio City, CA 91604, www.jbridges.com
Phone: +1 818-761-6650 Weds – Fri 12pm -
6pm Saturdays 12pm - 10pm.

When I first came out of the proverbial closet,
my friend Melissa Foster introduced me to Jim
Bridges. At that point in time, I had just started
presenting parties at the Back Bar of the Queen
Mary Night Club. Not satisfied with my
feminine image at the time it was Jim, with his
magic wands and 37 years of experience in the
beauty industry, who helped me get there! The
Jim Bridges Boutique has been helping ladies like
me out of the closet for the past 17 years with
make-overs wigs and advice and a unique range
of clothes and accessories. Jim's store is a safe,
warm and friendly place to shop for all your
cross-dressing needs in one location. With Jim

and his staff of professionals, who have literally transformed the looks of
thousands of trannies from around the world, you know that you are in the
hands of experts.

'REEL CLOTHES'

5525 Cahuenga Boulevard in NoHo
(between Chandler and Burbank)
(818) 508-7762.
e-mail: sales@reelclothes.com

Have you ever watched a movie, and wondered
what happened to those hot dresses, props and stuff after they finish filming?
The major movie studios like Disney, Universal, MGM, Sony and Warner
Brothers have huge wardrobe and prop departments. However, they also
have space limitations! Like all of us, they have to "clean out their closets"
every so often. Back in 1981, Elaine Volmer was working for the wardrobe
department of a major movie studio. Elaine decided to open up a shop that
had an orderly, systematic method of re-selling wardrobe and props to the
public. In 1991, Holly Hunter came on board as Elaine's partner and general
manager, and now the small boutique has grown into a thriving and very
"tranny friendly" business! Because of North Hollywood's proximity to the
movie production centres, many actors and actresses live, shop, and dine in
the area. Reel Clothes can claim a number of famous movie people who
have actually shopped at the store, including Amanda Plummer, Deborah
Harry, Lori Petty, Kathy Ireland, Geena Davis, Dave Foley, Leonard Maltin,
Judy Tenuta, Emo Phillips, and Marlon Brando. At the 2003 Tranny Guide
Party, I wore a shimmering gold dress from REEL CLOTHES. I was told by
a wardrobe expert that it was from the hit show Baywatch, and that Pamela
Anderson had previously worn it!! Now, every time that I visit Reel Clothes,
I head for the rack where I originally found this dress.

Now, the good news for you is that you can visit their shop and NEVER
leave your home! Yes, please check out their website, www.reelclothes.com
for fun and unique items from the movies and television. And, please tell
them you read about their "tranny friendly" shop in the TRANNY GUIDE
and that Marlayna Lacie sent you! www.marlaynasworld.com - email:
marlaynalacie@earthlink.net.

Showgirls

It's been twenty years since the legendary "La Cage" show first opened at the very 'drag friendly' Las Vegas Riviera Hotel and Casino on September 18th 1985. Sceptical casino owners first booked the show for only a three month run, but business mogul Norbert Aleman and determined twenty year old, Frank Marino both knew this was show was a winner. The rest is history!

Frank always knew he'd become a star. What he didn't realise is that he'd be dressed in Bob Mackie gowns, to do so. Frank says, "climbing the ladder of success was even harder wearing heels." Now an accomplished author, newscaster, columnist, spokesperson, and America's favourite "male actress". His ten year, ten million dollar contract makes him the longest running headliner in Las Vegas. If you haven't seen "La Cage" starring Frank Marino, I suggest you make your reservations ASAP. The show is a fast paced, energetic show in which a fabulous cast of female impersonators recreate a galaxy of stars. Frank entertains with dialogue and ad-libs in the persona of Joan Rivers with a change of costume between each and every act from a wardrobe which even the late Liberace would be jealous. The word is that when tourists visit Las Vegas there are three things they come for: gambling, a trip to the Hoover Dam, and a chance to see Frank Marino perform in this award-winning. For more information, call the Riviera Box Office at (702) 794-9433, or click on either **www.theriviera.com or www.frankmarino.com**

Marlayna: I have to congratulate you on your 20 year anniversary at the Riviera. After 13 years at the QMSL I know a just little bit about the hard work and sacrifices that come with the drag/stage lifestyle. Can you tell us how you feel after making history as the "premier drag diva" of the 20th Century. You ARE a living legend!

Frank: I don't know about a living legend, but I realise I have made a mark and opened the door for other female impersonaters to take their craft higher than some thought was possible.

M: When did the you realise that you were not like all the other boys?

F: I always liked the female Divas and never really cared much for the big male action starts.

M: A little please about the first time you got all dolled up?

F: I was 17 and it was Halloween and I got dressed up like the supreme diva Diana Ross.

M: Did you date in high school or did you know you were gay by then?

F: I always knew I was gay from the day I was born.

M: A little about the magic! How was it when people reacted to how hot you looked?

F: I feel people always react to glamour and the attention you get is such a great high.

M: When did you first hit the stage in drag doing your infamous 'Joan Rivers' impersonation?

F: After doing Diana Ross I wanted to do something a little less challenging with the make-up and tried Joan Rivers. I also wanted to be a live performer and tried stand-up as Joan Rivers in a nightclub on an open mic night.

M: Were you surprised or relieved or both when Joan dropped her lawsuit and you two bonded as friends?

F: I was surprised when Joan gave me the infamous law suit and was then relieved when we settled it. After all I was about 80 bucks short.

M: How long did you tour and perform before you signed with the Riviera?

F: I toured for about two years in the tri-state area and then 'lucked out' *(got lucky)* after a Joan Rivers performance for the producers of the 'La Cage' show.

M: There is always a first! A few words about the time you wore your own Bob Mackie gown!

F: Well, I had always heard of Bob Mackie. But when I finally had a chance to get one of his gowns for myself, I felt that I had really arrived!

M: A few words please about the good times and a few about the things that you lose when you have a career and it forces you to make sacrifices on many levels.

F: Most of the times here have been good. Although there are many sacrifices that must go along with. Like not being able to see your family or the amount of doors that close in your face when you try to meet a guy.

M: I appears all worthwhile! How do you feel when you look back and at the same time look forward to the future?

F: I look back in amazement and just smile. I could just hope the future is as bright as the past.

M: Can you tell our readers what they find then they visit your award-winning website

F: They will see the latest happenings of both Fran Marino and the La Cage Show plus some merchantry souvenirs.

M: I love your show! Please give all those globe trekking trannies making plans of visiting Las Vegas an update on your La Cage show at The Riviera?

F: Well, we pretty much are the Grand Divas of the 20th Century! Its a high energy, fast paced review with a lot of Glitz and Glamour!

M: OK Frank we are gonna call it "a wrap" for the Tranny Guide. I want to thank you for your time and attention and I will be watching for the UPS guy as I am hot for the Bob Mackie gown I begged you for!

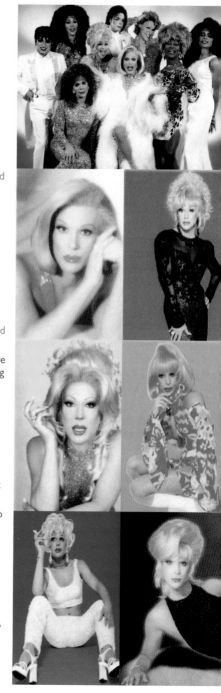

To say that Vicki Rene and I go "way back" would be an understatement. We met when I first started to venture into the cross-dressing lifestyle. She has become famous for being one of the most community-focused globe trekking trannies in our world-wide TG Community. Over the years, Vicki has become a leader and role model to many of us trannies, and I cherish her friendship. I also appreciate her hold-no-punches attitude, and she tells it like it is.

Marlayna: Please fill us in on the latest project that has you all excited.

Vicki Rene: My latest project has just ended with the conclusion of Southern Comfort Conference. Another year is over, and as always I had a great time. I think I have finally admitted to myself that I am part of the SCC family. I have been told that, for the last couple of years, by the two people that mean the most to me concerning this great event, Terry Murphy and Sabrina Marcus.

M: The Internet has truly changed us all. Can you give us a glimpse into the future, and predict where the Web will take our community?

V: Well like I tell everyone, the Internet has made us one! Before we were a bunch of little groups all over the world, fighting for our own rights, not thinking of others. Now we are united. Now when the word transgender comes up it is not just the TS in New York or California, but it also stands for the TV, TS, even the Drag Queen. Also it is not only for the male to female, but for the thousands of females to males that are out there, fighting for their rights also.

M: When did you realise that the Internet was going to revolutionise our world, and that trannies could (and would) be a part of it?

V: I have always kept an eye on the internet because I worked in a high tech job where we were always talking about the future. One day at work, back in the early 90's I typed in the word 'transvestite' into a search engine. I could not believe how many sites came up! Within a week I had my own brand new computer at home. I have always had contact adverts in magazines so a few people could get to know me, but once I saw other girls websites with more than one picture of themselves, I knew I needed my own site which was born in 1994. It start out with pictures of just me, then a few friends asked to be on it. Now I have over 5500 of my "Bestest Friends" on my site. I have over 600 pages of info on the site to look at.

M: What will our readers find when they visit your website www.vickirene.net?

V: Most likely they will find what ever they are looking for, with the exception of seeing girls with their "wee wee" showing. My site is all about beauty, and a girl with her penis showing to me is not pretty. I even have a few female to males on there if that is what you are looking for.

M: Can you share a Vicki Rene story with us?

V: Jim Thompson from Versatile Fashions, who also happened to be my room mate at the time. came over to me and told me his car had broke down, and he needed someone to help him push it. So wearing four inch heels and a dress up around my ass I helped push the car. All of a sudden

another car stopped and four of the biggest, best looking, men I have seen in years jumped out. I was not sure if they were there to help or kick the cute little ass of the "boy in a dress". One of them said to me, "Miss why don't you get into the car and drive and we will push it!" They pushed it about 100 yards to a parking space on the side of the road. Looking in the mirror, I saw one of the them was walking up to my drivers window, I thought ok, now it is ass kicking time, but no, this cute young man handed me his business card, and asked me to give him a call. I said "thank you" in my best girly voice and told him I would do that. I still have that card, 15 years later.

M: What have you been up to lately? It seems like you move from coast-to-coast about every year and a half?

V: I am now living in Jacksonville Florida, but you are right I do like to pack up and move a lot. I have moved coast to coast four times and even had a stop in Dallas for a while, it was mostly work related. Now I am unemployed and looking for a job - are you hiring?

M: What ARE your plans for the future?

V: I don't think I want another "high pressure" position I would like to live a few more years as a healthy YOUNG lady! I would like to find something that allows me to travel.

M: Do you find, since 9/11, that you feel travelling with drag items in your suitcase affects your attitude?

V: If 9/11 happened 20 years ago, it would have been different for all of us, I think it would have forced us, those who were out, back into the closet because security people did not understand us at all back then, if they asked us questions they would not have understood our answers. I flew about a week after it happened and I will tell you I was nervous about someone going through my luggage and finding all my makeup, hair, jewellery and everything else feminine and no male clothing at all, but nothing happened. I was going to an event in Denver the next year and I was questioned but I told them I was a transgendered and nothing happened. I guess if you are honest most of them do understand. To be truthful I am glad they ask questions, it makes me feel they are doing their job.

M: Let's wrap this up with some advice to trannies.

V: I get a lot of people that write me saying "what if I am seen by someone I know"? I tell them, "No one sees us on the internet by accident, they are looking at transgender site for one of two reasons, they are either one of us or want to be with us" But also say this, no one should ever put a picture of themselves on the internet until they are 100% ready to be there. You should make up your own mind, don't let anyone and I mean ANYONE try to talk you into it - if you are not ready.

Also if you have any questions at all, email me at **vickirene@aol.com** and if I can't help you, I will send you off to someone that can. I am not a doctor so please don't ask me to help you medically and above all I am not a dating service, so don't ask for me to help you there either. I have enough problems just helping me in the dating area.

www.vickirene.net

Gina Lance is the Editor-in-Chief of GIRL TALK Magazine (www.girltalkmag.com) which is available both in print and now on the web to download on subscription basis.

For the 12th edition of The Tranny Guide Vicky Lee asked me to write about the phenomena of TG Conventions in the USA.

I guess these events are almost unique to the U.S, as cross-dressing and being transgendered is unique in its variance from country to country.

TG or cross-dressing conventions began popping up in the United States about 25 years ago. In the U.S as in most countries, those who are transgendered, and afraid to venture out in their home town, feel more at ease in a city hundreds, if not thousands, of miles away from home. The safety of anonymity and the distance from people who know them in their male selves provides a barrier of protection for their feminine persona.

Most conventions in the U.S. that I've attended have sheltered those amongst us with this worry by offering a sanctuary in which we can relax. And many local transgendered join in the festivities as well. Although I've often said that I've never met a cross-dresser who was recognised in her femme mode, many people who are high profile or refuse to go out in the small towns in which they live, feel a convention is a much safer choice.

In general, all conventions include make-up seminars, fashion shows, award celebrations and Saturday night dances when you get to wear your favourite evening finery.

Many also include workshops dealing with poise, hormones and SRS surgery.

Here are some of my favourites:

JANUARY – "First Event"

Held in Woburn, Massachusette every January, this event kicks off TG conventions for the year. Sponsored by the Tiffany Club of New England, 2004 was their 24th annual get together. GIRL TALK columnist Brianna Austin from New York City usually braves the New England winter chill to make this event. You can reach the girls at the Tiffany Club at www.Tcne.org –

APRIL & OCTOBER – "Eureka En Femme"

Held in beautiful Eureka Springs, Arkansas; a Victorian historic town in the northwest part of the state. This is my favourite convention because hosts Becca and Dixie Nettle (husband and wife) urge attendees to get out of the hotel, visit the hundreds of local shops, and get used to being themselves. A great convention for "newbies". You can get more information at www.femmegetaway.com

JUNE – "The Be-All"

Usually held outside of Chicago, Illinois before the summer heat rolls into Midwest America. Lots of great people and great times! Reach them at www.be-all.org

SEPTEMBER - "Southern Comfort"

Held in beautiful Atlanta, Georgia this convention attracts probably the most diverse members of the TG community including many F to M's. In 2003 I ended up being a Keynote Speaker when author Noelle Howey fell ill in Chicago. This was an interesting turn of events for me, because SCC was one of my very first times out, many years ago. Find out more about Southern Comfort at www.sccatl.org

Here are a few more conventions you might also try.

MARCH

Colorado Goldrush www.cologoldrush.org held in Denver, Colorado

"Puttin' On The Glitz" www.tgharmony.org held in beautiful Phoenix, Arizona.

APRIL

California Dreamin, Co-sponsored by The Powder Puffs of Orange County and ETVC, RGA, and the Diablo Valley Girls Golden Gateway Holiday Inn 1500 Van Ness Ave. San Francisco

Annual IFGE Convention and Trans Youth Conference Hosted by the Greater Philadelphia Chapter, Renaissance Educational Association Write: Cioe Enterprises PO Box 61 Easton, PA 18044-0061 Phone: 610-759-1761Email: convention@ifge.org

JUNE

Be All You Can Be, Chicago, IL, contact Naomi Owen, POB 10240, Chicago, IL 60610

Second International Congress on Crossdressing, Sex and Gender Issues Renaissance Education, Assoc., Inc. Congress Registration 987 Old Eagle School Road, Suite 719 Wayne, PA 19087, Phone: (610) 640-9449, (610) 648-0257 FAX congrs2@cdspub.com

Be-All, P.O. Box 15237, Pittsburgh, PA 15230, http://users.aol.com/chitriess/trisss/beall.htm

JULY

Annual spouses and partners conference, Peggy Rudd, POB 5304, Katy, TX 77491, Ph. 915-343-1953 E-mail to: melpeg@phoenix.com

Gender, Sexuality, and Law Conference, "Reflections: New Directions", Keele University, Staffordshire, UK, GSL98 Conference Department of Law Keele University, Staffordshire ST5 5BG, England, UK, 01782-593218, 01782-593228 FAX, GSL98@keele.ac.uk

AUGUST

FTM Conference of the Americas, Massachusetts College of Art, Contact: Mykael Boston FTM Conference, POB 229, Waltham, MA 02254

SEPTEMBER

Southern Comfort Conference, Atlanta, GA, Southern Comfort Conference, P.O. Box 77591, Atlanta, GA 30357-1591, 404-633-6470, E-mail at: info@sccati.com web: www.sccati.com

Harry Benjamin International Gender Dysphoria Symposium, Vancouver, BC, Canada, HBIGDA, 3790 El Camino Real, #251, Palo Alto, CA 94306, Phone: (415) 322-2335, (415) 322-3260 FAX

OCTOBER

Fall Fling, Providence, MA, Tiffany Club of New England, P.O. Box 2283, Woburn, MA 01888-0483 1-617-891-9325 (Tues. 7:30-10:30 pm)

Rainbow Spirit Convergence, Kindred Spirits, P.O. Box 18332, Asheville, NC 28814, Phone: (704) 253-9882

Fantasia Fair, Provincetown, Cape Cod, MA, Registrar, P.O. Box 2734, Boston, MA 02208, 617-522-6033, http://www.cowart.com/outreach

Transgender & Transgender Cinema Film Fest, The Roxie Theater, San Francisco, 584 Castro St., #273, San Francisco, CA 94114, 415-552-4249

NOVEMBER

Queer spirits-- Transgender Spirituality Conference, Highlands, NC, Holly Boswell, P.O. Box 18332, Asheville, NC 28814, (704) 253-9882, aegis@mindspring.com

Holiday en Femme, Chicago, IL, Chi Chapter, P.O. Box 40, Wood Dale, IL 60191-0040, Phone: (708) 364-9514

Long Island Femme Expression, 11th Anniversary Ball, PlainView Plaza, 150 Sunnyside Blvd., PlaneView, NY, mail to LIFE, P.O. Box 3015, Lake Ronkonkoma,NY 11770-0417, 516-471-6037

"Conventions really are a great way to get out and meet new friends. If you're just coming out of the closet, they really will help you get used to your TG self. It worked for me!"

Beth Boye - Owner & Amanda

Charlene & Roxy

Transforming Faces

Amanda Wood

America - USA ■ *A Personal* Report

Austin. Nestled in the beautiful Texas hill country, is the state capital, home to a vibrant nightlife and is also famous for being the "Live Music Capital of the World".

If live music is not your thing, there is a thriving live theatre scene, art house cinemas and a vital club DJ scene. A variety of restaurants ranging from earthy ethnic to elegant fine dining surround us. There are also many little neighbourhoods, like South Congress Avenue and Hyde Park, with cozy coffee houses and designer boutiques. A new international airport has made this Texas treasure more accessible than ever before.

Beneath Congress Avenue Bridge, spanning the Colorado River, which divides the city's north and south sides, resides the largest urban bat colony in North America. Approximately 1.5 million Mexican free-tail bats have made the underside of the bridge their summer home, and in the process created one of the city's major tourist attractions. It can take up to 45 minutes for the bats to make their exit from beneath the bridge each evening at dusk.

Austin's unique party atmosphere begins on historic 6th Street. A cleaned up, funky version of New Orleans's famous Bourbon Street, Austin's 6th Street offers the busiest nightlife of any major city in the state. It's a diverse mix of dance clubs, bars, pool halls, restaurants, comedy clubs and live music venues in the midst of a virtual melting pot of people, from college kids to professionals, and teenyboppers to punks. Red River Street, which plays host to much of Austin's alternative live music scene, intersects 6th Street, as does the Warehouse District on the opposite side of Congress Avenue.

The Warehouse District features a more grown-up atmosphere, with a variety of elegant, upscale pubs, clubs and fine dining at some of the city's best restaurants. You'll even find a couple of queen friendly gays clubs here – the BOYZ CELLAR , home to the LIPSTICK LOUNGE, with shows featuring creative, young drag queens, and OILCAN HARRY'S, both near 4th Street and Lavaca.

The decidedly liberal attitude of the city (Austin has had a clause in its City Charter since the early 1980's expressly forbidding discrimination for sexual orientation, including transgenderism), along with its rolling green hills and beautiful lakes makes Austin a Mecca for fun seekers from all around the state. At the beginning and the end of each summer, the city is host to Splash Days, when gays from across the state converge on Lake Travis by day, and at night party at the many great dance clubs scattered throughout the downtown area.

"Austin has a colourful and exciting transgender scene".

BOUT TIME, can be found by taking the highway north toward Dallas it will bring you to 'this cross dresser's bar in the northern part of city. A favourite of the local tranny and cross dressing girls, it serves a mixed gay and lesbian crowd in a tavern style bar with a safe, relaxed and friendly atmosphere, and it is recommended as the #1 tranny bar in Austin by TRANSFORMATIONS MAKE UP & HAIR. Entertainment includes pool tables, video games, large screen TV, sand volleyball courts and the most fun drag shows in town.

122

CHARLIE'S is back downtown, standing in the shadow of the capital. It is the oldest gay bar in the city and still draws a crowd with nightly events. The crowd consists mainly of guys, gals and trannies of all shapes, sizes and ages. Special events are scheduled for every night of the week, whether its drag shows, pool tournaments or free buffets. Charlie's Sunday Show is the most professional drag show in the city.

THE 1920'S CLUB is an upscale martini bar just 2 blocks from the capitol building and is hosted by and is frequented by a growing number of transgender patrons seeking a quieter alternative to 6th Street. It boasts a very comfortable environment for transgirls and their spouses and also has a very elegant after theatre crowd. It's the kind of place a bi-curious F. Scott Fitzgerald would choose to take a nightcap.

SIDEKICKS, the newest club on the Austin T-scene, is a multi level dance club featuring three separate and distinct clubs in one arena. The standout being the Show Room, which features extravagant drag shows and pure Texan beauty as well as an enormous lesbian clientele. It also hosts pageants and other special events in the area.

Austin's own fabulous cross dressing make over service

TRANSFORMATIONS MAKEUP & HAIR was founded in 1990 and is owned and operated by myself - Jon Davis (aka Beth Boye).

Transformations is well known throughout America and is dedicated to serving all of our sisters in the transgender community. Beauty is my livelihood. As a licensed appearance designer and image consultant I work daily mostly with female clientele,. I may be doing ad campaigns, fashion shows or beauty pageants.

Transformations is a natural extension of my lifelong experience as a transgendered person and is the basis for my belief that every TG person, especially those new to the art, should have professional image counselling to ensure success in creating their own unique style.

Team Transformations' talented make up and hair artists are trained in our techniques of contouring make up and are very experienced in the proper use of cosmetics and how to fulfil the needs of our TG clients by educating and advising them on how to achieve a pretty and passable appearance, thus achieving an inspirational and positive effect on their cross-dressing activities.

Whether you are a first timer or a more experienced transsexual, we are ready to welcome you to Transformations Make-up & Hair. We offers something for everyone!

Beth and Girl Talk's Bijoux

Marlena , Beth & Lauren

Jon Davis at work

Team Transformations

Marlena & Stacy

America - USA ■ *A Personal* Report

Ms Bob

San Francisco is a great town for transgenders. There's protection under the law, helping professionals, support services, social groups, bars, events, films, pageants, drag shows, theatre and performance art. Natives call it "The City." There's a genial air of acceptance. The transgender scene is large and evolving. I doubt anyone knows everything that's going on. Everyone who contributed information to this article said, "I'm sure there's more." So, I assure you, there's more drag in San Francisco then this queen could uncover, so I'm bound to be missing wonderful events and turning friends in enemies through the sin of omission.

I've been wearing drag on the streets of San Francisco since I attended a Cockettes show on Halloween, 1971. I've cross-dressed at the opera, theatre, street fairs, restaurants, bars and when receiving tenure from the City College Board of Trustees, which got my photo on the cover of the campus newspaper. So, if you're visiting San Francisco remember that the City has laws and regulations on the books that protect gender expression, but they won't save you from poor judgement.

San Francisco divides itself into neighbourhoods. They're listed in tourist guides and marked on maps. If there really is a "Gay Mecca," I guess it's the *CASTRO*. Perhaps you've heard of it?

I won't call drag common place in the Castro, but you can buy neon wigs and rhinestone tiaras at *CLIFF'S*, the local variety store. *THE POLK* and *TENDERLOIN* are the older gay neighbourhoods. The Polk used to be a bit more up-scale. The Tenderloin never was. *SOUTH OF THE MARKET* and the MISSION are working class areas with clusters of trendy bars and shops, though these seem be overwhelming South of Market real estate recently. *THE HAIGHT* and *NORTH BEACH* are the old bohemian neighbourhoods. The Haight was home to hippies in the 1960's and the beats hung out in North Beach a decade earlier. Both neighbourhoods are fun to shop or walk around in and worth a visit, but you won't find many drag events in either.

Travellers and revellers are sometimes disappointed when they consider the number of things to do in San Francisco. "Oh, we liked San Francisco, just fine," they say, "It's just that there was so much more of, well, more of EVERYTHING in London." In place of London you could substitute New York, Paris or Rome it doesn't matter. San Franciscans find the comparison flattering. Of course there's more in those cities, they're ten times larger. More even. San Francisco's population is about 800,000. That's just a few thousand souls more than Jacksonville, Florida and smaller than either Indianapolis or San Jose San Francisco's Silicone Valley neighbour 55 miles to the south. On a per capital basis, San Francisco's nightlife is probably equal to any city's in the world, but that doesn't mean it has more drag bars than Tokyo.

photos with thanks to Asia and its glamourous girls

Primary Sources of Information:

This article is full of web sites you can visit from anywhere. It seems that every bar, club and queen has a web site. There are two sites that act as information clearing houses. They're very grass roots and are done with more heart than budget, which makes them both loveable and frustrating at the same time.

MADKATS, http://madkats.com/, is "about Drag, both Kings and Queens…Art, Music and bands: Madkats has always been about photography." Not all the bands are drag bands, "but they sure are cute, fun and just plain good music." The site is in transition, though they describe their future in optimistic terms.

KITHOLOGY, lists "queer things to do in the San Francisco Bay Area." Their Transgender Portal, www.kithology.com/transgender, is the most comprehensive listing of transgender fun spots and resources I've seen. The site works fairly well, too. But there are some messages on the site that made it sound like they, too, may be heading for a transition, too.

Once you get to town there are several newspaper you'll want.

These are most easily available at gay bars, magazine shops and cafes in the Castro, Polk and Tenderloin neighbourhoods. There are even metal racks on street corners. They're free, too.

B.A.R., short for Bay Area Reporter, is a 30-year-old GLBT weekly with a section of event listings you shouldn't miss. It comes out on Wednesdays. In every other issue they feature transgender activist Gwen Smith's column of cogent political and social insight, "Transmissions," www.gwensmith.com.

SAN FRANCISCO BAY TIMES. Is also weekly. It's queerer than the B.A.R. and has a more radical perspective on everything. Sister Dana Van Iquity covers the trans beat with wit and journalistic grace. Beside event listings, there's a "Trans" section in the Personals. Check out their "Transgenders" Resource Guide, too. It usually lists about 20 meetings of groups like Transgender Parents, Transgender Law Centre, Transmen's Alliance Against Racism and the TG, TS, Etc, Prayer Group.

SPECTRUM, www.sfspectrum.org, is the Castro's free neighbourhood monthly. It has two transgender columnists. Empress Chablis' required "Keepin' Up with the Courts" lists recent and up-coming doings of the Imperial Court, which is celebrating 40 years of service to the community in 2005. The advice column, "Dear Diva," by Queer TV reporter Dear Diva, dispenses plugs for events as well as pearls of wisdom and unapologetically progressive political commentary after she's finished counselling the confused.

GLOSS is a glossy bar mag that appears about twice a month. It's much more gay than trans. But don't miss "Vis à V," a column by transgender diva Veronica Klaus. Veronica covers the drag scene. A local cabaret legend herself, she highlights events by her talented friends.

BAY GUARDIAN and *SF WEEKLY* are two mainstream entertainment weeklies, Remember that "mainstream" is a relative term. The mainstream in San Francisco is the radical fringe in Oklahoma. Occasionally they cover tranny events. But if you're looking to date "a girl with something extra," you'll find ads for lonely, horny, fully functional ts's and tv's tucked in the back of these papers right between the escort services and masseuses.

125

Venues
Weekly & Monthly Events

These are on going, regularly scheduled events. I've usually listed them by venue, though not always. Most are drag shows or theme nights at gay bars. Call ahead. Things do change, especially in the world of drag shows.

ASIA SF Nightly, 201 – 9 St @ Howard, San Francisco, CA 94103, South of Market Tel: 415-255-2742, www.asiasf.com. This is a lucky combination of a 3-Star Cal-Asian restaurant with colourful, strong drinks and pretty young Asian drag queens waiting tables and entertaining between courses. About once an hour boys in slinky silk dresses dance on the Chinese-red runway above the bar. The club refers to them as "gender illusionists." AsiaSF is popular with tourists. It's also the venue of choice for many local bachelorette parties. Reservations are suggested. Seating in the restaurant is timed. If you plan your seating wisely it is sometimes possible to see two shows. There's a downstairs room, if you want to dance the night away.

AUNT CHARLIE'S LOUNGE Weekends at least, 10 PM, 133 Turk near Taylor, San Francisco, CA 94102, Tenderloin, Tel: 415-441-2922, www.auntcharlieslounge.com. There is a "sleazy drag show" every Friday and Saturday night. There's no stage. The humour is low and earthy. The shows are vibrant and professional without being polished. There's a raw honesty about the place and the performers are captivating. Aunt Charlie's is home to drag scene luminaries Vicki Marlene, Grand Marshal of the 2003 Gay Day Parade and reigning Grand Duchess Donna Rae.

CLUB RENDE-VOUS Every Friday, 11 PM and midnight, 1312 Polk, San Francisco, CA 94109 Polk Gulch, Tel: 415-673-7934. Drag Assault, hosted by Empress Cockatielia, has been running for about six years. Though Cockatielia is one glamourous queen, she says the shows are, "not only glamour. They're edgy and progressive. They're fun, comedy drag."

DIVA'S Nearly nightly. 1081 Post near Polk, San Francisco, CA 94109, Polk Gulch. Tel: 415-474-3482, www.divassf.com. Diva's clientele is mostly young transsexuals and their admirers. This bar is their club house and display window. Their skirts are the shortest in town. The club has three floors. The second floor is for dancing and the walls are lined with mirrors. I swear some queens go there to watch themselves wiggle. Shows are on the first floor. Tuesday is talent night with Tianna De Ville. Wednesday is Bad SchoolGirl Night. Divas' Darlins perform every Thursday at 10 PM and Alexis Miranda MC's the show every Friday and Saturday.

ESTA NOCHE Nearly nightly, 3079 – 16 St near Valencia, San Francisco, CA 94103, Mission St. Tel: 415-861-5757. This is the proud home of San Francisco's Latin drag scene with virtually continuous lip-syncing almost every night. Right now Las Fantasticas, Trans-International and Queens of the Night are performing in repertory and the stage is only dark on Fridays. Esta Noche also presents the annual Miss and Mr. Latino Contest in June.

GENDER ENDERS 1st Tuesday, 8:30 PM, Cherry Bar, 917 Folsom Street @ 5th St, San Francisco, CA 94103, South of Market www.genderenders.com. This features transgendered/intersexed/genderqueer artists, plus a queer performance open mic and "community bulletin board." The audience is encouraged to bring announcements, music, spoken word, stand-up comedy or performance art to the events.

HARVEY'S 2nd Sunday, 500 Castro St. @ 18 St, San Francisco, CA 94114 Tel: 415-431-4278. Harvey's is a bar and restaurant in the heart of the Castro. It's named for Harvey Milk. They're very drag friendly and there's usually a drag show. Right now the show is "Nice and Nasty" with Empress Chablis as Nice and Snatch, the Leather Empress as Nasty, www.snatchsf.com.

photos with thanks to Asia and its glamourous girls

SAN FRANCISCO ■ with Ms Bob

MARLENA'S Weekends, 488 Hayes near Octavia, San Francisco, CA 94102, Tel: 415-964-6672. This bar is the unofficial clubhouse of the San Francisco Imperial Court. Marlena herself is the 23rd Empress of San Francisco and 3rd Empress of San Mateo. There's a charming exhibit of SF Court memorabilia on the walls. Drag is at home at Marlena's. You're likely to see some dazzlingly bedecked queen no matter what day or time you arrive. There are lip-synch shows on Fridays and Saturdays. Faux Girls, MC'd by the scintillating Victoria Secret, is every second and fourth weekend. This show is a nightlife staple with a roomful of appreciative regulars. Performers include Nikki Starr, who can walk on water in heels as far as I'm concerned. She used to perform at the world famous Finocchio's, a showroom that presented female impersonators "at the same location" in North Beach from 1936 - 1999. Victoria is a real community builder. She has two sites for the drag curious: one for her fabulous Fauxgirls, www.fauxgirls.com. The other covers the doings of five acts Fauxgirls, Diva's, Aunt Charlie's Lounge and Club Rende-Vous, www.sfdrag.com.

TRANNYSHACK Every Tuesday, The Stud, 399 - 9 St @ Harrison, San Francisco, CA 94103, South of Market. www.heklina.com. This is San Francisco's more consistently on-the-edge drag club. Hostess and founder Heklina's formula is to bring in the talent push the envelope and pack the club. Anybody can have a Cher Night or a Dating Game (they've done both). But how many would have a David Lynch Tribute Night or a Hookers Night featuring a Biggest Load Contest. They've had drag queen in black face and been picket by the more humourless guardians of political correctness. Many performers use their own voices, though lip-synch is the norm all over town. Tranny Shack is also the venue most likely to present out-of-town drag celebrities, like Varla Jean Merman or Lady Bunny of Wigstock fame. Even Miss Chocolate, the "door whore" (do' ho') who stamps your wrist as you enter, is a nightlife institution. This is my kind of drag show, imaginative and under rehearsed.

TRANSBAY Every 2nd Wednesday, 7 – 10 PM, Quetzal Internet Cafe, 1234 Polk, between Sutter and Bush, San Francisco, CA 94109 Polk Gultch. www.transbay.org. The main goal of TransBay is to help build the SF Bay Area TG community. They do it two ways. First are their website's resource guide, social calendar and interactive bulletin boards. Second is the monthly get-together in Polk Gultch. More transgender women probably live in the Polk and the adjacent Tenderloin than in any other areas of the City. Quetzal Internet Cafe provides "a casual environment where people can let down their hair, so to speak and just have a good time. There is no group hierarchy-just people sipping cappuccinos and talking about everything from physics to dancing to entomology." They welcome all respectful people. TransBay,stresses "is not 'pick up centre'… We don't want folks to needlessly have to worry about individuals looking for a 'hot time.' There will be fun, and probably a touch or flirting here and there -- but if you're looking to meet your next lover, try somewhere else, please."

UNISEXY Every 4th Thursday, Makeout Room, 3225 – 22 St between Mission and Valencia, San Francisco, CA 94110, Mission. www.glamarama.com. This is a novelty, a beauty salon producing a theme night. Have your make-up and facials at the club. Have your wig restyled. Queer to the core, Glamarama, the salon, enjoys a special place in San Francisco's flaming firmament. Several of the stylists and employees are drag or queer theatre luminaries including Johnnie Kat, owner Deena Davenport and Princess Kennedy of tranny-rock band Pepperspray, www.peppersprayband.com. Deena used to do my hair, when I had hair now I take my wigs, if I wear wigs. 417 Van Ness, between 15 & 16 St, 415-861-GLAM (4526).

YOU WILL NEVER FALL
BEHIND
AT MARLAYNAS WORLD
www.MarlaynasWorld.com

Stores - Lets go shopping

Ms Bob

I'm really just scratching the surface here. Beside these shops that specialise in feminine clothing for the manly torso, there are dozens of women's clothing shops that will welcome your hard-earned tranny dollars.

FOXY LADY 2644 Mission St near 22 St, San Francisco, CA 94110, Mission Tel: 415-285-4980. This has been a community fixture for at least twenty years. Rumour is owner's son crossdresses and that's how she got interested in opening the shop. Now it's the Bay Area centre for plus size beaded dresses, shoes & wigs.

PEIDMONT BOUTIQUE 1452 Haight, San Francisco, CA Tel: 415-864-8075. This shop isn't only for queens. Glitzy local gals and clubs kids shop here and all along Haight Street. Don't despair if things are too small, and lots of them will be. They'll custom make anything in the store to your measurements. I bough a black mini skirt here years ago that's a staple of my wardrobe.

CARLA'S SALON & BOUTIQUE 124 Race Street, San Jose, CA 95126 Tel: 408-298-6900. www.carlas.com. This is the only out-of-town listing and I'm doing it because Carla is such a true friend to the transgender community and a major supporter of local groups. The girls at TGSF simply love her. They've even started to hold some of their events at her store.

A Personal Report

Annual Events

Many of these events are self-explanatory, since you all know what a street fair, film festival or drag beauty contest is. Some events drift from one month to another, especially those in the summer. So, checking the months on either side of you trip might be a good idea.

JANUARY TGSF COTILLION - www.tgsf.org.

TransGender San Francisco's big annual event featuring dinner, show, evening gowns, awards and the election of Miss and Mr. TGSF.

FEBRUARY IMPERIAL COURT CORONATION -www.impcourt.org.

Campaigning and parties begin three weeks before the elections. Voting takes place over several days in gay bar and everyone is eligible to vote.

MARCH MR. TRANNY SHACK DRAG KING COMPETITION – www.heklina.com.

Come out and support our Tranny Shack boys!

APRIL EASTER SILVER ANNIVERSARY IN 2004 - www.TheSisters.org.

Those philanthropic nuns, The Sisters of Perpetual Indulgence, are celebrating the Silver Anniversary in 2004. In recent years their Easter event started about noon-ish in Dolores Park, Mission District (on Dolores between 18&20 St)

MAY FAUX QUEEN CONTEST - www.klubstitute.com or 415-331-1500 x-DIET (3438). This Spring event is for drag queens trapped in women's bodies. Each year these genetically challenged drag queens claim their right to fabulousness. Sponsored by the Klubstitute Kollective, the venue varies.

JUNE INTERNATIONAL LESBIAN & GAY FILM FESTIVAL - www.frameline.org or info@frameline.org or 415-703-8650. Don't let the omission of B & T in the name fool you. This festival is a major outlet for new trans film.

PRIDE FESTIVAL - www.sfpride.org

JULY & AUGUST DRAG KING CONTEST - 415-282-5378 or www.madkats.com. A wild, howling beast of a show and trans scene fixture in its 9th year.

RUNWAY- www.gapa.org. The Gay Asian Pacific Alliance or GAPA presents this event. My informant says, "It's kind of hard to describe the event. It's formally the Mr. and Miss GAPA pageant, but it's more fun than serious ... and very fabulous.

UP YOUR ALLEY FAIR - www.folsomstreetfair.com. Drag is always welcome at this daylong leather scene event. Held on Dore Alley between Folsom and Howard. Always the last Sunday in July.

SEPTEMBER SS TRANNYSHACK– www.heklina.com.

Cruise the San Francisco Bay with a boatload of partying drag queens. Always the last Saturday in September, the night before Folsom St. Fair.

FOLSOM STREET FAIR - www.folsomstreetfair.com. Here's the culmination of San Francisco 8-day Leather Pride Week and reportedly the largest one-day event in California, a celebration SM, BD with over 200,000 in attendance. Always the last Sunday in September, South of Market on Folsom Street between 7th and 12th Streets. n Ness, between 15 & 16 St, 415-861-GLAM (4526).

OCTOBER *CASTRO STREET FAIR* -www.castrostreetfair.org. Always the first Sunday of October, one week after the Folsom Street Fair.

MISS & MR. GAY SAN FRANCISCO - www.impcourt.org

NOVEMBER *DAY OF REMEMBRANCE* -
www.rememberingourdead.org
Gwen Smith started the "Remembering Our Dead" website to honour, murdered, Rita Hester and held a candlelight vigil in 1999. Since then, the event has grown to encompass memorials in dozens more cities across the world. The march to the SF GLBT Community Center begins 6:30pm the second thursday in November at Harvey Milk Plaza (Castro & Market)

DUCAL COURT INVESTITURE - www.impcourt.org

MISS TRANNYSHACK CONTEST — www.heklina.com

TRANNY FEST - www.trannyfest.com. This is a bi-annual, four-day "extravaganza of performances; panels and parties climaxing in a marathon film festival showcasing cutting-edge films and videos on the sweet complexity, diversity, and sex appeal of lives lived on the gender continuum." The next one is Nov. '05. Besides producing events, Tranny Fest co-director Shawna Virago is front woman for the band Deadly Nightshade Family, www.shawnavirago.com.

DECEMBER *CHRISTMAS WITH THE CRAWFORDS* www.actsf.com. Artful Circle Theatre, This is the "Mommie Dearest" drag musical that has run 10 seasons in San Francisco and three in New York. There have been productions in Los Angeles, Seattle and Portland with productions planned for Omaha & Wichita. It's presented at Theatre Rhinoceros, the oldest GLBT theatre company in America. Artful Circle Theatre are inspired by classic Broadway musicals and Hollywood movies. Everyone sings in their own voices - no lip-syncing! The production values are on a par with local professional theatres and their sense of camp is much more refined. Other 2005 productions include "Acid Housewife: Six Trailers of Separation" and "Andrews Sisters Hollywood Canteen." You haven't really seen a drag show until you hear three drag queens sing the Andrews Sisters live or see Judy Garland impersonated by Connie Champagne, the sine qua non of drag queens trapped in women's body, www.conniechampagne.com.

THEATRE RHINOCEROS, www.therhino.org also has a season of shows. Many include gender issues and you'll see all flavours of gender impersonation during their season. They presented the world premiere of Kate Bornstein's "Strangers in Paradox" in 2003

Buttlicka at Trannyshack

Trannys embracing

Anger & Heklina

A Personal **Report**

The 'portal' to everything tranny on the Internet

Donnie Miles

MR. LYNNE CARTER

Lynne Carter press photos 1960s

The BOY with the PEARL BAILEY PERSONALITY

Finocchios Program Cover 1930s

Guy Doran "Belle of the Gay '90s"

America - USA ■ *Personal* **Report**

Organisations

FTM INTERNATIONAL 160 – 14 St., San Francisco, CA 94103 Mission 415-553-5987 info@ftmi.org www.ftmi.org. FTM stands for Female-to-Male and though Tranny Guide is decidedly MTF, its worth noting that San Francisco is the home of the largest, longest-running educational organisation serving FTM transgendered people and transsexual men in the world.

ITGSF – TransGender San Francisco PO Box 42486 San Francisco, CA 94142-6486 Tel: 415-564-3246 www.tgsf.org transgendersanfrancisco@yahoo.com. The City's social and support group. Their events are good, polite fun. Their membership policy is a model of unclusivity. They welcome "female and male cross dressers, transvestites, drag queens or kings, female or male impersonators, intersexed individuals, pre-operative, post-operative or non-operative transsexuals, masculine females, feminine males, all persons whose perceived gender or anatomical sex may be incongruent with their gender expression, and all persons exhibiting gender characteristics and identities which are perceived to be androgynous." Their newsletter, The Channel, is a good one and they try to make it available on their website. A good source for service providers, from psychologists to dress shops, it lists their events and meetings plus those of other regional groups. It is also available via mail.

The last Thursday of the month there's usually a social evening at the Blue

Muse near Civic Centre in SF, 409 Gough (between Hayes and Grove), 415-626-7505. Dinner starts around 7:30 with a short meeting at about 9 and hanging out after. It's pretty informal. Occasional mid-month social at various bars and restaurants in the area.

TG FORUM www.tgforum.com publish a weekly on-line magazine. They are a great resource for TG/TV/CD topics of interest and have many contests and pictorals on-line as well. It's well worth the $35per year to subscribe. They also have a chatroom where you can talk with others from all around the world

INTERNATIONAL MUSEUM OF GLBT HISTORY

657 Mission St. @ 3 St. #300, San Francisco, CA 94105, Downtown 415-777-5455 info @glbthistory.org.www.glbthistory.org.

One place you shouldn't miss is the country's only museum of GLBT history. You'll love the exhibit and be astounded by the archive. I know because I'm the secretary of the Board of Directors. The International Museum of GLBT History opened in May 2003 with SAINT HARVEY: The Life and Afterlife of a modern gay martyr, was curated by transgender scholar Dr. Susan Stryker.

The year 2003 was the 25th Anniversary of the assassination of Supervisor Harvey Milk and Mayor George Moscone. The exhibit runs until April 2004. The next exhibit will be about San Francisco's annual Dyke March.

The International Museum of GLBT History is a project of GLBT Historical Society. Our archive contains one of the world's largest collections of queer historical materials - unique manuscript collections, oral history transcripts, periodicals, photographs, and ephemeral in addition to a collection of fine art, graphic art, textiles, artifacts and memorabilia.

We have always been committed to the collection and preservation of transgender history. Lou Sullivan, the gay identified FTM transsexual who founded FTM International, was also a founder of the GLBT Historical Society. In addition to Lou's papers, we also archive the papers of Empress I Jose, the Widow Norton, founder of the Imperial Court System. Recent acquisitions include the papers of Dr. Ari Kane of the Outreach Institute and the Francine Logandice Collection of rare transgender books and periodicals.

Much of this collection is available on-line.

"The Greatest Show on Earth" 1960

Empress Chablis, Ms Bob, Dr Susan Stryker, Jordy Jones, Texas Starr & San Francisco Supervisor Bevan Duffy

Chorus Line from Princeton University Triangle Club " Tour De France" 1961 Top: Rehersals Bottom: Show

Ms Bob

A Personal Report

SCC Events - Tuesday

2:00 p.m. Registration Opens

6:00 p.m. Optional Dinner "The Palm Restaurant"

I got up at about 8:00 today because I knew I had a busy day. My first stop was the nail salon in the small mall that was attached to the hotel, this mall is mostly a food type court with many places to eat. Well I walked into the nail salon and to my surprise it was packed, funny thing it was full of girls like me. This salon just opened two weeks before the conference, the owner must have thought he had died and gone to heaven! After my manicure and pedicure, the girl told me they will be there on Sunday morning, starting at 5:30 AM to help remove the nails if I like.

Well my day has just begun, I went back to the hotel just in time for the picnic we were having at the local park right around the corner from the hotel…there we had all the hot dogs and hamburgers you could eat along with many other appetizers. We also had a kick ball game (that is like American baseball with the exception of no bat and we use a ball about the size of a soccer ball and the picture rolls it in to the batter). Now how would you like to be someone in the neighbourhood out walking your dog in the park and seeing this site<smile>. I would have loved to know what was going on in their mind!

Well the 2003 version of Southern Comfort Conference start off arriving at the really beautiful Sheraton Colony Square Hotel in Atlanta Georgia.

To my surprise there were already quite a few people there! Well I new I would be getting very little sleep the rest of the week so I decided that today was going to be an easy day. Tonight however there was a dinner at one of the local five star restaurants that was on the schedule that was always one of my favourite events but this year I declined, and decided a nice dinner in the hotel would work for me just fine.

After dinner I figured I would have a night cap at the hotel bar and then off to bed! The bar at the hotel is located right in the lobby of the hotel, once I got there and saw all the other ladies and guys, I knew this was not going to be that early night I was hoping. I found my room that night about 1:00 AM

I got back to the hotel about 2:00 PM and went down to registration to my little spot in the corner of the room where I help run the Big Brother/Big Sister program. This program is used for the girls (m-f) and

guys (f-m) that think they might need a helping hand with handling their first time in public. The funny thing is we get a lot of girl and guys that email us before hand asking for help but once they get there, they see all of us walking around the hotel and that makes them feel so much better. I always tell them that the people that run the hotel are super and love having us(especially the bar keeps) and we are the majority there, not the minority.

By now the conference is in full swing, there are lines at the registration table and the vendors are opening up and the hotel bars is going great guns.

That night is the Agatha's Mystery Dinner Theater. This is also a wonderful time, they bus us all off to a dinner theater where we take up about 50% of the place, the rest is full of people that came in off the street for a night out, not knowing we were coming. When you arrive there they give each of us a piece of paper with your lines and table number, yes lines, you become part of the show and as for the seating, you sit with both people from the conference and the other people that just showed up that night. It is very interesting at first, no one knows what to say to each other but by the end of the show everyone is talking to everyone. In all the years I have been going to this I have always had a ball.

After Agatha's it was back to the hotel and cocktails at the hotel with about 250 of my favourite people, the rest is history<smile> I found my room at about 2:30 AM that night!

SCC Events - Wednesday

11:00 a.m. Ken and Barbi-Q Picnic / SBS Kickball Game

2:00 p.m. Registration Open

6:00 p.m. Optional Dinner "Agatha's Mystery Theater"

SCC Events - Thursday

Thursday morning came so so early that day, I opened the Big Brother/Big Sister area and then went over and helped out with registration at 8:00 AM. Someone over slept and they were a person down on the registration desk and to our surprise there were about 30 people waiting for us to open up that morning. We got everyone under control in a matter of minutes, one thing I do like, about registration, is if there is a problem, no matter the size, with someone's registration, it does not hold up things, we send them off to another area where we have the people that you email your stuff off to, when you register on line and they have all the needed info there and it is cleared up very quickly. That is also the area we send them if they did not register on line, things go really quick.

Thursday also starts the meals that Southern Comfort provides with the package you bought. Lunch was served to about 3.50 that day, it is a sit down lunch and very nice. At the luncheon we have a both the chair people, this year Cat(m-f) and Sam(f-m) as co-chairs, stand and say a few things, and then we have the key-note speaker for the day get up and speak. This year it was Lacey Leigh, a great gal from Arizona. In the past we had anywhere from 1-3 speakers that day but we found people got restless and it is just not fair to them(a couple of years ago I was a speaker, I was not restless, just a nervous wreck, waiting on my turn<smile>)

What I forgot to tell you is the vendor open officially today and we also start are workshops, here is Thursdays schedule for workshops:

9:00-10:30 a.m. Head To Toe - Jim Bridges

9:00-10:30 a.m Getting Buff (for FTMs) - Krista

9:00-10:30 a.m A Personal TG History - Christina Young

9:00-10:30 a.m TG Homeless - Lisa Mottet

10:30 – Noon Managing Your Transition - Donna Rose

10:30 – Noon TG Alternative - Holly Boswell

10:30-Noon TG Veterans Monica Helms & Angela Brightfeather

11:00-Noon Partners, Family & Friends Welcome by SCC Partners Program

Noon- 1:45 LUNCH Address - Lacey Leigh: "Living the Impossible Dream"

1:45-3:15 pm Wig and Hair Care - Jon Davis

1:45-3:15pm Male Presentation - Jami Ward

1:45-4:00pm History & Spiritual Trads - Marisa Richmond & Ken Dollarhide

3:30-5:00pm PassionQuesting - Kim Danbert & Walter Willis

3:30-5:00pm Beyond SRS - Donna Rose

3:30-5:00pm Masculinity 101 - Louis Mitchell

3:30-5:00pm Wine 101 - Hollis Clark

As you can see we have many work shops going on at that same time, for both the male to female and female to male, sometimes it can very hard to pick one and not another.

We also have a shopping trip to Atlanta's famous "little 5 corners" shopping area, this is always a fun time, you can find just about anything there and the people are just outstanding to all of us, they have discovered, our money is just as good as everyone else's, if not better<smile>.

Thursday at 5:00 we have reception for the "Newcomer". These are people that might be there for the first time there or out. There is wine and soda's and we talk about what SCC is all about and what are some of the things to look out for and also some of the things you should and should not do (drink and drive, restrooms to use, attire around the hotel and so on)

Thursday there is an optional dinner at Agnes and Muriel's, another top restaurant here in Atlanta, think we had two bus loads of people going

A Personal Report

135

there. I was not one of them! I decided to go have dinner with four of my best friends, that I only get to see once a year, Gina Martine from California, Chrissie Darling, from Tennessee, and Kathy Taylor also from Tennessee. We had a great time at a really nice restaurant, the food, drink and companionship could not be any better. The City of Atlanta knows we are coming so all the restaurants are very friendly and a lot of them that are near the hotel put on extra help because they want us to come back next year.

After dinner we took a cap back to the hotel just in time to get a bus to one of the local clubs called the Armory. These buses start running at 10:30 PM and go on till 2 or 3 PM every 20 minutes, back and forth between the club and the hotel.

I decided to stay and drink and also attend an event that happens every year but is not part of Southern Comfort in any way, it is the world famous Roxy DuMonde pajama party! This year there must have been 150 in Roxy's suite, lots to drink and lots to see, always a high light for all of us!

It was now 2:30 AM so I decided it was time for bed!

SCC Events - Friday

Friday things opened up again at 8:00 AM with a full house waiting for us at registration and Big Brother/Big Sister areas but by 9:00 AM all was cleared up and it was time to chit chat with friends again.

At 9:00 AM Vendors area and workshops started up:

9:00-10:30am Freeing Me to Be - Lacey Leigh

9:00-10:30am MTF Facial Feminization Surgery - Douglas Ousterhout, MD

9:00-10:30am FTM Hormones - Sara Becker, MD

9:00-10:30am The Wilderness of Intimacy - Virginia Erhardt

9:00-10:30am Let's Pass A Local Law ! - Mara Keisling & Lisa Mottet

10:00-Noon The Perils of Passing - Jessie McGowen , Heather O'Malley, Marc Eden, Hollis Clark, Divinity, Zantui Rose

10:30-Noon Top Ten Mistakes (CDs Do To Get Read) - Denae Doyle

10:30-Noon FTM SRS - Peter Raphael, MD

10:30-Noon Two Nice Girls Say the F-Word: TG Feminism Pt1 - Krista & Alaina

10:30-Noon TG People Of Colour - DeeDee Chamblee & Diego Sanchez

Noon -1:45 pm LUNCH Entertainment The Sissy Show

1:45-3:15pm Everything You Ever Wanted to Know About BDSM - Catherine Gross

1:45-3:15pm Wrapped In Blue: Book Discussion & Signing - Donna Rose

1:45-3:15pm Internalized Transphobia - Verba & Zeek

1:45-3:15pm Successfully Transition in Your Employment - Hawk Stone

1:45-3:15pm How To Create Ceremonies All Your Own - Rev.Barbara J (Becca Laughlin)

1:45-3:15pm Transgender Rights at the Federal Level - Mara Keisling & Lisa Mottet

1:45-3:15pm Gay Transmen and Non-Transmen Relationships - Chase & Chris

3:30-5:00pm Delicious Deportment - Anndrea Daniels

3:30-5:00pm Welcome To The Circle of Women - Virginia Erhardt

3:30-5:00pm Moving Into Your Body - Heather O'Malley

3:30-5:00pm Aging & TG Elders - Hawk Stone

3:30-5:00pm "Admirers" & The TG Community - Sam Allen & Michele Angelo

Friday lunch was another great meal served by the hotel as part of the SCC package, at this luncheon we had a show put on by a couple of girls called "The Sissy Show" they did a number of their own songs and it was really kind of funny!

After lunch you had your choice of two things to do outside the vendor and workshop area, one was an outing to a Shopping Trip called"Phipps Plaza" and the other was the "SCC Pool Party", guess which one I picked? Well I do not look that good these days in a bathing suit but I do like looking at the other girls in their bathing suit....we got about 100 people show up for the pool party, good time was had by all.

Friday night was special, we start off with a sit down dinner, which about 500 attended. It was a fantastic meal and after that we had a talent show. You would be surprised how much talent is in the transgender family.

After dinner there were buses going to one of the local clubs called Le Buzz, this started at 10:30 and went on till 3:00 AM, I think. I again stayed in the hotel bar and just had a great time. I did slip out for about 2 hours, to a local drag club called Model T's and seen the show, they were giving special drink prices for people from SCC, you just needed to show your SCC name tag. I got back about midnight and met an old friend that showed up and we had a few drinks at the lobby bar and then we went off to a party in one of the rooms.

SCC Events - Saturday

Saturday morning came really early that day, I was down at the registration table again at 8:00 AM and believe it or not there were people there waiting to register. It was going to be another full day of workshops and today is always a good day to shop in the vendor area.

9:00-10:30am MTF SRS Presentation - Gary Alter, MD

9:00-10:30am Lip Sync - Anndrea Daniels

9:00 -10:45am Gender Variance: Holly Boswell

9:00-10:30am TG HIV & AIDS Issues - Diego Sanchez

9:00-10:30am Family Psychotherapy - Hawk Stone

9:00-10:30am Transgender Activism - Monica Helms

10:30-Noon Transgender & Sexuality - Zelda Rose,

10:30-Noon Feminine Poise - Denae Doyle

10:30-Noon Generations - George Juge & Avery Jasper

11:00-Noon Gender Outlaws - Holly Boswell

Noon- 1:45pm Lunch & Keynote Address -
Noelle Howey- Author of "Dress Codes: Of Three Girlhoods--- My Mother's, My Father's, and Mine

1:45-3:15pm MTF Hormones - Sara Becker, MD

1:45-3:15pm FTM Sexuality - Michael Tipton

1:45-3:15pm TG Feminism Pt 2 - Krista & Alaina

1:45-3:15pm The Legislative - Mara & Lisa Mottet

1:45-3:15pm Make-up A to Z - Susie Paris

1:45-4pm Transgender Spirit Circle - Kindred Spirits

3:30-5pm Your Personal Feminine Style - Lori Fox

3:30-5pm Hair Removal & Electrolysis - Andrea Orr

3:30-5pm FTM Show & Tell - Michael Tipton

3:30-5pm Our Trans Families - P-FLAG Panel

3:30-5pm Transgender Equality - Mara Keisling

Lunch was served at 12 noon and our key note speaker called in sick but the back up we had was sensational! It was Gina Lance, the editor and owner of Girl Talk magazine (who by the way donated 600 copies to SCC). She was sensational, besides that she is a good friend.

That afternoon myself and Kelly Price represented Southern Comfort Staff and hosted a reception that

A Personal Report

Mara Keisling put on for the National Center for Transgender Equality, she is located in Washington DC and is kind of a lobbyist that fights for all our rights, here in the USA.

Saturday night is always a special night for me, it is a night that everyone gets dressed to the nines and dances the night away. It all starts with cocktails in the hotel lobby....I think I have the bar keeps trained, when they see me they know it is a Bombay Gin Martini, very dry, but dirty, with 3 olives, 2 in the class and one in my hand.

Lots of pictures, and it kind of made me feel good that a lot of people asked me to have a picture taken with them, they must be fans of my website.

Then it was off to dinner, it was another great meal and a lot more pictures taken, after dinner the heads of the Southern Comfort Committee got up and chitted and chatted with all of us for a bit then to my surprised named off and gave a lovely rose to all the staff(including me) for all our help and also named all the volunteers that helped with registration, decorations for the Saturday Dinner, the pool party and so on. You know it takes almost 50 of us to put this event on each year, we have 3 meetings in Atlanta prior to the event during the year.

After dinner there was a beautiful woman named Francine Reed sing for us, outstanding is all I can say about her!

About 10:00 PM we all made our way upstairs to a dance with the theme of the 60's 70's and 80's. That was also a great time but it was also a time for saying our good byes, and tears were shed. Some girls I will see during the year but a lot it will take a whole year before we lift our glasses again with each other...

All toll we had about 625 people paid for the event and another 150 just came for the fun in the lobby area.

Events on Saturday

8:00 a.m. Registration Open

8:30 a.m. Marketplace Open

9:00 a.m. Seminars Continue

Noon Lunch – Keynote Speaker "Noelle Howey" She was sick so Gina Lance filled in.

2:00 p.m. Southern Belle Society Reception

3:30 p.m. National Center for Transgender Equality Reception

4:30 p.m. Transgender Affirmation Ceremony

7:00 p.m. Cocktail Hour "Vicki D'Salle"

8:00 p.m. Dinner

9:15 p.m. Showtime "Francine Reed"

10:00 p.m. "60s, 70s, 80s Dance and Costume Party"

Sunday morning, time to pack up and drive those 6 hours back to Florida....but first there is a meeting to attend, A time to say what went right and what went wrong. It is also the kick off meeting for Southern Comfort Conference for 2004.

Southern Comfort is an annual event

All details including booking information and this years dates

www.sccatl.org

info@sccatl.org

Southern Comfort Conferences

c/o Shamrock Conventions

56 College Street, Ste 304, Ashville, NC 28801, USA

ATLANTA, GEORGIA

BACKSTREET

845 Peachtree Street, NE, Atlanta, GA 30308
www.backstreetatlanta.com. Backstreet is open 24 hours a day and 7
days a week. They do this legally by operating as a private club. You
must buy a membership to get in. However, it only costs $10 for a
three-month's membership. You enter from the rear of the building.
The parking lots along the side of the building and in the rear, which are
well lighted, cost about $10 for your car. Each of the three levels of the
club is quite large. You enter on the ground level into a large bar with
pool tables. One level down is a disco with a very large dance floor. At
the head of the stairs on the second level, they have Black Jack tables.
There is a large bar and a stage set up to view the
drag show. There is a back room on this level that also has a show at
times. Although I did not see any Trannies there beside myself, the
management assured me that Backstreet is the Tranny scene in Atlanta. I
saw mostly hetero couples there and spoke to some gay men.

FORT LAUDERDALE, FLORIDA

WILTON MANOR is a neighbourhood in Fort Lauderdale that is a totally
gay community and Trannies are welcome in most places. I have visited:

CHARDEE'S 2209 Wilton Drive (NE 4 Ave), Wilton Manor, Fort
Lauderdale, 1-954/563-1800. This is a gay restaurant. Wednesdays they
offer 2 for 1 entrees but if you are alone, they charge half price. The
food is good. There is a bar in an adjoining room. The bar section has a
piano bar section. Terry Hammond plays the piano Wednesday through
Saturday. Sunday is Karaoke night. They draw a middle aged gay crowd
that welcomes Trannies.

TROPICS 2000 Wilton Drive, Wilton Manor, Fort Lauderdale 33305, 1-
954/563-4269. This is a gay restaurant with a bar along side and a piano
bar in the front of the bar section. Miguel is at the pianist
Wednesday, Friday and Saturday. They also draw a middle aged gay
crowd. They have another restaurant in Tampa, Florida by the same
name at 2801 South MacDill, Tampa, FL 33609, 813/837-1836. Which I
understand that it is similar to the Fort Lauderdale one.

THE HIDEAWAY 2022 N.E. 18 Street, 1-954/566-8622. It is located just
off Federal Highway, but you can see the place easily when you turn off
Federal Highway. Go one block, make a U turn; head back toward
Federal Highway and you will see it on the right. The Hideaway is a gay
bar with a stage in one corner. They have a Drag Show on Saturday
night. When I was there I counted seven Trannies in the bar. Six of them
were in the show. I understand that if you want to be in the show, just
be there, bring your music and let them know your feelings.

NEW YORK CITY

INA'S SILVER SWAN (at the Silver Swan, formally Karalyn's Oasis) 41
East 20th Street (between Broadway and Park Ave, South)
Tel: 1-212/254-3611, Renate Moscatt (owner). The restaurant serves
very good German food. On Saturdays only, after 10pm, the kitchen
closes and it becomes the most Tranny place in New York. Every Tranny
in and out of New York knows Ina's. It operates until 4am. Trannies
there are dressed in every mode imaginable - from proper ladies to
exhibitionists. There is a long bar at the front with tables along side. In
the rear, there are more tables. The rear is also where all the dancing
takes place. There are dressing facilities downstairs. A checkroom has
been added recently. There are plenty of "admirers" at all times. From
time to time there are costume parties and special dancers are hired to
entertain. There is an admission charge of $5

Joanne wrote to us from her
home in the USA to tell us of
her visit to New York of which
she said:

" **It is a wonderful place for
Trannies, since the laws
are in our favour. In public
accommodations, the law
basically states that you
are to be treated in
accordance with the sex
that you appear to be.
However, I would not go
anywhere where you may
not be wanted - such as
perhaps blue-collar bars or
similar macho places**".

With same good sense she tells
us of some of her other "finds"
in Atlanta Georgia and Fort
Lauderdale in Florida.

She also said

"**I want to mention
DIGNITY CRUISES. run
by Peggy and her husband
Melanie www.pmpub.com.
They arrange cruises for
groups of Trannies. I am
going on my first one
January, 24, 2004. They
have another one this
summer in the
Meditteranian**".
See Page 148-149.

A Personal Report

LONG ISLAND, NEW YORK

FEMME FEVER
www.femmefever.com.
This is a make-over, shopping and party service. Joining them is free and allows you to enter their website where you can get emails and announcements regarding all kinds of transgender activities. They mostly cover the New York Tri-State area; however, some activities from all over the country are posted.

CLUB 608, 608 Sunrise Highway, Babylon, NY. A gay bar that is Tranny friendly.

HONEYS, 667 Montauk Highway, Bayport, NY.
www.honeyscafe.info. This is mostly a lesbian club that I found Tranny friendly. They have a nice dance floor. The place is busy on weekends and operate 7 nights a week. It is not far from the Fire Island Ferry.

RATTLESNAKE JONES
Sometimes referred to as RS Jones 153 Merrick Avenue, Merrick, NY, Tel: 1-516/378-7177. You enter the restaurant through the bar. They serve good food and have live music on weekends. Mostly hetero couple come here but they are Tranny friendly.

BLANCHE'S 47-2 Boundary Avenue, South Farmingdale Tel: 1-516/694-6906. A Friendly gay bar.

CHUNKY'S 267 Mineola Blvd, Mineola Tel: 1-516/739-3009. Best on Friday nights.

THE MONSTER Corner of Grove and West 4th Street (Sheridan Square subway stop) 1-212-924-3557. Another gay oriented bar, across from the 'Stonewall Inn', though at times a bit livelier due to a piano bar in one corner. The musician will play standard favourites or any request song. Best nights there for us "ladies" are Wednesdays. when drag shows are presented several times during the night, as well as Fridays and Saturdays when the patrons are in a "party mood". Phone for details of special events or guest performers.

LIPS 2 Bank Street (off Greenwich St. bet. 7 & 8 Avenue, nearest Subway stop, 14th Street) 1-212-675-7710 (reservations are necessary) Small, intimate restaurant with cross-dressed waitresses. While most customers are "curious" tourist, those who go 'dressed' are also appreciated and made very welcome. In fact ask to be seated at Ginger's table and you'll receive excellent service as well as a few T-girl "tips" to make you a better lady. Thursdays are the best since it is 'Dinner with the Divas Night'. The girls, between serving tables, present a show of song and dance impersonations of famous celebrities (Cher, Cindy Lauper, Joan Rivers). All sorts of hijinx can occur including dragging diner's or passers-by off the street into the shows. Entrees are named after the waitresses, portions are more than generous. The dining area is limited in size but after dining you can linger at the bar in the rear for drinks and watch another hour's show.

PENNYFEATHERS 99 Seventh Ave. South (1/2 block south of Sheridan Square, nearest subway stop, Christopher St.) 1-212-242-9567. Nancy's all-time favourite place to dine in the City. Small, candle-lit restaurant with intimate indoor sidewalk café style dining. T-girls are always well cared for by the two waiters, Isaac & Eddie. You're guaranteed to be treated like the well-dressed lady you are. A great variety of food is available without reservations. Call in any time, even for a late night post-club snack and drinks at the bar. Your bartender is Mike and who is just as kind and attentive to us gals as the owners and staff.

NOW BAR Leroy St. and 7th Avenue South. Probably the most reliable weekly venue, , where transsexual legend 'Glorya Wholesome' and husband and DJ 'Gil T.

CDI (Cross Dressers International) located at 404 West 40th Street, Apartment #2, Hot Line 1-212/564-4847 answered on Wednesdays from 6 P.M. to about 10pm. www.CDINYC.org. You can come dressed, dress there or stay in drab. There is a $10 charge. The money goes to pay for dinner that is served. In the summer a barbeque is held in the backyard garden. Don't let the $10 scare you Rochelle & Wendi are great cooks. In the winter and in bad weather when no one cooks, it's pizza, chinese or other restaurant food. At about 10pm, some of the girls go out to a club or what have you. They also hold special events frequently (e.g. Halloween, Debutante Ball, Prom etc) usually on a Thursday. The Events telephone, in operation at all times is 1-212/570-7380

STEPHANIE JOHNSON West 23rd Street, 1-212/330-8366. www.MyFemSpirit.bigstep.com. She does make-overs, makes custom clothes and provides escorted nights on the town. You can dress there anytime for $10. She is very talented in the services she provides. If you think that you are too masculine to go out and blend-in in public, call Stephanie.

ARTHUR'S TAVERN 57 Grove Street Tel: 1-212/675-6879 is a small bar with some tables along side the bar. There is a stage in the rear where jazz bands play 7 nights a week. A lively fun place that is very Tranny friendly.

ROSES TURN 55 Grove Street is a piano bar with lots of customers singing. It is next door to Arthur's (above). They are both just across Seventh Avenue from Pennyfeathers.

MANATUS RESTAURANT, 340 Bleaker Street, at Christopher Street Tel: 1-212/989-7042 is a plain diner like restaurant that is Tranny friendly. The prices are low and the food is good even if the ambiance is rather plain.

CAJUN RESTAURANT 129 Eighth Avenue at 16th Street Tel: 1-212/691-6174 is owned by Herb Maslin. He and Sean, the bartender, are very friendly to Trannies. There is a bar with tables in the front and more tables in the rear where a band plays ragtime in the evening. The food is mostly New Orleans spicy but some mild dishes are available.

EAST OF EIGHTH 254 West 23rd Street Tel: 1-212/352-0075 is a restaurant just east of Eighth Avenue on 23rd Street. Downstairs has a bar and a couple of tables. In the rear there are tables usually used for serving meals. The second floor is also a nice area to have dinner. The food is quite good and the people are Tranny friendly on all days and hours. On Saturday night, several Trannies can be found in the bar before they head over to Ina's at the Silver Swan.

REGENTS, 317 East 53rd Street (between First & Second Avenues) Tel: 1-212/593-309 A gay bar catering to an older crowd that is Tranny friendly. Good food, moderate prices and very large portions. The upstairs bar has two tables and the piano goes on most nights with customers singing mainly show tunes. At 10:00 P.M the music moves downstairs. Downstairs there is a bar and tables along side. In the rear are tables where dinner is served, similar music and singing continues. Dinner is served until 11:30 P.M. (sometimes a bit later, if conditions warrant it).

THE TOWN HOUSE BAR 236 East 58th Street (between 2nd & 3rd Avenues) Tel: 1-212/754-4649 www.townhouseny.com. This gay bar has three bars. On the main floor the bar is quite long and the music is continuous. There are a couple of couches at the rear. The back bar is a larger room with tables, sofas and a piano where customers sing mostly show type songs. All the piano players are good, but try to catch Eddie Lawrence on Monday, Wednesday and Friday. He has a great voice and personality. Downstairs, past the coat-check room is a small bar. The bartender also doubles a DJ. Probably the best bartender in New York is Anthony. He has an infectious smile, great laugh, and although gay, loves Trannies. All are friendly here. The place gets very crowded on weekends.

TOWNHOUSE (RESTAURANT) 206 East 58th Street Tel: 1-212/826-6241 is also friendly and serves good food. It is mentioned mostly so that it is not confused with the Townhouse Bar (above).

PANDA RESTAURANT 987 First Avenue at 54th Street Tel: 1-212/752-8822 This TG friendly Chinese restaurant serves the usual Chinese/American food; however, their fish dishes are unusual for a Chinese restaurant and are very good.

BISTRO AT STONEWALL 113 Seventh Ave, Tel: 1-917/661-1335. This is a gay/lesbian restaurant and bar. Tables are along side of the bar. Jerry Scott is at the piano on Wednesday Nights. Eddie Lawrence plays here Sunday and every other Saturday. Other nights have different piano players and sometimes a DJ. The food is good and the bartender, John, is friendly as are all the others there. John does a great imitation of Louie Armstrong singing.

DONT TELL MAMA 343 West 46th St., Tel: 1-212-757-0788. This is strictly a piano bar and show place on 'Restaurant Row' in the theatre district. They do not serve food. The piano bar is going every night. They have about three rooms where they have various shows for $10 or $15 plus a 2-drink minimum. Sometimes a drag show, sometimes a Tranny doing a Judy Garland imitation show or at other times a gay stand up comedy show. Call ahead to find out what is happening and, if you like, make a reservation because seating is limited.

CELINA'S in the Chelsea Hotel, 222 East 23rd Street. They serve good food.

LUCKY CHENGS 24 First Avenue www.planetluckychengs.com. This is a famous drag show, drag waitresses, restaurant and club.

PIECES 8 Christofer Street. They have a very good drag performer on Wednesday nights.

NYC HOTELS
That are friendly to Trannies

CHELSEA PINES INN 317 West 14th Street, Tel: 1-212-929-1023. $89 single/$119 double.

CHELSEA HOTEL 222 West 23rd Street, Tel: 1-212/243-3700, Up to $2000 single. This is probably the most famous hotel catering to the GLBT community, as well as others.

CHELSEA SAVOY HOTEL 204 West 23rd Street, Tel: 1-212-929-9553.$145 single/$155 double.

CHELSEA LODGE 318 West 20th Street, Tel: 1-212-243-4499. $85 single/$100 double.

COLONIAL HOUSE INN 318 West 22nd Street, Tel: 1-212-243-9669.$80 single/$140 double.

HOLIDAY INN DOWNTOWN 138 Lafayette Street, Tel:1-212-966-8898. $229.

HOTEL 17 225 East 17th Street, Tel: 1-212- 475-2845. $75 single/$109 double.

HOTEL 31 120 East 31st Street, Tel: 1-212-685-3060. $110 single.

A Personal Report

David pulled his gleaming new Toyota Yaris up alongside the young Czech guard and as I was on what he perceived to be the driver's side, I duly handed over our passports, David's on top. As is my custom, the page bearing my picture was covered by my TS 'legitimisation' letter from my Doctor plus a laminated NUJ press card featuring my photo en femme.

'Do you speak English?' I asked the border policeman.

'No - Deutsch und Czech,' he replied, mixing up his languages fluently.

He perused David's ID and - after stooping to look beyond me and check that my travelling companion matched his picture – he opened my passport. Ignoring my Doctor's letter and Donna's press card, he sought to match the passport photo up with the ever-more-nervous woman before him - and instead found a shaven-headed male face staring out from the page.

His forehead creased into a frown and his expression said it all. 'Vot is this?' he wanted to know.

I leant out through the window, opened my Doctor's letter, pointed to Donna's card and said softly: 'Transsexual, do you understand?'

'One moment'. He guided us into a lay-by alongside the prefab and went off to seek help. A couple of minutes later he re-emerged, my documents still in his hand and babbling into a walkie-talkie.

Another border officer arrived on the scene and examined the documents. More walkie-talkie animation followed and finally, official No.2 came over, brandishing my letter in one hand and my passport in the other, to tell me in halting English: 'These not same people.'

Then, indicating the male picture in my passport, he added: 'This is not you.'

He pointed to the name 'Donna Gee' on my Doctor's letter and the totally different male monicker on the passport (Gee is actually the first letter of my birth surname).

'These not same person. 'I'm sorry. You go back."

With that, he indicated that David should turn round and return from whence we came. In other words, I was not going to be allowed into the Czech Republic.

My first reaction was one of despair - and anger at the cheek of these 'Praguer louts' to refuse entry to an obviously unthreatening woman. I had so wanted to see Prague. I had heard so much about its beauty and all the wonderful sights. Now we were going to have to re-route our entire holiday.

David, God bless him, was remarkably relaxed about it all. 'What would you like to do?' he asked, aware of how upset I was. 'Go back to Vienna - or head for somewhere else like Linz?'

Having just spent three days in Vienna, I was loathe to return when there were so many other places I had not seen. 'I don't care,' I said, 'but I don't really want to go back where we've come from.'

As we drove westwards along the Austrian-Czech border, the heavens opened and the skies did my crying for me.

Suddenly I had a thought. Why didn't we try to get into the Czech Republic at a different crossing point? David was immediately game for it - in fact, we both jumped at the idea. After all, the border guards would probably be less fussy in the rain. This was a real challenge . . . to get me into the country as an illegal alien!

I checked the map for border crossings. There appeared to be one about 15 miles to the west - but when we got there it didn't exist. The next one was 50-odd miles further on. We decided to head for it. After all, if we failed to make it we were heading in the right direction towards Linz anyway.

An hour plus a couple of detours, a wrong turning and a coffee stop later, we found ourselves at the Teplice crossing point.

Instead of a prefabricated booth, we drove into a modern white-concrete complex, at which point David put our pre-arranged plan into operation. Instead of me handing the passports over, he stopped the car, got out and took the item round to the police officer himself. This time, at David's suggestion, my Doctor's letter and my visiting card were not part of the package.

David had felt the guy might not look at my passport once he had seen that the driver's credentials were in order. He thought wrong.

The guard opened my passport, saw old baldie staring back at him - and was, not surprisingly, bemused. Again, the word 'transsexual' meant nothing to him.

He emitted a loud whistle. Seconds later a more-senior officer in a peaked-cap came over. God, I thought - the guys at the first crossing had warned them to expect us. Cop number one handed over my passport and the two men began muttering together.

DONNA GEE... in Prague on her 18-day summer trip across Europe after a couple of "Praguer Louts" tried to spoil her Czech Dream

Here we go again, I thought. Would I just be turned back - or be marched away in handcuffs this time for trying to enter the country illegally?

I decided to try the Doctor's letter approach. Brandishing his letter confirming that 'Donna Gee is having treatment for male to female transsexualism', I asked: "Do you speak English?"

"A little," replied the more senior officer, who had assumed control of the matter. He took the letter and began to read it.

"I am transsexual, you understand?" I said softly, in my most feminine voice. He kept reading. 'Transsexual," I repeated. 'You know what a transsexual is?"

After what seemed an age, he looked up. 'I understand,' he said, turning to his colleague, his lips breaking into a somewhat nervous smile. 'Sexuality.'

With that, he folded up the letter, handed it back with my passport, and ushered us to drive on.

'OK, you can go through," he said.

I let out a silent whoop of delight - and stuck two imaginary fingers up at the ignorant guards who had turned me back at the first border crossing.

My Prague dream had been reborn.

P.S. After six years of living two lives Donna finally became a full-time woman last September. She now has a female passport .... to everyone's relief!

For 10 days, and 1,200 miles across Europe, I hadn't even looked in my handbag for my passport. Into France, on to Germany and across the scarcely visible border into Austria, there had not been even a suspicion of a document check. David's passport had sufficed at all the hotels, so mine remained well and truly private - since it remained at that time in my male name.

But as we approached the prefabricated booth that served as the main entry point on the road from Vienna into the Czech Republic, I had no idea of the pitfall that lay just ahead. Leaving Austria was no problem. The border guards didn't even look at our passports...they were seemingly only interested in Austrian citizens leaving the country with something to hide. For one fleeting second, I thought we had got in to the Czech Republic and en route to Prague, the jewel in our holiday crown.
How wrong I was!

A Personal Report

Continued page 142

Donna773@aol.com

143

Exploration of this reveals the vast cultural differences we have between east and west, and how the western mindset has evolved from what was once a global norm in sexual mores. As far back as the late 60's there were stories of Arab boys in Port Said who had been sculpted into young women by surgery paid for by their rich lovers, probably done in Casablanca, although details are sketchy. The News of the World bravely tried to cover the story, but photographs were, even then, banned from publication, and still are. Doubtless the Anti Slavery League has more information.

The commonly known eastern ethic that 'women are for babies, boys are for sex/fun' is true. Reasons for this can be varied, but overall and mostly to blame is the Islamic demands on both sexes to remain pure. The only good news for victims of this endemic channelling process, is that they are not culturally obliged to become or remain homosexual, despite their experiences. Whereas, it is not tolerated but, secretly expected, that they will be bisexual.

In some areas of the Middle East, their goal in the first place is to earn enough from the trade to afford to marry a woman. The most clear model of this, is in the Xanith (pronounced H'anith) of Oman. Their nationally acknowledged job in life is to act as cheap prostitutes in order so that women should not have to. They wear their hair loose and long, usually shoulder length, their kaftans belted and are excused beards and moustache's, but they pray with the men in the mosque. And apart from a little kohl pencil and ochre, they are not allowed to transform their appearance to feminine, and certainly not in public. To do so, would be to effectively 'become a woman', and therefore sully a woman's honour. The punishment for this is public whipping, in the least. Many Xanith have always been known to only work for a short time, earning enough to marry, and despite their sexual passive role in their career days, they have been known to make a success of that. Some, of course, are true TG's, others, true Gays.

There has always been a form of primitive penectomy surgery in the Middle East, the same gruesome routine described in many other cultures, and means to acquire a bosom; a balm known as Bombay Salve, probably made from certain herbs and the urine of pregnant mares or cattle. In truth, the massage with it in the area probably does more, with psychosomatic self-belief, to enhance the bust.

But modern TG Xanith are aware of the TS operation, although, they would have to leave Oman to have it, return to change their papers, and henceforth live a virtuous life, probably to marry a man.

They are seldom heard of even in Oman, our agent there found only four references in as many years. In one case a couple of the girls tried a shopping trip 'a la femme' and were caught out on a bus, but authorities were tolerant and only fined them. Indicating that TG has evolved there, to be known and tolerated.

There are other names for it from the area - Batchah, Achnatschik and Schopan. Some may be derogatory and others new word sets created by an evolving community.

The Saudi Arabian term is Khwajasara, and probably means much the same as the old Afghanistan name, Kuchi-Safari, or, 'travelling wives'. They are now known as Kumari and show many similarities to their Pakistani sisters the Khushra, (related though different to India's Hijra).

The Kuchi-Safari were first identified for the westerner by travelling 19th century sexologist Sir Richard Burton. He wrote "The Afghans are commercial travellers, in a large scale. Each caravan is accompanied by a number of boys and lads almost in women's attire with kohl'd eyes and rouged cheeks, long tresses and hennaed fingers and toes, riding luxuriously in Kajawas or camel-panniers. They are called Kuchi-safari, or travelling wives, and the husbands trudge patiently by their sides."

Their role was agreed and acknowledged by the men's real wives. This was to keep their men from alliances with other women which might end in difficulty for the whole family, and displacement for a wife, who had no real rights to property before, during or after marriage. Burton does not record the age of the Kuchi-safari, although we may expect that he disapproved of underage abuse as much as we do today. Despite that at the time, there was no clear age for consensual sex in England, and as Dickens revealed, abuses were endemic to the poor of the cities, and conditions were not dissimilar to the east, throughout Europe.

Later in the same study, The Erotic Traveller, he describes the sexual acts used on boys or girls, which offer good reason why the Kuchi-Safari would scurry about as soon as a caravan stopped, to insure the ground was clear of stones for sleeping. They were taken on their backs, like women, but with a painful addition, the dominant partner guided his passage and tightened theirs with a hand gripped around their genitalia.

Burton interestingly reveals, that heterosexual TG's were frowned upon, their motive not unlike that of those admonished in The Law of Moses, in Deuteronomy. He writes; "In Afghanistan also a frantic debauchery broke out amongst the women when they found incubi who were not pederasts; and the scandal was not the most insignificant cause of the general rising in Cabal (November 1841), and the slaughter of Macnagten, Burnes and other British officers." For those unaware, the Law of Moses fully translated, insists that women should not disguise themselves as men for the purpose of being preachers, nor men disguised as women in order to slip into women's tents at night for illicit sex. Something like the latter seems to have occurred in Cabul in 1841, and perhaps involved some British officers.

The use of the term 'incubi' is interesting, a male demon that draws on women's sexual energy at night, evolved no doubt out of attempts at religious celibacy and the post pubescent ID, or deep subconscious, creating a psycho-chemical reaction. It has been observed that whenever the eastern rules are broken sexually, there's a tendency for people to react with superstition and attack the person as a 'djinn' or 'genie'. Then dehumanising them and easing the act of punishment for themselves, whilst probably killing the victim, horribly.

Modern Kumari were found in Afghanistan, just prior to the recent war there. They were working as dancers in the border town

Just ahead of the first Gulf War an eager American junior officer turned up to give an inspiring speech, with the prop of a bag of assorted women's G strings and panties; casting them out dramatically before the men, he intoned in his "best John Wayne; 'If anyone's in doubt, this is what we are fighting for...'.

There were more laughs than cheers and whoops, perhaps because the news of this incident came to be first reported in Renaissance News, the journal of one of North America's top Transgender organisations.

The UK's TG groups scanned around to find some closet members in the forces, and also came up with some of 'our boys' who were would-be girls, under their camouflage and boots.

The International Gender Transient Affinity, being the first and only TG human rights network, gets into the thick of war zones on a close and personal level. They wanted to find out whether our boy/girls were going to encounter sisters on the other side. A high probability of it was found, although, they were more likely to be among the civilians than 'undie-cover' as it were, in the armed forces.

Samantha Kane is one of the most well known Transsexuals born in Iraq. Though now (despite £35,000 of surgery and what she wrote in her book) has, it is reported, reverted to living male.

A Personal Report

Peshawar, in Qissa. Selim, one of the Kumari, was the child of an Afghan merchant family, which until her father lost his fortunes due to the wars with Russia, was quite well off. She was 19 years old when last contacted, working in a restaurant by day, dancing with her sisters by night to help support her family back in Cabul, who were also arranging Selim's marriage to a woman. She said; "if they knew my real work they would kill me. 'They think I work in a meat shop. Little do they know that the butcher is my boyfriend, and I am interested in other meat".

The other Kumari sisters were working legitimately by day, one was a student of Islam, (which is what Taliban means, but one must doubt that she was of that fundamentalist institution). Another had just began to grow facial hair and dared not shave it off, she had to bleach it instead. What they did most was to meet at night and go off in a van supplied by an agency, to dance at weddings and births like Hijra. Their clients were in danger with them, as this performance is not Islamic but 'animist', to bring fertility, and all dance and music was banned by the Taliban. It was as much a rebellion as was the lipstick worn by a Serejevo secretary.

The people made an effort at glamour and entertainment as a reaction to the depression of war and dictatorial oppression. The punishment if caught, would certainly have ended in the football stadium, where 'homosexuals' were variously shot, hung or had a wall collapsed onto them, a version of stoning.

We know that the Kumari survived the war, because The Sun newspaper revealed that Whiskey Company, 45 Commando, were complaining about 'men' in lipstick walking hand in hand, inviting them to dance with them. What a great pity that the MOD did not supply a social anthropologist to explain to the British troops, that they would be seen as brave liberators, and invited to dance only as an honour to them, with no strings attached. After all, the Kumari are passive, so if the men made no moves then nothing would be expected or done about that.

The Sun's Littlejohn threw in that; "our boys in Bagram are being pursued by men wearing pink lipstick, nail varnish and perfume", adding; "Obviously the Taliban weren't quite as thorough as we have been led to believe". - It is not possible to pass comment about that statement from a western journalist.

Just ahead of the new Gulf conflict, the Sunday Sport has come up with "Saddam is a woman". Their writer Ben Borland asserts that "Saddam Hussien is a rampant Transvestite who likes to be called 'Sandra' when he is a la femme, and trawls the gay bars of Baghdad, picking up 'chick-boys'". The Sport has been seen to be kind of TG's in the past, even making newspaper-publishing history in the 80's when they allowed me to enter their Face & Figure competition, in which I was short-listed for the finals. But, they do like their 'was a woman' stories, which they pick up from the USA's Weekly World News. When they did 'Hitler was a woman', despite a theory running among students of the subject, there was no way to prove it. Whereas Saddass Insane is very much alive in the here and now, and as revealed, there's even a 50/50% chance of a vestige of truth in the matter. Naturally, I dropped them a line, telling them that I will afford them the benefit of the doubt, if they accept my challenge to get to Baghdad, to prove it. I supplied two pics of myself as Barb Wire with pump action shotgun, to let them know that a feisty British Gender Transient is up to the job. To date, there has been no reply. Mr Borland claims to have rung the Ministry of Defence where a spokesman said, "This sounds absolutely ridiculous. I strongly suggest you double-check your sources. We have never heard anything about Saddam Hussein dressing as a woman named Sandra or anything else for that matter. I honestly haven't got time to answer any more questions on the subject". No one, Mr Borland writes, 'was available for comment at the Iraqi Ministry of Information or the Pentagon.' Apparently, the Sport may have come up with something that the MOD is still blind to. But at the time of writing only time itself will tell.

If I've been fighting human rights abuses against TG's in the 3rd world, while one of its biggest dictators was a sister, responsible for a chunk of it, I'll be somewhat miffed!

In the early part of 2003 a task force was built up in the Kuwait desert just off the border of Iraq. On the face of it this has very little to do with Transvestites. To most people it was the start of a sequence of events, which was to include some good explosions on telly, a lot of strong opinions being voiced and political squirming and back covering on a monolithic scale. To me as a member of the MOD, that task force and a tranny it meant a bit more.

Cross dressing although always popular as a bit of a laugh on a night out in the mob, is still some what frowned on in battle fields. As such my chances of some time to let my feminine side run free were looking a bit thin in the near future. In fact dress regulations in war zones are quite strict and for good reason. Sequins although essential on some outfits are prone to twinkling and giving your position away to the enemy when worn on battle fatigues. Heels are prone to sinking in the sand and are a devil to run in and hobble skirts are a non starter. I have thought that as stilettos leave smaller foot prints than boots they may be useful in mine fields but to be honest I can't see me being issued anti-mine stilettos any time soon.

After much hanging around for weeks on end, we eventually charged across the border and got our first look at Iraq. To be honest it wasn't very impressive, but few places are after an artillery bombardment, and the people, who I have to say my heart went out to. Most people seemed genuinely pleased to see us but if you live in a hut with absolutely nothing you to would be pleased to see someone that gave you some food and a bottle of water.

You may think from the pictures of Sadam's palaces that Iraq was quite a glamorous place, but the average member of the Iraq population has very little glamour in their lives. The Iraq girls although very beautiful had few clothes and often no shoes, so an Iraq tranny, if such thing exists, probably has even less. It made me put my own problems like zero privacy and dressing time a bit more in perspective.

As time passed I came to several conclusions about Iraq. 'A'. Don't move to Iraq. Although Muslim women's dress would make it very easy to pass as most of their body and face is covered, it's not the sort of thing that works for me. 'B' Don't move to Iraq. If you think attitudes in UK are intolerant then you would be shocked to see what happens to people outside the norm in a country like this. 'C' If you do move to Iraq, unless you look good in a bikini you will have to move back soon as it is too hot to wear anything else.

I thought perhaps that if men let their feminine side out a bit more there would be fewer wars. Less bombs and guns and more bars and garters sort of thing. Tony Blair in a teddy and George Bush in a ball gown would be sight to see. Although it was Maggie in charge for the Falklands Campaign, perhaps iron knickers don't count. I don't mean to trivialize the war as people lost their lives, some good friends of mine. But life goes on and some of us like to spend ours in a dress and you can bet the freedom to do that has been hard fought for by somebody. When you do spare a thought for the would be tranny's around the world who must suppress the need to dress, not for fear of what the neighbours might think but of a more real fear of what the authorities may do.

Kirsty's full Personal Profile was published in the 11th Tranny Guide

---

What is your name and what is your background?
My name is Julia Leggs, I now live in Richmond , Surrey. I am divorced and single now. My background is quite varied, I left school when I was 15 and joined the British Army, Serving in the Infantry for 6 years before becoming a Combat Med Tech with the Medical Corps. I got married when I was 18, became a father for the first time when I was 20 and she will be 21 this year! I also have a son who is 10 this year. I have done several jobs since leaving the forces which include HM Prison service, Retail management, Timber preservation, Nursing and now direct marketing for an Ex Service charity for disabled Ex Servicemen and Women. I also live on site, which does cramp my lifestyle a bit!

Julia Leggs full Personal Profile was published in the 11th Tranny Guide

A Personal Report

Formal Dinner

Caroline & Martha

Mel, Peg, Sharene

Peggy & Melanie

were 16 crossdressers and an equal number of spouses, girl friends and supportive friends as well as many from the Houston area GLBT community. This group was small compared to the 2,200 other passengers on board. Several crossdressers in the group developed friendships with attractive, educated and supportive women who want to continue the relationship established on the cruise. Some of the pictures that follow show this friendship developing during the week long cruise.

By the second day of the cruise most of the 2,200 passengers knew that there were "men in dresses" on the cruise. Many began asking the usual questions: "Are you gay? Your wife is with you! How does she deal with your crossdressing? Why do you want to go to all the trouble to be beautiful? Why would you want the torture of waist clinchers, panty hose and high heels? By the third and fourth day of the cruise, passengers and especially the many women alone on the cruise or with groups of other women wanted to spend time and party late at night with the fun loving beauties in the Dignity Cruise group. Dignity Cruises were named "Dignity Cruises" because of the conviction of Dr. Peggy Rudd, author of 'My Husband Wears My Clothes', and 'Crossdressing With Dignity' plus two other books on the topic of men and women who cross gender lines, that transgendered individuals needed a safe and supportive environment to cross-dress with dignity. Cruises provide this environment and frequently are less expensive than many of the transgender conventions and conferences.

Since 1988, over 800 transgendered individuals together with spouses, girlfriends, family members and supportive friends have enjoyed the ultimate en-femme adventure. Many of the fellow passengers have been educated about our dignified transgender worldwide community. On every cruise passengers request time with our group to have their questions answered and have their pictures taken with members of the group. On the second formal night of the cruise, the group has a formal picture taken by the ship photographer posed on the winding staircase of the ship's atrium. On every cruise there are hundreds of fellow passengers who also take pictures and videos of the posed group. These pictures and the positive interactions between the group and passengers are then shared with family members and friends upon their return home. In 15 years the participants in the past Dignity Cruises may have educated over 30,000 passengers and many

Transgendered individuals are looking for love and romance. Many say that have difficulty finding a woman who will love, support, understand and accept their crossdressing. On past Dignity Cruises two crossdressers met women who later became their wives. On the Dignity Cruise 20 cruise out of Houston/Galveston November 16-23, 2003 there

others on their return home. On one of the cruises there was a group of 48 Jerry Falwell "Christian Coalition" followers. This group asked to meet with our group. After their questions were answered, this group of men and women became the group's biggest supporters. We were later told that they reported back to Falwell who said that any transgendered person who presented themselves in a dignified manner was welcome at any time at Thomas Street Baptist Church in North Carolina. We did hear that several attended services and were warmly welcomed.

On the last morning of the past cruise we overheard many people including couples who were making very positive statements about the transgendered people on board. We did not hear any negative remarks which is not to say that the few "rednecks" on board did not voice their negative comments.

Celebrate the Freedom of Gender Expression at "The TG Convention at Sea"

DIGNITY CRUISE 21

The next Dignity Cruises are planned for January 24-31, 2004 out of New Orleans to the Western Caribbean and September 18-23, 2004 out of Barcelona - Spain to: Cannes/Monte Carlo, Florence, Rome, Naples and Malta.

DIGNITY CRUISE 22

February 25 - March 6 2005. Sailing from Miami on the RCCL Brilliance of the Sea to the Panama Canal, Aruba, Grand Cayman and Costa Rico

Information on Dignity Cruises arranged through Absolute Best Cruises, Florida is found at **www.pmpub.com** or by contacting **digntycruises@mindspring.com**

Celebrate the freedom of gender expression, join Dr. Peggy Rudd and Melanie Rudd and many from the TG community in North American and Europe, sailing from fun filled, historic Barcelona, Spain aboard the magnificent Royal Caribbean Splendor of the Seas September 18-25, 2004 to Cannes/Monte Carlo, Florence/Pisa, Rome, Naples, and Malta before returning to Barcelona. This journey through history begins and ends in Barcelona, a city known for its festive spirit, flamboyant architecture and savoury cuisine. This luxurious ship will take you to see classical works of art, ancient ruins and sweeping cityscapes, surrounded by olive groves and the beautiful blue sea.

Your initial deposit of $250 per person will hold your choice of cabin with final payment prior to July 1, 2004. Pre and post cruise hotel packages will be available in Barcelona. Air packages from your home city are also available.

Excursions and additional information on this cruise can be found at **www.rccl.com**

The rates are exceptional for 7 days/nights of luxury and pampering while experiencing the grandeur of ancient Europe.

To book this magnificent adventure call Dignity Cruises, associated with Absolute Best Cruises at **281-347-SAIL (7245), Fax: 281-347-8747** or email: **melpeg@mindspring.com. www.pmpub.com**

Inside cabin (Q) $644 per person
Outside cabin (I) $844 per person
Balconies (D) $1144 per person
Port and government taxes are additional

A Personal Report

Vienna

SELF-HELP GROUP / TG - MEETING

TRANSX – TransGender - Union Rosa-Lila-Villa, 1060 Vienna, Linke Wienzeile 102 (next U4-station Pilgramgasse), http://transx.transgender.at. Meetings each first Monday and third Wednesday of the month at 20:00, Club on the 1st Floor.

TRANSGENDER – FETISH:

LESWING Hannovergasse 5, 1200 Vienna. Transvestites and Gay night on Tues. Changing and Make-Up rooms available.

SMART-CAFE Köstlergasse 9, 1060 Vienna. www.smartcafe.at. Viennese SadoMaso and Fetish Café, Tues to Sat evening. Each 1st Sat of month: SMart Extreme Party with dress code.

PERVS@PARADISE Fuenfhausgasse 1, 1150 Vienna. A fetish event each 2nd Sat 22:00, [lo:sch], Dress code: Fetish/SM/TV. SM-Sunday-Brunch: each second Sunday from 12:00 at Café Benno, 1090 Vienna, Alserstrasse 67. www.bdsm.at/embm.

GOING OUT

WILLENDORF Rosa-Lila-Villa, 1060 Vienna, Linke Wienzeile 102 (next U4-station Pilgramgasse). Excellent mixed-gay-lesbian restaurant, 18:00 – 2:00,

CAFÉ BERG Berggasse 8, 1090 Vienna. Cofeeshop and restaurant. 10:00 – 1:00.

CAFÉ SAVOY Linke Wienzeile 36, 1060 Vienna (next U4-station Kettenbrueckengasse). Traditional Viennese Cofeeshop. Mon to Sat.

CAFÉ X-BAR Mariahilferstrasse 45, Raimundpassage, 1060 Vienna (next U4-stationKettenbrueckengasse) Queer Pub, daily from 16:00,

LIVING ROOM Queer restaurant, 1050 Vienna, Franzensgasse 18. 18:00 – 4:00, except Sunday. Frauencafé Lange Gasse 11, 1080 Vienna Women - lesbian pub. Tuesday – Saturday, 18:30 – 2:00.

NACHTSCHICHT Wagramerstr. 69, 1220 Vienna. TG-friendly discotheque, where you usually will meet some of us on Fridays. Monday to Saturday from 21:00.

ROSAS Tanzbar Langegasse 50, 1080 Vienna. Classic dance for Lesbian, Gays and Transgenders. Each last Sunday of the month starting 19:00, "Cheek2Cheek",

U4, HEAVEN Schoenbrunnerstrasse 22, 1120 Vienna, U4-Station Meidling. Mixed-gay disco. Every Thursday night from 22:00.

WHY NOT www.why-not.at, Tiefer Graben 22, 1010 Vienna. Mixed-gay disco. Friday and Saturday, best to visit on Saturday,

Graz

Self-help Group / TG - Meeting

GRAZ.TRANSGENDER Each 2nd Sunday of the month at 19:00 at the SBZ (Maiffredygasse 4) and each 4th Wednesday at 21:00 at the Traminer Weinstube at the corner Jakominiplatz - Klosterwiesgasse 2. For more information and contacts visit http://graz.transgender.at/ or Michaela http://members.tripod.de/rouxii/michaela.html, michaela@trangender.at.

Going Out

TRAMINER Weinstube a TG-friendly wine house (see above)

DARKWAVE, HipHop, Electro, Industrial and Metal is played, after 24:00 on Friday and Saturday there are a lot of freaky people (punks, Gothic's, fetish, transgender). Tuesday to Saturday 23:00 - 06:00 at Luthergasse 4.

BLACK FANTASIE a club for fetish, bdsm and transgenders. Griesgasse 38, Tuesday - Thursday 18:00 - 24:00, Friday and Saturday 20:00 - 01:00, www.blackfantasie.at.

YAMAMOTO a nice sushi-bar. Prokopgasse 4, Tuesday to Sunday.

Linz

SELF-HELP GROUP / TG - MEETING

AT COFFEE CORNER, Bethlehemstr. 30, 4020 Linz. Contact Alexandra (sandyTS@gmx.at) or Nadja (nadja_tg@hotmail.com) Each 1st Monday and 3rd Wednesday of the month from 19:00,

Going Out

COFFEE CORNER Bethlehemstr. 30, 4020 Linz, Tel.: 0732/77 08 62. Monday to Saturday, opens at 19:00, Gasthaus Bratwurstglöckerl Angerholzweg 38, 4030 Linz, Tel. 0732/34 20 24. TG-friendly restaurant,

STONEWALL Rainerstr. 22, 4020 Linz, www.stonewall.at, Tel. 0732/60 04 38. Bar each day from 20.00 h, Edith's Disco for TGs on Tues, general Disco on Fri and Sat at 23:00, be careful on Turkish gay-bashing gangs hanging around the entrance area - especially on weekends!

MY WAY Goethestrasse 51, 4020 Linz, daily from 19.00; www.myway.at, Tel. 0732/65 27 60

NACHTSCHICHT Im Bäckerfeld 1, 4060 Leonding, TG-friendly discotheque. Wed to Sun from 21:00

Salzburg

SELF-HELP GROUP / TG - MEETING

TRANSGENDER.AT Each 2nd and 4th Wednesday of the month from 20:00, HOSI-Salzburg, Office at Muellner Hauptstrasse 11, 5020 Salzburg. Contact Dani (dany@transgender.at).

One of the curious things concerning TG's is that they seem to have no history. Once Trans-women were just recognised as queerly dressed gays. Transvestites were discovered for the first time at the beginning of the last century by the sexologist Magnus Hirschfeld, who recognised that many of them were not interested in having sex with men at all. Then transsexuals were invented 50 years later in operating theatres.

In fact European TG's have a long history too. It is mainly a history of pursuance, of mental houses, jails and concentration camps.

Remembering our personal histories implies the memorisation of insulting, irreverence and serious troubles in the labour market. Now, here in Austria, we have no longer fear getting beaten up at the next corner or even getting killed. But not far from here – in Serbia – the well known transvestite Merlinka was murdered in March 2003.

"Austria has its history of lynching TG's too".

The first documented murder of a transgender person in Vienna goes back to the year 1863. On 14th July the Turk Army started to besiege Vienna. Some houses stood in fire and people became psyched. A 17 years old Cross-Dresser, who just passed by, immediately was blamed to be the reason for all the misery. It is well documented that the riffraff beat him, undressed and lynched. The blood-covered corps was dragged to the Peters church where a butcher tore off his skin encouraged by the enthusiastic cheers of the crowd.

As our transgender-organisation TransX learned these facts, we felt that it would be good to mourn once for that young person and all for all those persecuted since then. Exactly 320 years after that cruel event we planned a funeral procession following just along the same way the dead corps was hauled.

It would become the first Austrian transgender-demonstration, but we were not sure, if we were strong enough to organise an impressing event. So we looked for the solidarity of other groups: Gay groups declared their support (although – as we know now - they didn't help very much in fact). But the Green-party, several left-wing groups and two Sado-Masochist organisations showed much solidarity and helped a lot by informing the public. The week around the 320-years memorial became an action week where transgender-events took place on almost each day: free transgender-movies, lectures, discussions and parties took place.

For the first time there was a broad alliance against prejudice against TG-persons and we got the feeling that times really will change now.

The memorial march took palace on 14th July – exactly 320 years after the cruel event. About 200 persons participated - probably the largest transgender demonstration that took place in Europe this year, and it was an impressing street-theatre performance as well. Many participants dressed in black like people at an entombment.

At the place where the murder happened we held an oration. Gloria G., a well known transgender author, recapitulated the historical events and remembered that discrimination of TG's still exists as a form of sexism, that forces everybody to live life as either a 'real man' or 'real woman' rather than to express one's emotions freely.

Then we marched to the centre where the poor guy was skinned. With loudspeakers we read the 280 names and short histories of murdered transvestites and transsexuals published by an American transgender organisation at **www.gender.org/remember**. It became a quite dramatic and creepy march through the centre of Vienna. Although some people, passing by, still laughed at us, it became a very honourific demonstration for the persecution and suffering of all people that are 'different'.

At the final ceremony I gave a talk about that useless horror. We laid down an annulus and kept silent for a minute. Sad music was played. Then I started talking again. But this time I spoke about our political demands and about the fact that the "chains of gender" must lose their power now. I pointed out that reclusively the fact that this demonstration could take place proves this. I mentioned that this 320 years cruel history is passing by and a new age is starting. To demonstrate that we can leave all the fear of persecution behind, I invited all transgender folks to drop their old skin of shame and shyness. I took a sharp knife, held it up upon my chest and pulled it down along my body such that my black memorial dress was cut in parts and fell down to earth. Loudspeakers played out "Tommy's - I'm free" as a declaration of the end of a cruel blind period.

Has the world changed since that time?
The legal situation is still the same: In Austria trans-women are still forced by law to undergo surgery before they are accepted to go officially by a female first name and get female identity cards. Coming out still implies the risk of long phases of unemployment, but in the last years we observed more and more cases, where transsexuals could change their gender without loosing their jobs.

Maybe it was only the transgender-community that has changed a bit since then. Recollecting our history of pursuance, remembering centuries of suffering and maltreatment, helps us to resist all forms of sexism, that discriminate against people due to their gender performance and helps us remember that everybody has the right to express his/her gender freely!

Central TG web site:
www.transgender.at

A Personal Report

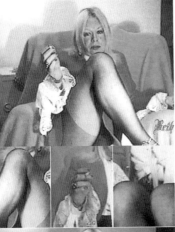

Are you happy to be called a tranny and what does this name mean to you?

Depends on who calls me so. Not in the supermarket, because I walk as a regular man, in life. Except that I'm a man with long blond hair. Once I'm transformed and moving in the TV or clubs world, I feel proud to be a tranny, demanding and giving respect to all sisters. I never felt any competition, not from my side. I'm proud being' myself, satisfied being Beth.

How old are you and how young can you remember thinking about or actually cross-dressing?

I'm 52. It started when I was 9 with my mom's heels. Never stopped. Went on and on.

Where do you buy clothes?

Preferably in small shops, in other towns. Cos it would embarrass me to meet anybody who knows me, but not my "other life". I do mail orders as well.

What leads you to choose the styles you wear?

I choose stuff that looks sexy to me - like I'd like a woman to wear for me. I like to be kinda extravagant. I like lace, satin stuff, miniskirts & heels. I've got no style in particular. I can use nearly everything as long as it's not too indecent.

Do you have one look or many images?

When I go out, I'm never indecent, (clothed like the hookers). Although some years ago I was always as shocking as possible. At home, when I'm expecting someone I like doin' the style of "the ancient queen" which I feel a lot alike. In this role anything can be possible, like a Xmas tree, covered in all kinds of gold and silver beads hung on me by the meter & all kinds of jewellery from top to toe, even a crown.

Is make-up and hair important to you and if so how do you achieve your look?

I'm dark blonde and coloured high blonde, For years and years I have gone every week to my hairdresser for a hair wash and have it in good shape everyday, because you never know who you could meet. Colouring once every 6 weeks. I never leave home without an umbrella. About my make-up, I guess I'm old fashioned, I have always done the same thing for years. I like it, but I do need to get some new ideas and have variation in styles.

To what degree do you practice hair removal, and other body feminisation?

I like to be smooth all over, always.

Who knows that you dress?

My ex-wife. She never saw me, but found some TV stuff of mine, three times actually, over 25 years. She then declared that she couldn't live with such thoughts of me anymore and wanted a divorce. . I told my mom when I was 50 because I felt she was blamin' my ex-wife too much.

How often do you dress and if you go out where to?

I always dress at night. How often, depends on my opportunities There isn't so much around here to go to, It is about a 150 kilometres drive for me. So once or twice in a month I go on my

What is your name and what is your background?

I am Beth. I'm 3/4 Belgian and1/4 English. Livin' in Belgium. I'm a performer as singer/musician. I've got the strong impression that both of my talents, being a musician and being a tranny, are coursed by the English part of my genes. My grandma was a London nurse. I'm divorced and single for the last 5 years.

own sometimes or I contact friends by e-mail to meet me there. I have many experiences in everything considering my age. But in the last year I have been building on these. I already have a lot of tranny friends.

How much of a sexual turn on is trannying for you?

I couldn't think of one other reason than sex. But a certain power is also involved. I mean as a tranny you try to create what, in your own eyes, looks like an attractive woman. If you bring that woman successfully out, you'll have power over men. I get excited from the first line of lipstick on my mouth, I need my face painted and then grow really horny when I get ready to be Beth. I couldn't and wouldn't allow anyone to touch me when I'm not in tranny.

What is your definition of feminine?

Soft skin, breasts, long hair and more tenderly build.

To what degree do you feel gender dysphoric?

It's like fulltime in my mind. Though the older I become, I seem to get more and more involved in tranny things, like a reason for living.

To what degree would you consider permanent hair removal, hormones, surgery?

Permanent hair removal would be very practical, hormones I'm scared of. I'd like some bigger breasts, though not too large. Other things like an operation to make the genitals feminine looks like a horror show to me.

What one piece of advice would you give to someone that has just found they are not the only tranny in the world?

Try to make the most beautiful of the woman that's in you. Listen to advice from sisters, but don't take everything for truth.

Photos on this page with thanks to Pamela from Belgium

Copenhagen ■ *A Personal* Report

BARS, RESTAURANTS & NIGHTCLUBBING

ALLEENBERG
Allégade 4 Tel: +45 33254442. Old-fashioned bar with a very mixed clientele giving this place a most joyous atmosphere. Very crowded late night. Trannies most welcome, and we're always having a good night out at Alléenberg.

AMIGO BAR
Schønbergsgade 4 Tel: +45 33214915. Gay/mixed crowd. Several sisters have made their way singing karaoke late night in front of an audience. Very crowded late night, but if you are not shy you'll have a ball at Amigo Bar.

BUTTERFLY CLUB AT NEVER MIND
Nørre Voldgade 2 Tel: +45 33118886. Never Mind is a most friendly and relaxed gay bar with a small dance floor, occasionally drag show, stand-up comedians and live jazz music. Trannies and friends meet here in Butterfly Club the first Friday every month since 1998. They have become a tranny institution in in the past four years and we'll be there for many years to come.

CENTRALHJORNET
Kattesundet 18 Tel: +45 33118549. Might be the oldest gay bar in the world, but has a most joyous atmosphere. If not shy you'll meet new friends immediately! Trannies are warmly welcome

COSY BAR
Studiestræde 24 Tel: +45 33127427 www.cosybar.dk One of the most popular late night gay bar with a small dance floor. Live DJ's and drag show during weekend. Cosy Bar has been one of the most popular 'waterholes' in the gay community for decades, and trannies and drags have always been a big part of the game. Being totally renovated last year with a new dance floor and live DJ's it's become even more popular. Want a good night out try Cosy Bar. Check out their website for further information.

HEAVEN
Bar Café & Restaurant, Kompagnistræde 18, Tel: +45 33151900 www.heaven-copenhagen.dk Heaven might be the most popular new gay bar, café & restaurant in town. Nice, friendly atmosphere, and trannies are most welcome. Gay/mixed crowd. Very busy during evening and weekend. Their website is well worth checking out for further information about the gay club scene in Copenhagen right now.

INTIME
Allégade 25, Tel: +45 38341958 Website: www.cafeintime.dk Old-fashioned gay/mixed piano bar situated vis-à-vis the spot where TiD had their regular meetings through decades. We often drop by and are a most welcome part of the crowd. The new ownership on Café Intime keeps up the tradition having live music during the evening. Fellow musicians or even guests are often invited to join the sessions. If you have a good jazz feeling you might be the next guest star on Café Intime.

MADAME ARTHUR
Bar & Nightclub* Vester Farimagsgade 3 Tel: +45 33932936 www.siliconedolls.net Drag Cabaret with the most popular drag artists in Denmark right now. Madame Arthur is very popular with trannies and several sisters have had a good time here. Check out their website for further information.

MANIFEST FETISH CLUB
E-mail: stig@manifestfetishclub.dk www.manifestfetishclub.dk Monthly Fetish-Club which often arrange Gender bender parties with focus on TV, TS, TG, & Drag. Check out their web site for further information on the fetish scene.

NEVER MIND
Nørre Voldgade 2 Tel: +45 33118886 A most friendly, relaxed gay bar with a small dance floor, drag show, stand-up and live jazz music. Trannies and friends meet here in Butterfly Club the first Friday every month since 1998.

PAN CLUB
Knabrostræde 3 Tel: +45 33113784 www.pan-cph.dk Most popular gay/mixed Disco. 2 dance floors and 3 bars. Drag show during weekend, live performances and special events. Very popular with younger trannies.

QUEEN VICTORIA
Restaurant, Snaregade 4 Tel: +45 33910191 Run by actor/singer Hardy Dræbye, formerly known as Mona Lisa, performing drag for decades, and this restaurant is a must among trannies. You're most welcome, and even the menu is excellent! TiD arrange a most popular candlelight dinner for all members on Queen Victoria every year in May.

ROSIE MCGEE
Vesterbrogade 2A Tel: +45 33321923 www.rosiemcgees.dk Straight Pub and Dance Hall situated next to Town Hall Square. A very popular with trannies and several sisters have had a good time here. Check out their website

SILICONE DOLLS *
at Madame Arthur* Vester Farimagsgade 3 Web Site: www.siliconedolls.net Copenhagen's top travestie and drag night club at Madame Arthur run by Katarina Collins Check out their web site for further information.

HOTELS

ABSALON HOTEL*
Helgolandsgade 15 Tel: +45 33242211 Fax: +45 33243411 E-mail: info@absalon-hotel.dk www.absalon-hotel.dk. Situated in the heart of Copenhagen next to Madame Arthur, Silicone Dolls, Never Mind, Town Hall Square/Pedestrian Street and Tivoli.

AVENUE HOTEL
Åboulevard 29 Tel: +45 35373111 Fax: +45 35373486. This hotel is a legend among Swedish and Norwegian trannies staying in Copenhagen. Nice rooms and nice prices. In walking distance to Town Hall

Square/Pedestrian Street, Tivoli and all the interesting places mentioned in this list.

JORGENSENS HOTEL*
Rømersgade 11 Tel: +45 33138186 Fax: +45 33155105 E-mail: hotel@post12.tele.dk Web Site: www.hoteljoergensen.dk. Nice and friendly low-budget hotel in quiet area. Central situated. In walking distance to Never Mind. Popular with trannies who rather spend their money on shopping and clubbing than hotel bills while visiting Copenhagen.

LEDA HOTEL
Svanevej 6 Tel: +45 35831222 Fax: +45 35831224 E-mail: leda@ledahotel.dk www.ledahotel.dk. Located at Nørrebro a little out of Centrum. Only 10 minutes to Town Hall Square/Pedestrian Street by bus/car. Nice rooms, nice prices and very friendly staff. Recommended by sisters from Scandinavia. Special price when you place your order via e-mail.

PARK HOTEL*
Jarmers Plads 3 Tel: +45 33133000 E-mail: park@copenhagenparkhotel.dk. Situated in the heart of Copenhagen, next to Never Mind, Town Hall Square/Pedestrian Street and Tivoli this might be the most expensive hotel on the list. Friendly and professional staff makes you feel welcome at once. Walking distance to all the interesting places mentioned in this list. Park Hotel has become the new favourite hotel with trannies from abroad because of the central position right in the heart of Copenhagen.

IBIS COPENHAGEN STAR HOTEL*
Colbjørnsensgade 13 Tel: +45 33221100 Fax: +45 33212186 E-mail: star@accorhotel.com www.ibishotel.com. Situated in the heart of city next to Madame Arthur, Silicone Dolls, Never Mind, Town Hall Square/Pedestrian Street and Tivoli.

IBIS COPENHAGEN TRITON HOTEL
Helgolandsgade 7-11 Tel: +45 33313266 Fax: +45 33316970 E-mail: triton@accorhotel.com Web Site: www.ibishotel.com. Situated in the heart of city next to Madame Arthur, Silicone Dolls, Never Mind, Town Hall Square/Pedestrian Street and Tivoli.

IBSENS HOTEL
Vendersgade 23 Tel: +45 33331913 Fax: +45 33131916 Nice and friendly all woman run hotel in quiet area. Central situated. Nice rooms and nice prices. In walking distance to Never Mind. Very popular hotel for trannies to stay visiting Copenhagen

BEAUTY & MAKEUP

ELSE LOVENOVS SPECIALKLINIK
Ordrupvej 46A Tel: +45 39636763 This specialist (with 60 years experience) understands and cares about TS/TV's with unwanted hair. Skin treatment and semi permanent makeup. During the season they visit the tranny organisation TiD to inform about the latest techniques in laser.

GLAMOUR TRANSITIONS *,
Tuborgvej 266a, 2400 Copenhagen NV, tel +45 35 815 814 www.glamourtransitions.com Miss Katarina

BARS, RESTAURANTS & NIGHTCLUBBING

All dressed up for a wonderful candlelight dinner on a nice restaurant, dancing or meeting new friends at a cosy little bar is a big part of enjoying the life of a woman. This list includes the most frequented and popular bars, restaurants and discotheques amongst trannies in Copenhagen right now.

BEAUTY & MAKEUP

Maybe you want to try a new colour in lipstick or a sexy new perfume. Then you'll be happy to know that it is very easy buying makeup in Copenhagen, as most makeup shops are utmost friendly to trannies. If you have special needs try out Teaterhjørnet. They have it all. If you're looking for specialist shops for hair removal, a beauty treatment or a full makeup service you'll find our favourites here.

BREAST FORMS

These specialist shops have a lot of trannies amongst customers. They know us through years and are fully aware of our specific needs. Do make an appointment in advance for better time and better service.

HOTELS

It's strictly business to run a hotel and I've never heard about any hotel in Copenhagen that wouldn't welcome you as a tranny as long as you behave properly and pay your bill. On the other hand we love to choose our own favourites, and this list includes the most visited hotels by trannies staying in Copenhagen.

A Personal Report

Copenhagen ■ *A Personal* Report

Collins new make-over salon is located in a very discrete part of Copenhagen offering make-overs, hair removal, facials, make-up lessons and a variety of accessories, shoes, wigs, make-up, jewellery and breastforms. The salon offers dressing sessions, photos-sessions and escorted tours and evenings. Other services include production and hosting of websites - travel packages throughout the world

INGEMIL
Haraldsgade 83 Tel: +45 3920331. Beauty treatment and makeup service. Many trannies just love this place. Nice, relaxed atmosphere, and very friendly staff.

TEATERHJORNET
Vesterbrogade 175 Tel: +45 33222247. Full range of Theatrical Makeup - and the place to buy beard-covering makeup. Many trannies and drags amongst costumers in mix with actors and professional make-up artists. Nice, friendly staff (they've seen it all!)

BREAST FORMS

DAN CHRISTIANSEN
Toftegårds Allé 10 Tel: + 45 36160017 Runs a wide choice of styles and sizes in breast forms. Discretion assured. Ask for special offers (breast forms used only for demonstration at low prices)

SIMONSEN & WEEL
Dag Hammarskjölds Allé 33 Tel: +45 35381477 Runs a wide choice of styles and sizes in breast forms. .

LINGERIE

EMMA LINGERI
Gammel Kongevej 107 Tel: +45 33247870 Beautiful lingerie, stockings and bridal wear. Trannies most welcome.

RENATE BUCCONE
Vesterbrogade 51 Tel: +45 33221041. If you're into corsets try Renate Buccone. Full range of Victorians, Sexy Satin and Lace Corsets and the most beautiful French lingerie. Call for their catalogue.

ORGANISATIONS & INFORMATION

BOSSEHUSET
Bådsmandstræde 43 Tel: +45 32959872 E-mail: boessehuset@hotmail.com Web site: www.christiania.org/~bhust. The place for gay theatre, drag show, cabaret, music and other events around the gay scene. Their biggest event is the very alternative Miss World Contest held every 2. Year. Next time will be in August 2004. Join their special mailing list frkverden@hotmail.com for further information. Maybe you wish to join the contest next time around.

DUNST
Sommerstedsgade 30 Web site: www.dunst.dk Internet-café for gay and tranny people Dunst might become a quite interesting new place to go, as their efforts are to cross the unspoken barriers between gay and tranny people. They'll arrange cultural events, crazy parties and film festivals. Dunst BIO run gay and

tranny cult movies every week. Check out their web site for further information.

LBL Teglgårdsstræde 13 Tel: +45 33131948 E-Mail: lbl@lbl.dk Web site: www.lbl.dk Gay/lesbian Organisation LBL runs their own house in the heart of Copenhagen with a small café, bookshop, library and Gay Radio Rosa at 91.4 MHz every night. Check out their website or call for information about what's going on in the tranny scene right now.

MERMAID PRIDE ORGANISATION
www.mermaidpride.dk. www.copenhagen-pride.dk Check out their information for Mermaid Pride Parade in August and other events during the season. They know what's worth knowing about the gay and tranny scene in Copenhagen right now.

PAN INFORMATION
Tel: +45 33360086 www.gayguide.dk. Gay/lesbian switchboard. Check out their website or call for information about what's going on in the gay world and the tranny scene right now.

SMIL
Sorgenfrigade 8A Tel: +45 35835569 www.sado.dk. S&M organisation located in the heart of Copenhagen. Membership/guests welcome. Having their own accommodation they'll arrange meetings during the week and different kind of weekend parties. Trannies into fetish and S&M welcome. Check their web site or call for information.

TID TRANSVESTITFORENINGEN
Danmark Favrholmvænget 10 DK – 3400 Hillerød Tel: +45 70229977 E-mail: tid@transvestit.dk www.transvestit.dk. This organisation support the transgender people in Denmark, arranging social gatherings in Copenhagen twice a month. Check out their web site for further information.

SHOES

HOOK SKO
Amagercentret 308 Tel: +45 32570184 Full range of fashion-shoes up to size 41-42 (Euro) and a small selection up to 43-44 (Euro)

KAJ LARSEN & SON
A/S H. C. Ørstedsvej 57 Tel: +45 35355966. Full range of ladies shoes. Most classic style up to size 46 (Euro).

KONGENS NYTORV SKO
Kongens Nytorv 21 Tel: +45 33330717. Full range of fashion-shoes up to size 41-42 (Euro) and a small selection up to 43-44 (Euro)

PEHRSSON SKO
Vesterbrogade 31Tel: +45 33319633. Besides having a full range of fashion shoes up to size 41-42 (Euro) and a small selection up to size 44-45 (Euro) the shop deals with high-heeled stilettos up to size 45 (or more).

PERFECT SKO
(Annette Lassen) Nærumvænge Torv 1Tel: +45 45800504. Full range of ladies shoes, most classic style, up to size 47 (Euro). You'll find the staff most helpful and confident with trannies through decades.

* **New indicates new entries in my list of favourite places this year.**

WIGS

AMICA PARYKBAR
(Annette Hagemann) Vesterbrogade 96 Tel: +45 33311013. Full range of wigs. Annette is very helpful and confident with trannies through decades.

FINWA WALDORF
Thorvaldsensvej 112 Tel: +45 335363562. Full range of wigs. Customised, handmade wigs can also be ordered.

FRIDA DAVIDSENS EFTF
(Elisabeth Simonsen) Nørre Farimagsgade 17 Tel: +45 33130372. Full range of wigs, and my absolute favourite amid wig suppliers. You'll find Elisabeth most helpful and confident with trannies. During the season she makes special arrangements in the shop for tranny people demonstrating new styles in wigs.

PARYKCENTRET
(Ellen Andersen) Store Strandstræde 3 Tel: +45 33128410 Full range of wigs. You'll find Ellen most helpful and confident with trannies

Long time friend of The Tranny Guide/Jenni Sands

LINGERIE

If you're looking out for beautiful lingerie and stockings you'll be happy to know that it is very easy shopping in Copenhagen, as most shops are utmost friendly to trannies.

This list brings you some of our favourite shops in town.

ORGANISATIONS & INFORMATION

Visiting a new town for the first time it's a great help to know where to go and ask for further information about the gay and tranny scene. Here you'll find the answer on most questions wanting to join the game in Copenhagen.

SHOES

If you're lucky too fit less than size 41 (Euro) you might have all the opportunity in the world to buy a lovely pair of shoes. But needing bigger size it's a problem wherever you are to get a nice shoe in the right size. I've made this list to ease your way.

WIGS

Unfortunately wigs are pretty expensive in Denmark, especially compared to prices in France and US. Anyway we do have a string of helpful wig suppliers in town, and these shops are the most sought by trannies. Please make an appointment for better time and service.

A Personal Report

Where do you buy clothes?

All over the planet. Started at the internet as I found this way very discrete and I guess I was some kind of embarrassed. These days I simply walk into a store - see what I like and try it on.. even when in male mode. I mean.. what could possible happen? except maybe for giving the Ladies working in the store a good laugh and a story to tell at the dinner table.. A good thing I have learned is to bring a picture of Kat when shopping in male mode. Showing that always breaks the ice and very often the people you deal with are both impressed and finds it fantastic. I have so far never experienced negative things in this matter... I still do a lot of shopping on the internet, but these days only when I know for sure about sizing and quality. I am avoiding the Internet tranny stores - most of them is a rip off with poor quality and just there to take advantage of the trannys of the world.

What leads you to choose the style you wear?

I have always loved Glamour, glitter, heels and rhinestones... The biggest Diva of them all - Joan Collins has had a big influence on me she is one of the most attractive women on the planet. Joan moves like a Cat.. and Collins - Katarina Collins - get the picture

Do you have one look or many images?

I have many looks - sexy elegant, classy elegant or even a bit naughty elegant (if such a term exists?). Almost all my looks includes shoes or boots with heels, and preferably lots of stones in the ears or around the neck

Is make-up and hair important to you and if so how do you achieve your look?

YES!! the most important without proper make-up and a beautiful wig I would jump into the ocean. Its crucial and one of the reasons that I am so happy that I am a tranny and not a person saying "I am a girl - so I don need make-up". I do all sorts of make-up from natural looking to totally over the top - it all depends on the occasion and the clothes I wear. This is an area where Pandora has been a crutial part of my life. She has helped me choose the right products. I attended two make-up lessons so far and I practice as much as I can. It is the same with my wigs. I used to buy expensive ones, but have learnt that with the proper styling and care - a cheap wig can do the job. And the advantage is that when going for cheaper, you can buy a few extra to get different looks.... gosh life is wonderful

To what degree do you practice hair removal and other body feminisation?

Every three weeks I have my legs, bikini-line (ouch!) and under my arms waxed by a pro. Arms, stomach and chest is shaven every day. I did that even as a "man-only" and simply hates bodyhair. I enjoy having a nice tan, uses a lot of creams as day cream and night cream, as well as serums for my eyes...

Who knows that you dress?

Everybody who wants to.... Cant say it simpler. here is nothing wrong with me so why not let the world know. A few former friends found it disgusting and turned their backs at me, which I respect and lives with. Its

What is your name and what is your background?

My name is Katarina Collins and I'm a Danish T-girl. Fully out there to be noticed. I run my own businesses which are "Glamour Transitions" (make-over and transition service) and "Silicone Dolls" (a nightclub) I live in the Copenhagen, I am single and have my wonderful daughter living with me.

Are you happy to be called a Tranny and what does this name mean to you?

Yes I am excited - I think the term "Tranny" as well as "T-Girl" covers every aspect in the transgendered community. I saves me from thinking on the known labels as TV,TS, CD, Shemale, drag and what else do we have... I am a Tranny - a guy in a dress and I love it!!

How old are you and how young can you remember thinking about or actually cross dressing?

Age?..hmm.. what a question to a Lady! I am in the better part of my thirties okay...I dressed and had make-up on my face for the first time in my life February 2003 - I guess one of the best days ever - with huge thanks to Pandora De Pledge who made me fabulous!! Until then I have had the thought but always suppressed finding thoughts like that rather odd and kinky...:-)

their loss:-) Have since that day in February 2003 found so many new and wonderful friends in the community, so I could not be more happy..

How often do you dress and if you go out where to?

I Dress every second weekend.. (oct to april)(when my kid visits her mum) and I go out all 3 nights those weekends. During the summer months I stay low, since its simply to hot to wear make-up and wigs.. I love travelling and are privileged enough to be able to do so..and an expert in finding cheap airline tickets. Mostly and as often as possible I go to London, where I have been many times to Way Out Club (love that place and the people coming there) but also the other clubs or just going out amongst other people. I have got to know many friends around the world and I both enjoy clubbing as well as restaurants or shopping on Oxford Street all dressed up.. In Copenhagen its the same with either my own club Silicone Dolls (scandinavian answer to what London offers) or bars and cafe

How much of a sexual turn on is trannying for you?

I feel sexy as Kat. But what turns me on is the same as for most of you.. Nice, attractive, cultured people...with this sexy wink in the eyes....:-)

What is your definition of feminine?

First of all beauty, elegance and glamour! How you move, sit, smoke, hold your glass etc... A perfect tranny is the same as the ultimate in feminism..simply because we try harder...

To what degree do you feel gender dysphoric (i.e. that your brain is feminine?)

I don't feel born in the wrong body. I feel great as a guy and stunning, wonderful and fab as a girl..

To what degree would you consider permanent hair removal, hormones,surgery?

I would simply adore to have all my body and facial hairs removed... If it was not so painful, Hormones and feminisation surgery is not my cup of tea and I can't imagine it ever will be. I do respect those going that route and especially the ones trapped in the wrong "suit" - that must be awful..

What one piece of advice would you give to someone that has just found they are not the only tranny in the world?

I would say Congratulations Girl!! Now get a beautiful make-over, then get out there, be yourself, knock em dead and have a wonderful life.... you'll never regret it...

www.misskatarina.com

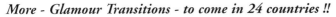

Wonderful Copenhagen - the city of changes!! And indeed things have changed here. Its full of tranny action with a new, full service, tranny make-over salon called *'GLAMOUR TRANSITIONS'* and a super new, very elegant and exclusive new nightclub named *'SILICONE DOLLS'* at 'Madame Arthurs'

With attractive prices Copenhagen has really become the perfect place to visit for any travelling tranny. Many tranny treats await you including *MADAM ARTHUR* located in the centre of Copenhagen very close to the Central station. Madam Arthur is open Wednesday & Thursday for dance and karaoke from 9pm and is only a few minutes walk from many hotels offering very reasonable deals from as little as £45 pounds for a double room in a 3 star hotel.

'GLAMOUR TRANSITIONS' is my new, exclusive, make-over service (or make-over salon). The salon is located in a very discrete part of Copenhagen but still only 10 minutes away from the centre with its bars, restaurants and club life. The salon's decoration is stunning and offers everything a tranny can wish for including wardrobe, wigs, shoes and styling services for make-overs, dressing sessions, photo sessions. We also sell accessories like shoes (wide), wigs (styled), make-up, jewellery, breastforms, and whatever else you can imagine you need when you go femme as a glam queen - and the pricing we'll bet will keep you smiling. Visiting is by appointment only. Enjoy an hour, 5 hours, a day or longer in fabulous femme surroundings accompanied by the best make-up artists and stylists Denmark and Scandinavia can offer. The best discretion is offered for those of you a bit shy.

At Glamour Transitions we also offer production and hosting of websites where the results of your make-overs can be displayed. We also offer escorted trips for shopping, events and nights out including travel packages for trips throughout the world.

I plan for it to be the first of a chain of salons opening in 24 countries. www.glamourtransitions.com

Copenhagen ■ Katarina Collins

to 2am and Friday & Saturday for spectacular drag shows from 10pm to 5am.

I host Silicone Dolls night every Saturday with new themes almost every week and guaranteed fun!!. A special night for trannies and their crowd - though obviously trannies are more than welcome every night at Madam Arthur.

After the grand opening of Silicone Dolls in January .- the magazines and television described the place as Copenhagen's "Las Vegas". We feel honoured and will do whatever possible to live up to that description with excellent entertainment and very reasonable drink prices and last but not least a very mixed fun loving straight-gay crowd. On the launch night it was wonderful to see Nikki, Debs, Fiona, Stella (Tranny Grange) and Ms. Debonair (Image Works & The WayOut Club) from the UK.

All Photos taken at the launch of Sillicone Dolls

The 'portal' to everything tranny on the Internet

A Personal **Report**

This survey is put in order of German zip-code.
This map gives a guideline.

This survey was finished in January 2004 it is as accurate as possible but it can not claim to be complete - Space here does not allow. Any ommision is in no way meant as a criticism.

For a wider overlook go to the website

www.TransGenderLife.de

where you will find a survey, which is kept actual all over the year and which is filled as complete as possible.

"Language need not be a barrier ..."
Just try out

www.babelfish.com

The web site www.babelfish.com allows you to enter the website address that you wish to read and it will translate the total site for you within a few minutes.

For up to date local information pick up the free gay-magazines from bars and shops of the gay community. Look out for these magazine names:

SIEGESSÄULE at Berlin HINNERK at Hamburg RIK at Cologne / Düsseldorf SERGEJ at Munich and at Berlin BOX for all regions of Germany

If you have specific questions, or if you want to add supplements or corrections, please address to the editor Charis Berger via e-mail to:
CharisBerger@gmx.de

Special thanks to Maren, webmaster at www.tginfo.de (menue "TG-Treffs"). Her database was very helpful in completing this survey for TRANNY GUIDE 2004 edition.

All phone-numbers are given from abroad to Germany, i.e. >0049 - 30 - 33 33 33<. -- If you phone from Germany, drop >00 49< and dial >0< before the local code, i.e. >030 - 33 33 33<

ZIP-CODE "0" (Eastern parts)

DRESDEN:
TRANSID at Stadteilhaus, Prießnitzstr. 18, D - 01 099 Dresden T:0049 351 4640220 www.trans-id.de - info@trans-id.de. A self-help organisation for TG's, friends and relatives, which meets every 2nd and 4th Saturday of month from 8pm at "Gerede e.V." or at "Info-Café" of local Aids-selfsupportgroup address above. Besides the meetings transID is active in political affairs, in party organisation, in photo-sessions, movie-evenings and so on;

"SACHSENWEIBER" at "Mezcalero", Königsbrücker Str. 64, 01099 Dresden-Neustadt, www.sachsenweiber.de T: 0049 351 5636235 or mob: 0049 177 5765865 A regular meeting for TG's partners and friends 3rd Friday of month no pre-registration necessary.

ATELIER-CHANGEABLE www.atelier-changeable.de. Lydia. offers transformations and make-up services, tranny-parties held in several cities in Germany tranny-weekends, and a online tranny-shop, Her parties offer discos, election of Miss Changeable and a little show-program. For customers from far away bed-and-breakfast-accommodation is possible. A new party concept is announced for 2nd half of 2004.

LEIPZIG:
TRANSGENDERTOWN at Rosa Linde e.V., Bruhl 64-66, D - 04 177 Leipzig Alexander or Grit. T: 0049 341 48 41511 beratung@rosalinde.de. A newly established group of transgendered women and men, and intersexual people. 7pm every 2nd Friday of month Individual councelling is available.

BI-STAMMTISCH at Rosa Linde e.V.,Brühl 64 - 66, D - 04 177 Leipzig-city; www.rosalinde.de sabinewaage@firemail.de. Informal meeting for bi-sexual people every 3rd Tuesday of month at 8pm. CD's and TG's welcome

BLAUE TRUDE Katharinenstr. 17 (near Sachsenplatz), D - 04109 Leipzig, T:0049 341 2126679 www.blaue-trude.de. This is the most popular gay pub, disco and bar. Occassional Drag-shows

HALLE:
TRANSVISION at Aids-Hilfe (Bölberger Weg 189) Contact: Michaela Lindner T:0049 34977 22111 A Self support Group. Meetings and councelling every last Wednesday of month from 7pm

CHEMNITZ:
CHEMNITZER TRANSGENDER INTITATIVE (CheTI) at "Different People" (c/o AWO, Wiesenstr. 10, 09 111 Chemnitz); Contact: Andrea and Claudia T:0049 371 3303070; René (FtoM) T:0049 174 2828176 www.cheti.de info@cheti.de Meetings every Tuesday from 7 to 10pm. Twice a year CheTI used to organise an over-regional weekend-meeting for TG's

ZIP-CODE "1"

(Berlin, and eastern parts)

BERLIN:

GROUPS, MEETINGS AND COUNCELLING

SONNTAGS-CLUB (SC) Greifenhagerstr. 28, D - 10 437 Berlin T:0049 30 78703630 "Trans-Line Info" T: 0049 30 4423702 Email Sam.Lennard@t-online.de www.sonntags-club.de. The best known self-support organisation for gays that offers councelling. Meetings for TG's at "biz-café".

TRANS-X An active group of TG's offering lectures, video- and movie-evenings etc.

"TRANSANDERS" for discussion of transgeder-related questions. Every Friday from 6 to 9pm a special phone-service for info and councelling of TG's is available (above). Once a year (usually in October) an over-regional congress on transgender-subjects is arranged.

TRANSSISTERS at pub "Margies Together - Cafe and Bar",Hohenstaufenstr. 53 (near corner to Martin-Luther Str.), D-10 779 Berlin www.TransSisters.de info@transsisters.de or T:0049 30 60972744. A local "club" of TG's. Numerous members communicate via internet, meet occasionally one-to-one. They organise parties twice a year. TransSisters meet for shopping, for celebrating birthdays, or for visiting shows, theatres or concerts. Every last Friday of the month an informal meeting is offered at 8pm guests and friends welcome.

QUEER-GROUP AT HUMBOLDT-UNIVERSITY www.mutvilla.de which unites gay, lesbian, bi and TG's, offers weekly

LAMBDA BERLIN-BRANDENBURG E.V. www.lambda-bb.de Individual councelling is offered.

LONG YANG CLUB Jürgen Müller, Perleberger Str. 7, D -10 559 Berlin; T: 00 49 - 30 - 39 61 541, www.longyangclub.com/berlin This club is for gays lesbians and TG's from Asia

Charis Berger (53, living at Munich) is editing the Germany-part of Tranny Guide for five years. She is well known to readers of Tranny Guide as well as in the German tranny community, as she published a tranny-magazine for a couple of years. She was also active in tranny related social and political affairs. As Charis has lived as a transgendered woman for more than 25 years she can indeed pass on many tranny life experiences. "I hope a lot of ‚sisters' will gain from my experiences. I'm glad if I can help somebody to grow in self-consciousness and in skills in styling and making up". Charis offers a transformation-service on a very private basis, just for some hours of experiencing female impersonation, and to enjoy the challenge of a change "From Him to Her".

Charis also likes to discuss tranny life with young people, some times at colleges, some times at seminars for social workers. "I want them to realise that life between fixed genders is as normal as having red hair or being a good long distance runner. To be a tranny is just a special skill that gives a twofold sight of life", she explains with a smile.

Though semi retired from public affairs, she still edits two highly informative tranny websites >www.TransGenderLife.de< and >www.TGnews.de<, and she publishes an e-mail-newsletter for trannies, full of news about the tranny world at and around Germany.

Dear "Sisters",

The 12 th edition of "Tranny Guide -- Way Out World" offers you a very extensive survey where to meet "sisters" and where to go out for fun, if you travel to Germany. Never before a tranny-survey of this extent has been published, not even in German language. If you combine this survey with survey of Germany's tranny-websites in the 11th Tranny Guide, you will have the best start for experiencing Germany's tranny world.

If you read German and if you are interested in actual news about tranny life around Germany, you are cordially invited to visit the websites >http://www.TransGenderLife.de< and >http.//www.TGnews.de<. News on events, on groups, on meetings etc. are published here consecutively. Both websites are considered again and again to be "the most informative and most actual information source on transgender-related subjects and news in the internet in German language".

An e-mail-newsletter in German can be sent to you free of charge. Subscribe for your FREE e-mail-copy at newsletter@tgnews.de<

Thank you for being with us ! Have a nice time and enjoy the tranny life of Germany !

Charis Berger

You want to get in touch with Charis preferably by e-mail to >CharisBerger@gmx.de< or write a letter to Charis Berger, Postfach 86 08 08, D - 81 635 München (please enclose 2 international reply coupons for an answer)

A Personal Report

PARTIES, EVENTS, SHOWS & BARS:

SCHWULES MUSEUM ("GAY MUSEUM") is always worth a visit. Changing expositions sometimes focused on transgendered people. Mehringdamm 61, D - 10961 Berlin , open Monday, Wednesday to Friday from 2 to 6 p.m. Saturday 2 to 7pm, T:0049 30 69311 72, www.schwulesmuseum.de

WIGSTÖCKEL-FESTIVAL www.wigstoeckel.net (translate: "Little Wigstock") takes place once a year, usually first weekend of October. The one-day festival offers usually a memorial gallery ("Walk of Fame"), an information market with booths of groups and institutions, and show-programs of professionals and newcomers and disco-party.

REGENBOGENBALL Regenbogenfonds der schwulen Wirte e.V., Fuggerstraße 7, 10 777 Berlin, eMail: info@regenbogenfonds.de or regenbogenfonds@t-online.de; T:0049 30 21473586. Once a year elegant people, dressed in "black and white" and evening gowns meet here for a night with dancing and shows. Gays mix with celebrities of the city. Tranny-women are welcome.

BAR JEDER VERNUNFT Schaperstraße 24, D - 10719 Berlin-Neukölln, T:0049 30 8831582 www.bar-jeder-vernunft.de. Cabaret-programs of high quality. Georgette Dee, Duo Malediva and a lot of transgendered artists perform here.

CABARET CHEZ NOUS at Marburger Str. 14 (near to Europa-Center), D - 10 798 Berlin, T: 0049 30 2131810 www.cabaret-chez-nous.de. Famous Tranny-Shows Showtime daily 8.30 and 11 p.m.

NEUBRANDENBURG:

INITIATIVE ROSA LILA at: Zu den Hufen 6, 17 034 Neubrandenburg , contact: Christoph Zachow, T: 0049 0395 19 446 or 0049 395 544207 post@rosalila.de. Group of TG's meets every last Tuesday of the month. Personal councelling is offered on Wednesdays from 4 to 6 p.m.

ROSTOCK:

SCHWULES ROSTOCK (formerly "Rat und Tat e.V.", Leonardstr. 20, 18 057 Rostock, T: 0049 381 453156; istud966@fh-nb.de (Christopher Zachow) www.schwules-rostock.de. A self-support group for TG's 1st Friday of month at 4 p.m

ZIP-CODE "2" (Hamburg, and the north)

HAMBURG:

GROUPS, MEETINGS & COUNCELLING

TRANSVESTITEN / CROSS-DRESSER SELBSTHILFEGRUPPE 4th Saturday of the month from 3 p.m. at "Blauer Raum" (1st floor at the location of KISS-Altona , Gaussstr. 21, D - 22765 Hamburg-Altona; T: 0049 40 395767 Sabrinahh@gmx.de http://crossdressinghamburg.de

TRANSSEXUELLEN SELBSTHILFEGRUPPE AND TS / TV STAMMTISCH HAMBURG Support group and formal meeting mainly for male-to-female TS's, but open to CD's as well. Participants are welcome at the pub "Marathea" at Goldbek-House for an informal meeting. The group also maintains a highly informative website: www.hanse-trans.de Contact Marianne and Lena, T:0049 40 67379679 lena@hanse-trans.de

TRANS-STAMMTISCH HAMBURG at "Villa Kunterbunt" (Detlev-Bremer-Str. 37, Hamburg-St.Pauli;h.s.t@gmx.net www.transgender-club-party.de.vu. This is an informal meeting every Thursday from 7:30 p.m. Welcomes all different TG's and friends. Twice a year, in spring and in autumn, a tranny-party is organised by this group.

PARTIES, EVENTS, SHOWS & BARS:

"HAMBURGER TUNTENBALL" usually at end of February, more than 1000 gays and trannies and drag-queens and friends at Curio House, near to Hamburg University. This is the top-event of the year www.tuntenball-hamburg.de.vu.

PULVERFASS Reeperbahn 147, D - 20 359 Hamburg, T:0049 40 28 02121; www.pulverfass.de. "The first tranny cabaret in Germany" features two shows per night 8:30 and 11:30 p.m., and 2:30am on Saturday. Travestie artists from Germany and abroad. Adjoined to Pulverfass is a bistro which is open from 5 pm. At the theatre pre-show-dinners are offered from 7:30 pm.

ACCOMMODATION

HOTEL KÖNIGSHOF Pulverteich 18 (near railroad- and bus-mainstation), D - 20 099 Hamburg-St.George, T:0049 40 28407474 e-mail: hotelkhh@aol.com www.koenigshof-hamburg.de. Klaus-Werner Held and Erik Springer the gay managers of this 3 star hotel promise a "royal service for trannies and friends."

KIEL:

TRANSIDENTEN-GRUPPE KIEL http://tgkiel.trans-info.de. Contact: Baerbel Gau T: 0049 431 6409574 e-mail: baerbel.gau@kielnet.net. Is the most active selfsupport-group of Schleswig-Holstein offering personal councelling Last Thursday of month at "Huch" (located at "HaKi-Zentrum", Westring 278, D - 24 116 Kiel, T: 0049 43119446). Highly informative TS website with photo-documentation of surgery from male to female.

FLENSBURG / SCHLESWIG:

SELBSTHILFEGRUPPE TRANSIDENTEN FLENSBURG / SCHLESWIG aimed to help TG's out of self-isolation. Occasional meetings, contact first Carolin Köhn 9am-1pm.Tues, Weds & Thurs T: 0049 4621 27748

BREMEN:

GROUPS, MEETINGS & COUNCELLING

SELBSTHILFEGRUPPE TRANSSEXUELLE MENSCHEN BREMEN is a private group for selfsupport. Swen-Björn Grupe Gesundheits-Treffpunkt West (Gröpelinger Heerstr. 120, D - 28 237 Bremen). e-mail: BarbaraWoman@t-online.de T: 0049 421617079 mobile: 0049 1726646340 (ring during meetings only). Group meetings are every last Friday of month at 7:30pm.

BREMER SELBSTHILFEGRUPPE FÜR TRANSIDENTITÄT http://de.groups.yahoo.com/group/TransgenderBremen. This is a web group It's aim is to announce trans-meetings from Hannover to Hamburg & from Bremen to Rostock.

PARTIES, EVENTS, SHOWS & BARS:

MADAME LOTHAR Kolpingstr. 9, D - 28 195 Bremen, T:0049 421 3379191 http://www.madamelothar.com. A very small Tranny-Cabaret bar.

OLDENBURG:

SELBSTHILFEGRUPPE FÜR TRANSVESTITEN UND TRANSSEXUELLE "Cafe Hempels" Schwulen- & Lesbenzentrum Ziegelhofstr. 83, D - 26 131 Oldenburg, T: 0049 441 7775990 Contact: Sabine Email: sabinexd@aol.com Meetings usually every 2nd Tuesday of month at 8 pm details on http://bremen.gay-web.de

ZIP-CODE "3" (Hannover, and the north)

HANNOVER:

WWW.EN-FEMME.DE for info on tranny-meetings in Hannover and surrounding areas.

GROUPS, MEETINGS & COUNCELLING

TRANSSEXUELL IN HANNOVER T: 0049 178 6123121 Valerie or 0049 162 4566671 Chris. Email: ts-han@gmx.de, :www.transsexuell-in-hannover.de.vu Valerie & Chris founded this group in 2002.
BODY AND SOUL held at Café Belvedere Gretchenstr. 16, D - 30 161 Hannover Contact: Josef T: 0049 551 801840 www.bodyundsoul.de.vu. A self support-group for TG's. Meetings most Tuesdays of month at 7:30pm.

PARTIES, EVENTS, SHOWS & BARS:

ALCAZAR Leonhardtstr. 11, D - 30 175 Hannover, T: 0049 511 344610 www.alcazar.de. This night-club is now run by Daphne de Luxe and Kay Ray. Two shows nightly at 10pm & 1:30am, Fri & Sats an additional show at 3am. A "talent search competition", held once a year.

WOLFSBURG:

TRANSGENDER-STAMMTISCH WOLFSBURG held at Café Extrem, Breslauerstr. 198, D - 38 440 Wolfsburg www.stammtisch.trannie-angehoerige.de Email: Stammtisch@trannie-angehoerige.de T: 0049 5362 500030 Contact: Chantal C. or Vera B. An informal meeting for MtoF and FtoM's every 1st Saturday of month at 7pm. Contact first before attending.
ROSA WOLFSBURG E.V. (Pink Wolfsburg Association) Schachtweg 5a , D - 38 440 Wolfsburg, T: 0049 5361 292929 Email: rosawolf@wolfsburg.de. Holds meetings every Tuesday. Individual councelling is offered via this number T: 0049 5361 19446

GOSLAR:

SKY Selbsthilfegruppe für transidentische Menschen at AWO Goslar Bähringer Strasse 24/25 Contact: Karin Reichel T: 0049 3943630376 Email: ReichelKarin@aol.com or Carola Burghardt T: 0049 5321 29376. www.shg-sky.de/ Holds meetings for people with gender issues last Friday of the month from 7pm.

KASSEL:

TRANSX KASSEL at Kurt-Schumacher-Straße 2, 1st floor, room "Johanna Wischer", D - 34117 Kassel Contact Melanie Nayyal T: 0049 561 8708451 / 0049 561 7875399 Email: Melanie.Nayyal@t-online.de. www.geocities.com/melly_ks/start.html. Selfsupport-group Meetings at 8pm every 2nd & 4th Friday of month.

The 'portal' to everything tranny on the Internet

Personal Profile of RAMONA

What is your name and what is your background ?

My female name is "Ramona". I live near Hannover and my job is in aircraft maintenance. I'm married but without children.

Are you happy to be called a "Tranny" and what does this name mean to you ?

The name is o.k. as long as it is not used in an offending manner. I do not want to be on one level with gays, fetishists or "sweet homos".

How old are you and how young can you remember thinking about or actually practicing cross-dressing ?

I am 52 now, I was a little Boy when I dreamt about wearing girls dresses.

Where do you buy clothes ?

Usually in department stores, sometimes together with my wife. Occasionally I buy via mail order.

How would you describe your style ? ?

First of all it has to look feminine. Further more I like my clothes elegant, somtimes sporty.

Do you have one look or many images ?

I always stick to my basic style

Is make-up and hair important to you and how do you achieve your look ?

Both is very important to me. My make-up is from drug-discounters, my wigs are from mailorder-shops

To what degree do you practice hair removal, and other body feminisation ?

I do not like any hair on my body. I remove hair as soon as they grow, everywhere on my body. Of course I shave every day.

Conutinued page 167

A Personal Report

Germany ■ *A Personal* Report

BIELEFELD:

GROUPS, MEETINGS & COUNCELLING

TRANSGENDER-INTERESSENGEMEINSCHAFT BIELEFELD at Schäfer´s Cafe at Kunsthalle (art museum, Arthur-Ladebeck-Str. www.transgender-bielefeld.com kontakt@transgender-bielefeld.de T: 0049 178 2347980. Started a few years ago by 2 drag-queens mainly intended for cross-dressers but welcomes TS's as well. Wednesdays at 8pm for talking. Saturday meeting are for fun & enjoyment. Special events and a quarterly newsletter "MakeUp". Web has info about meetings in northeast Westfalen and southwest Niedersachsen.

PARTIES, EVENTS, SHOWS & BARS:

ROLANDSECK Heeper Str. 28, D - 33 607 Bielefeld. Is one of the oldest pubs in town. All groups of gays, lesbians, bi-sexuals & TG's gather here for talking and having pleasure. Pub is open till 5am. Occassional travestie-shows.

TRANSGENDERLESBENFRAUEN-CAFE ajz-kneipe Heeper Str. 132, Contact Knut Email flref@uni-bielefeld.de. A disco organised for "woman only" by the lesbians of Bielefeld University. Trans-Woman are heartily welcome.

MAGDEBURG:

TRANS-SELBSTHILFEGRUPPE MAGDEBURG Gesundheitszentrum Hasselbachplatz, Breiter Weg 251, D - 39 104 Magdeburg T: 0049 391 6108320 Email: kerstin-l@onlinehome.de. Meetings for TG's and relatives every last Wednesday of month at 6pm. Individual councelling is offered at "KOBES" Klosterhof 1a, D - 39122 Magdeburg, T: 0049 391 5614616.

ZIP-CODE "4" (Dusseldorf, Ruhr, Munster)

DÜSSELDORF:

GROUPS, MEETINGS & COUNCELLING

TransX is the nearest support group about 40 km from Dusseldorf at Cologne, (see below, zip-code "5"). However Michaela Heckers T: 0049 2151 774057 Email: j.heckers@t-online.de provides some contact in this area.

2.) PARTIES, EVENTS, SHOWS & BARS:

CAFE ROSA MOND E. V. Oberbilker Allee 310, D - 40 227 Düsseldorf, T: 0049 211 992377 www.rosamond.de. Mainly aimed for supporting gays and lesbians but drag-queens and cross-dressers are always welcome at the parties and events.

MÖNCHENGLADBACH at AIDS-Hilfe (Hindenburgstraße 113 (2nd floor on top of shoe-shop Wintzen), D - 41 061 Mönchengladbach, T: 0049 2161 19411. www.westwerk.de/aidshilfe-mg/ts-forum/ Contact Nicole Günter Email devoted@t-online.de T: 0049 160 442953. Meetings every 2nd Tuesday from 8pm.

ATOMAGE Kleinbroicher Str. 3, D - 41 232 Moenchengladbach-Giesenkirchen, info-phone: 0049 2166 87 530, www.lustgarten.de/atomage. A disco for fetish-people. Cross-dressers, drag-queens and-kings welcome.

C'EST LA VIE Gasthausstr. 67, Moenchengladbach; T: 0049 2161 175764. A small travestie-theatre.

DORTMUND:

GROUPS AND MEETINGS

SHG DORTMUND at Aidshilfe Möllerstr. 15, D - 44137 Dortmund, T: 0049 231 20705 or 0049 231 2000919. Selfsupport-group for TG's meetings at 5pm every 1st and 3rd Friday of month.

TRANSGENDER-CLUB www.transgenderclub.de is organised by Jackeline Lior and Arminia mainly as an internet-"club" Also they hold a party twice a year called "TransGender-Gala".

PARTIES, EVENTS, SHOWS & BARS:

"TV-GELI" www.tv-geli.de. Tranny-Parties organised by Angelika.

LA LUNA Harkortstr. 57a, D - 44 225 Dortmund, T: 0049 231 976760 www.luna-variete.de. A typical music-hall which performs travestie-shows at 8pm.

CABARET QUEUE Hermannstr. 74, D - 44 263 Dortmund-Hoerde, T: 0231 413146 www.company-of-thundermen.de. A small travestie cabaret which performs mostly "Thundermen-Company"

BURGTORCLUB at Café Extrablatt, Burgwall 17, D - 44 135 Dortmund, T: 0049 231 571748 www.burgtorclub.de/index2.html. A small travestie theatre and dancing club. The shows are performed by "The sweet Devil´s". Every first Thursday of month they hold a talent evening for travestie performers.

HERNE:

TRANSGENDER-SELBSTHILFEGRUPPE MITTLERES RUHRGEBIET at CVJM-Haus, Sodinger Str. 3, D - 44 623 Herne, near U-station Kreuzkirche / corner to pedestrians area, www.gitti-t.de Email: Brigitte.Schramm@web.de. Meets every 2nd and 4th Tuesday of month from 8-10pm. Individual councelling is available from 7-8pm but book first. Drinks are available.

BOCHUM:

STARGATE Hans-Böckler-Str. 12 (City-Passage at Townhall), D - 44 787 Bochum, T: 0049 234 13888 www.stargate-club.de. A disco mainly frequented by gay people, trannies are welcome.

ESSEN:

TRANSSEXUELLEN SELBSTHILFEGRUPPE ESSEN at "Lore-Agnes-Haus" of AWO (Arbeiterwohlfahrt), Lützow Str. 32, D - 45 101 Essen, T: 0049 201 31050, www.transsexuell.de Email airin@transsexuell.de. Meets every 2nd week on Monday from 6pm. For individual consulting T: 0049 201 3105122 or 0049 221 6085715. Contact: Airin.

HERTEN:

TRANSGENDER-STAMMTISCH at pub "Schick" Ewaldstr. 25. Email: Tenere2@aol.com. Meetings every 3rd Thursday of month for all TG's.

OBERHAUSEN:

EN-FEMME STAMMTISCH at pub Ärwins Brauhaus, Oberhausen-CentrO / Neue Mitte, Promenade Nr. 30, D - 46 047 Oberhausen T: 0049 175 8924385 www.claudia-tv.de Email: claudia@claudiasworld.de, An informal meeting for TG's, CD's and friends1st Thursday of month at 8pm.

MÜNSTER:

TRANSMAUS www.transmaus.de Email: jenny@transmaus.de or Lisa@transmaus.de. An informal group of cross-dressers Last Friday at 8pm. You can dress up in the meeting-room. Pre-registration is required.

SELBSTHILFEGRUPPE TRANSIDENTITÄT MÜNSTER Contact: Heiko or Lydia, at the office of KCM Schwulenzentrum Münster E.V., Am Hawerkamp 31, D - 48155 Münster, T: 0049 251 665686 Email: Fraktion_TImuenster@gmx.de www.terhaer.de/shg-muenster.html. An open group for all TG's, video evenings, lectures & discussions, informal parties. They also print a magazine. 2nd Saturday at 3pm.

OSNABRÜCK:

SELFSUPPORT-GROUP at "Café M", Bramscher Strasse, 49 048 Osnabrück; Contact: Ina Nora Teetzen, T: 0049 541 7120240. 1st and 3rd Saturday of month. at 7pm

ZIP-CODE "5" (Cologne, Bonn, Aachen, Bergisches Land)

KÖLN (COLOGNE)

GROUPS, MEETINGS &COUNCELLING

TXKÖLN at Café (Gruppenraum 310) at Bürgerzentrum Stollwerck, Dreikönigenstr. 23, D - 50 678 Köln www.txkoeln.de Email: txkoeln@txkoeln.de. One of Germany's most active selfsupport-groups for TG's. Meet every Friday from 8pm. They have an Email-newsletter "tg-info", which is free.

DEUTSCHE GESELLSCHAFT FÜR TRANSINDENTITÄT UND INTERSEXUALITÄT Godorfer Hauptstr. 60, D - 50 997 Köln; T: 0049 2236 839019 www.dgti.org. Email: info@dgti.org. Germany's "over all organisation" for TG's and intersexual people. managed by Katrin Helma Alter. It is aimed as "voice of TG and intersexual people in the public & political affairs". The website gives news of legal status for TG's in Germany, surgery, doctors, psychologists, attorneys of law etc. Individual councelling is offered too, Also run seminars to help TG's to obtain better self conciousness and develop better styling.

PARTIES, EVENTS, SHOWS & BARS:

GENDER CHANGE PARTY www.transgender-net.de GCParties are famous party-events for trannies and open to all TG's and friends. Disco, travestie-sketches and the election of "Mr and Mrs Transformation" at midnight are part of the program.

ID-EVENTS www.tginfo.de or www.ident-evenTS.de, Email: info@tginfo.de. Also hold styling workshops, Free weekly Email-newsletter.

PRIVATE TRANS-PARTIES Email: info-party@netcologne.de, www.transparty.de Organised by Christin and Verona. Is a rather new party & contact organisation; Severl parties a year for members only (short time membership available), The fee covers "Dinner", drinks, and room-cleaning. Trannies can also get a professional make-over but booking is necessary.

KULTURSCHOCK www.kulturschock-cologne.de performed by the "Schockletts" is travestie-comedy at its best as far as non-professional actors performing.

Conutinued from page 165

To what degree would you consider permanent hair-removal, hormonal treatment or surgery ?

If possible, I would like to have my hair permanently removed on the face and on my legs and as well I would undergo hormonal treatment to grow real breasts. I never though about surgery. That's not my way.

Who knows that you dress ?

Only my wife and as well some "sisters" which I met at tranny-parties, but they do not know my real identity, and in Munich where we bought some second-hand clothes some time ago.

How often do you dress and if you go out where to ?

I dress almost daily, after work and on weekends, usually at home. Out of the house I dress only for special tranny-parties.

How much of a sexual turn is trannying for you ?

Cross-dressing doesn't have any sexual temptation or stimulation to me.

To what degree do you feel gender dysphoric (i.e. that your brain is feminine) ?

If I can judge it definitively, I'd say in my male body lives a female soul.

What one piece advice would you give to someone that has just found that he is not the only tranny in the world ?

Enjoy your life, you have got only this one ! And go for contacts and friendship to "sisters" who share your hobby or inclination.

A Personal Report

The 'portal' to everything tranny on the Internet

Germany ■ A Personal Report

TIMP Heumarkt 25, just vis-à-vis Maritim-Hotel, D - 50 677 Köln, T: 0049 221 2581409 www.timp.de. A famous tranny-night-cabaret with shemale-shows from midnight until morning. It is run by Willi Geloneck and his son. "Timp-Girls" come from all parts of the world. No entrance fee, but there is a minimum consumption fee. Many celebrities show up late nights.

ZUR ZICKE Rheingasse 34 - 36 (Altstadt of Cologne), D - 50 676 Köln, T: 0049 221 2408958. A gay bar where trannies are welcome at any time. 1st Saturday of the month travestie-shows are performed.

KÖLNER TUNTENBALL is a glamourous dance event, frequented by drag-queens and cross-dressers. For more information ask the managers of "Die Zicke"

AACHEN:

TRANSGENDER-GRUPPE DES RAINBOW E.V. in the Café of Rainbow e.V., Gasborn 13, D - 52 062 Aachen. Contact: David (c.o. Akis) T: 0049 241 49 009, Email Marvingendernaut@web.de or Maren T: 0049 163 8007241 Email: BittnerMaren@aol.com. www.transaachen.de.vu. Meetings from 8-10pm every 1st and 3rd Wednesday of month.

YOUNG TRANSGENDERED PERSONS at Rainbow-House, Gasborn 13, D - 52 062 Aachen; T: 0049 241 16035515 Email: info@lambda-nrw.de, www.lambda-nrw.de. Lamda e.V. is established all over Germany. It is an organisation for all varieties of younger gay people.

BONN:

TRANSSEXUAL-SELBSTHILFEGRUPPE BONN (c/o Gruppenraum 1, SEKIS, Lotharstr. 95, D - 53 115 Bonn, T: 0049 228 9145917 on/Mon, Wed, Thu. 9-12am and Thu 2-6pm. Contact: Desirèe Heynemann-Günther T: 0049 2202 932827. 1st and 3rd Friday of month at 8pm.

MAINZ:

TRANSMAINZ at pub Senfkorn, Gaustr. 38 (near to main rr-station), D - 55 116 Mainz. Contact Uschi T: 0049 6131 613240 Email uschi@uschi-herz.net, or Audrey T: 0049 67249 39460 www.trans-mainz.genderline.de/ 2nd Wednesday of month at 7pm.

SIEGEN:

TRANSSEXUELLENGRUPPE SIEGEN at Gesundheitshaus, Koblenzer Str. 78 (besides Aral-gasoline, opposite to Kreishaus), D - 57 072 Siegen, T: 0049 271 2380205 c/o. Bastian Klappert or Heike Tönnes at K.I.S.S. www.transgender-siegerland.info/ Initiated by Ehe, Familien- and Lebensberatungsstelle (Burgstr. 23, D - 57 076 Siegen). Meetings from 5:45 to 7:15pm every 2nd & 4th Friday of month

HAGEN:

INFORMAL MEETINGS FOR TRANSGENDERED PERSONS at Café Krönchen, Körnerstr., 58 095 Hagen Contact: Michaela Email: MichaelaTV58@aol.com. 2nd Thursday of month

WERL:

MARION AND ALEXANDRA Meetings at Büdericher Str. 10, 59 457 Werl / Westfalen, www.alexandras.de.vu Email ats.werl@tiscali.de T: 0049 2922 870804. Private rooms and transformation-services are offered on a commercial basis. The meetings are mainly meant for trannies, who do not yet dare to show up in the public. You can dress up and have help with your make-up at Marion & Alexandra's apartment. They also run a little tranny-shop.

HAMM:

TRANSGENDER HAMM Contact: Fabian Email:fabian@fabians-welt.com www.transgender-hamm.2xt.de. A recently established group for TG's and friends. Meetings on Tuesday held in the local "AIDS-Hilfe".

ZIP-CODE "6" (Frankfurt, Saarland, Heidelberg)

FRANKFURT (MAIN)

GROUPS, MEETINGS & COUNCELLING

TRANSVESTITEN-VEREINIGUNG (TTV) Postfach 1148, D - 65780 Hattersheim, T: 0049 6192 46985, www.geocities.com/tvvfrankfurt Email: aimeecross@gmx.de. The group was founded many years ago. It meets every Tuesday-evening. The location where they meet is kept secret. New "sisters" who want to join the meetings have to apply. Once a year they hold a Gala-Ball, but only for "sisters" that are part of the group or have a special invitation.

PARTIES, EVENTS, SHOWS & BARS:

THEATER IN DER TANZSCHULE (TITS) at Friedberger Landstr. 296, D - 60 389 Frankfurt, T: 0049 069 593701, www.tits-theater.de performs travestie-revues of and with Bäppi la Belle (alias Thomas Bäppler) the famous travestie artist of Frankfurt. Friday and Saturday at 9pm. Very popular so book early.

MUHLHEIM AM MAIN

GERDAS KLEINE WELTBÜHNE Offenbacher Str. 11, D - 63 165 Muhlheim/Main (near Frankfurt), T: 0049 6108 75491 www.gerdas.de/ A small, but famous travestie cabaret with Gerda, the "impresario". Wed to Sat .

NEU ISENBURG

TRANSSEXUELLEN-STAMMTISCH Naturfreunde-Haus, Neuhöfer Str. 55, D - 63 263 Neu-Isenburg, T: 0049 6102326032. Contact: Petra Henderson petrahenderson@yahoo.com or Angelika Email angelika_Lr@yahoo.de www.geocities.com/petrahenderson/nitreff.htm Informal meeting for TG's, partners and friends at 8pm every 1st Saturday of month

MARBURG

SELFSUPPORT-GROUP c/o AIDS - Hilfe, Bahnhofstr. 27, D - 35 037 Marburg, T: 0049 421 64523. Meetings for TG's & CD's 2nd Sunday of month at 3pm at the location of AIDS-Hilfe. Email TS-MR@gmx.de.

HEIDELBERG

SELFSUPPORT-GROUP c/o Selbsthilfebüro, Alte Eppelheimer Str. 38, D - 69 115 Heidelberg. Contact: Kerstin Erlewein T: 0049 632292250, kerstin.erlewein@t-online.de or Contact: Sabine Bolland T:0049 6202 271343 bolland@addcom.de Meetings for TG's at 7pm every 2nd Friday of month.

KAISERSLAUTERN

SELFSUPPORT-GROUP FOR TRANSSEXUALITY Beate Biundo, Bergstr. 46, D - 67 697 Otterberg, T: 0049 6301 37592 Email:Beate.Biundo@freenet.de Meetings once a month on a Saturday at 4pm

TRIER

TIM TRANSIDENTISCHE MENSCHEN TRIER Contact: Karin Hauth T:00 49 6531 970556 Email Wil.Karin@t-online.de. Contact them for more details.

SAARBRUCKEN

INDIVIDUAL COUNCELLING FOR TG'S Schloßstr. 6, D - 66 117 Saarbrücken, T: 0049 681 583912 Dr. Waltraud Schiffels who is male-to-female transgender herself and writer of some very interesting books on transgendered life offers councelling.

ZIP-CODE "7" (Stuttgart, Black Forest, Bodensee, Ulm)

STUTTGART

GROUPS, MEETINGS & COUNCELLING

SELBSTHILFEGRUPPE STUTTGART held at KISS, Marienstr. 9, D - 70178 Stuttgart This is an active selfsupport-group of TG's Meetings from 7:30 to 10pm every Wednesday pre-registration is required. contact: Astrid Volz T: 0049 7031 762895 Email AstridVolz@t-online.de www.trans-stuttgart.de

INFORMAL MEETINGS FOR TG'S AND TRANNIES at restaurant "i-Pünktle", Urbanstr. 48, near Staatsgalerie of Fine Arts, D - 70 182 Stuttgart. Meetings from 8:30pm For more info contact Petra Grandel Email PetraEBE@aol.comT:0049 7031 658060, www.trans-stuttgart.de

TRANSIDENT X at KISS, 3rd floor, room 5, Marienstr. 9, D - 70178 Stuttgart. Contact: Chantal Karrer T:0049 160 5774140 (only 7-9pm please!) or Wolfgang Zakrzewski 0049 7032 794078 (only 7-9 pm please!) Email ChantalKarrer@web.de www.transidentx.de . Meetings are 7:30 - 9:30pm every last Friday of month.

PARTIES, EVENTS, SHOWS & BARS:

RENITENZ-THEATER www.wommy.de Usually two shows a year are performed by Frl. Wommy Wonder (alias Mike Erdmann), the local and regional "star" of lady-impersonators. More info from WW-Kontakte, Adlerstr. 25, D - 73 760 Ostfildern-Nellingen T: 0049 711 9079792; info@wommy.de

KARLSRUHE

TRANSTALK held at disco 'Check-In' located in the building of rr-mainstation, 76 137 Karlsruhe Email: transtalk@gmx.de www.transtalk.de.ms One of the most active meetings for TG's from 8pm 3rd Friday of month. Tranny parties are held twice a year.

FREIBURG

SELFSUPPORT-GROUP FREIBURG at Deutscher Paritätischer Wohlfahrtsverband, Schwarzwaldstr. 29, D - 79 110 Freiburg/Breisgau T: 0049 761 472270 Meetings every 1st and 3rd Friday of month

TRANSGENDER BREISGAU held at Beratungsstelle "Drobs", Faulerstr. 8, D - 79 098 Freiburg / Breisgau or at AWO, Markgrafenstr. 13, Freiburg-Haslach. transgender-breisgau@online.de 7pm every 2nd Thursday of month.

Personal Profile of ROSY

What is your name and what is your background ?

My female name is "Rosy". for many many years I live at Moers. My profession is in the CNC-business. My hobby is music, often in a little band for local dancing events. I'm married, my son is grown up and made me granny some years ago.

Are you happy to be called a "Tranny" and what does this name mean to you ?

Usually I look at myself as a member of third gender .... and that's what I try to tell people who ask me or look at me shaking their heads.

How old are you and how young can you remember thinking about or actually practicing cross-dressing ?

I am over 60 now and I can remember I had some girls dresses already when I was 6. Crossdressing was a focus in my life as long as I can remember.

Where do you buy clothes ?

Usually from mail order shops

How would you describe your style ??

I like it fashionable and sexy. But I also wear elegant and ladylike dresses which fit to my "middle-age"

Do you have one look or many images ?

It is nice to change styles. You can be a totally different person, as you change from one style to another ...

Is make-up and hair important to you and if so how do you achieve your look ?

Make-up and well fitting wigs are very important to me indeed. I buy make-up and wigs at mail-order-shops.

To what degree do you practice hair removal, and other body feminisation ?

I remove hair everywhere on my body, except on my head, but there isn't too much left. Unfortunately I have to shave daily, if I dress up I have to shave a second time before doing my make-up.

A Personal Report

Conutinued page 171

The 'portal' to everything tranny on the Internet

ZIP-CODE "8" (Munich, southern Bavaria)

GROUPS, MEETINGS & COUNCELLING

TRANSGENDER-STAMMTISCH MÜNCHEN at little bistro "10vorne", Reichenbachstr. 33, near Gärtnerpatz, nearest U-station: Fraunhoferstr.; tram. #17, Fraunhoferstr. bus: Gärtnerplatz. Contact: Vanessa T: 0049 174 4203131(best Mon from 8-10pm) Email: TG-Stammtisch-Muenchen@gmx.de
www.TG-Stammtisch-Muenchen.de.vu. Informal meeting for all varieties of TG's, drag-queens & friends. 1st Tuesday and 3rd Thursday from 9pm. dressed in a way which is appropriate for the public.

INFORMAL TRANNY-MEETINGS AT SCHWABINGER KOJE Kurfürstenstr.11 (zwischen Georgen- und Adalbertstr., M.-Schwabing), T: 0049 89 2717744 open daily from 8pm till late. Since April 2003 "Trucker-Tina" and her spouce Brigitte run this cosy little night-bar. Trannies are welcome any day, but especially Mondays and Saturdays Tina has established a little "cabinet" with good light and mirror for doing the make-up and for dressing up.

VIVA E.V. Baumgartnerstr. 15 M.-Sendling / backside of former fair-areal. T:0049 89 89161965. www.vivats.de Email: info@vivats.de. Local selfsupport-association for transsexual people, mainly men-to-female, but CD's and FtoM's are welcome. Fridays from 7:30pm. The last Friday of month is "Open Evening", just to meet new "sisters". On Tuesdays from 7 to 9pm. VIVA offers personal councelling via phone.

STAMMTISCH "FREIES MÜNCHEN E.V. held at gay-bar Cook Augsburger Str. 1, near to Sendlingertorplatz, M.-Center Contact: Ellen T:0049 89 41074630 Email: FreiesMuenchenEV@aol.com. Weekly informal meeting of fetish-people. CD's and drag-queens are heartily invited. The meetings take place 9:30 to 11:30pm.No dresscode applies to these meetings.

TRANSFORMATION-SERVICES AND -COUNCELLING www.ChangeAway.de Councelling offered on a private basis by Charis Berger (52, She-Male "by birth"). A special room is reserved for this service offered on basis of an individual contribution to cost. Charis wants to help CD's, who are not skilled yet or who cannot exercise their "hobby" at home. Charis gives good and individual advice for self-understanding and self-conciousness of trannywise inclined persons. Everything necessary for transformation is available. (and can also be bought at ressonable prices) Photos can be taken. Companionship by going out is offered as well.

TRANS-MUENCHEN is a newly established virtual meeting-point first of all for trannies from the Munich area, but meanwhile a lot of guests from far away have joined. Meeting place: http://groups.yahoo.com/group/Trans-Muencheu

PARTIES, EVENTS, SHOWS & BARS:

BEL ÉTAGE THEATER, Feilitzschstr. 12 (1st floor), D - 80 802 München T: 0049 89 33 90139 www.beletagetheater.de A little theatre managed by Johnny Kleczsz and Susanne Braeuninger. Performing travestie-shows. Wednesday till Saturday at 8:30pm and Sundays at 7:30.

VOLLMAR-HAUS Am Oberanger 38, D - 80 331 München T:0049 89 26018010 www.vollmarhaus.de Email: info@vollmarhaus.de Frequent travestie-shows

OLD MRS. HENDERSEN Müllerstr. 1 (corner to Rumfordstr.), D - 80 469 München T: 0049 89 26469 www.old-mrs-hendersen.de. A a disco, night bar and a little show-theatre which performs travestie-shows on Thursdays and Sundays at 9pm.

CARMEN'S LOUNGE Theklastr. 1 (between Müllerstr. and Blumenstr.), D - 80 469 München, T: 0049 89 23000496 www.carmenslounge.de. Managed by well known Carmen Thurs-Sat from 9pm parties & travestie-shows.

SHOPPING:

DER DICKE DEAL Elsenheimerstr. 6/ corner to Landsberger Str., München-Laim T:0049 89 57967580 www.derdickedeal.de A second hand boutique for "tall girls". The boutique is run by Eva Harrer, who is a very friend of trannies.

SECOND-HAND-FUNDUS "FROM TRANSGENDER FOR TRANSGENDER Contact: Charis T: 0049 177 5520699 Email CharisBerger@gmx.de www.TransAuktion.de or www.TransGenderLife.de. On a private basis Charis Berger started a special "flea-market" for trannies. Clothes (skirts, tops, trousers, coats, shoes, boots, wigs almost all sizes and styles, also availabe are dessous, stockings, panties. Accessoires i.e. bags, belts, fancy "jewellery", fingernails, make-up etc. There is no actual "shop" to look therefore arrange a date with Charis. www.TransAuktion.de was created as a sort of tranny-special "eBay"-site.

ATELIER CHANGEABLE Gerlachweg 9, D - 80 999 München T: 0049 89 55064173 Email muenchen@atelier-changeable.de www.atelier-changeable.de. Managed by Mattea. Transformation services and mail-order-services.

TRAUNSTEIN

CHANGE WAY Contact: Michelle T: 0049 8669 902986 on Thurs from 8 to 9pm Email MichellePorst@aol.com http://members.aol.com/SHGChangeWay Michelle will give you information or you can contact AWO Traunstein refer to selfsupport-initiative "Change Way", Güterhallenstr. 2 , D - 83 278 Traunstein and ask for Vera T:0049 861 16169 from Mon til Fri 9 to 12am

NEUÖTTING (SÜDOST-BAYERN)

GENDER-STAMMTISCH at pub "El Loquito" (formerly known as "Müllerbräu", Burghausener Str. 2, D - 84 524 Neuötting Email: viva1@gmx.de. 3rd Tue a month informal meeting for all TG's, CD's and friends at 8pm . This meeting is managed by "Viva1" a nice, mature CD who likes to meet "sisters" for a nice talk and also undertakings together, i.e. skiing in winter or a visit performances at Munich or Salzburg.

ZIP-CODE "9" (Nueremberg, Bavaria, Sachsen)

NÜRNBERG

GROUPS, MEETINGS & COUNCELLING

TRANS-LIFE E.V TransPeople, Postfach 81 01 01, D - 90 246 Nürnberg T:0049 911 313426 ask for Inge transpeople.manni@gmx.de www.transpeople-nuernberg.de. Selfsupport-group for TG's and CD's. Meetings from 7 till 9pm every 1st Monday of month held at Nachbarschaftshaus Gostenhof, Adam-Klein-Str. 6, room113, 3rd floor. Individual councelling to TG's is offered every 1st and 3rd Tuesday of month, contact Inge Ellen Hildner, mobile 0049 170 9229956.

SMALLTALK E.V. at Kühlenfelser Str. 5, D - 91 257 Pegnitz-Bronn T:0049 160 99281662 smt-bayern@gmx.de www.smalltalk-ev.de. A special "association" for fetish and "SM"-people. Informal meetings every Fri and Sat from 9pm. CD's and TG's welcome. No dress-code applies.

PARTIES, EVENTS, SHOWS & BARS:
PARADIES-REVUE-THEATER Bogenstraße 26 (U-station Aufseßplatz), D - 90 459 Nürnberg T:0049 911 44399 Once was famous for excellent travestie-shows, but meanwhile interest of public has diminished a lot, but the theatre is still open. Shows changing monthly.

ERLANGEN:
TRANSPEOPLE Postfach 31 28, D - 91 019 Erlangen T: Christine: 0049 174 2617219 www.trans-people.de. Meetings are every 3rd Thurs of month at 7pm at Bürgertreff "Die Villa", Äussere Brucker Str. 49, D - 91 019 Erlangen

BRUCK IN DER OBERPFALZ:
TRANSBAVARIA at Discothek "Musik-Café Blue Moon" (on the country-side between D - 92 436 Bruck and Nittenau) transbavaria@abacho.de http://grenzenlos.fairserver.biz. A private initiative by Gaby. Meetings every 4th Fri of month in a separate room in disco. Gabi asks for pre-appointment at least one week in advance Occassionally she arranges tranny-parties with travestie-show. Dressing-up and make-up is possible at the disco-rooms.

OBERKOTZAU
SELBSTHILFEGRUPPE EVITA Email Claudia_K.OP98-EVITA@t-online.de

WÜRZBURG
TRANSITAS E. V. Contact: Gisela Helga Plettner Kapellenplatz 6 / Frenshof, D - 96 185 Schönbrunn T:0049 931 573160 (only 1st and 2nd Wed of month) SHGTransitaswue@aol.com www.transitas-wuerzburg.de.vu. Local selfsupport-group meeting 4 till 7pm every 1st Saturday of month at "Selbsthilfehaus", Scanzonistr. 4, D - 97 080 Würzburg. Personal councelling available.

BAD - KISSINGEN:
SELFSUPPORT-GROUP Carmen & Christiane, Hartmannstr. 2 a, D - 97 688 Bad Kissingen T:0049 9734 5271. TG's Meets every last Friday of month at 8:30 p.m.

ERFURT
TRANSITAS at SwiB-Center A selfsupport-group for TG's and CD's. Meetings every 1st Wednesday of month at 7pm at Café and a separate group-room for individual councelling at SwiB-Zentrum, Windthorststr. 43a , D - 99 096 Erfurt T: 0049 3613462290). http://swib-zentrum.gay-thueringen.de

---

Conutinued from page 169

To what degree would you consider permanent hair-removal, hormonal treatment or surgery ?

Not any more. I guess my age is beyond thinking or dreaming of a gender change, or just wishing some treatment to adopt my body to a more female look-alike.

Who knows that you dress ?

All my family, all my friends, a lot of "sisters" in the tranny community of Germany and of Switzerland, where I lived for some years.

How often do you dress and if you go out where to ?

As time allows and as my mind is like, I dress up at home as often as I want. Dressing-up for going out is only sometimes for a special tranny party. i.e. at Cologne

How much of a sexual turn is trannying for you ?

Yes ! To dress-up is a lot of temptation and stimulation to me, but not only in a sexual sense. Dressing-up makes me happy and turns me into an other person. Rüdiger is a shy and reserved person, but Rosy is open minded and likes to be in the centre of attention.

To what degree do you feel gender dysphoric (i.e.that your brain is feminine) ?

Well, if I look at myself, I'd say I'm female at least inside. But my body is male that's my outside. And yet: I feel female and the trouble is that most of people cannot see that I am a woman ....

What one piece advice would you give to someone that has just found that he is not the only tranny in the world?

Accept you are part of the 3rd gender community. You are not a freak, you are not sick, and you are not perverted. You are someone special! Don't hide, be proud.! Don't bother about stupid comments, it's just because they do not know better. It's up to you to help them out of their ignorance.

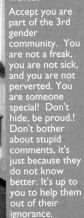

The 'portal' to everything tranny on the Internet

Holland ■ *A Personal* **Report**

Shopping, as you all know, is a real treat. The more I do it the more I discover how easy it is. One of the reasons the following listings I put together does not contain any of the large chains of shops is that at most of these places shopping as a tranny, or as a man shopping for feminine stuff, is simply not a problem. As a man I have bought underwear, tights, skirts, handbags, a hat and jewellery at branches of **C&A, H&M, V&D, M&S** and **P&C**, as a tranny I've been to branches of the **HEMA**, the **BIJENKORF, DOUGLAS, BRISTOL** and **SCAPINO** for lingerie, perfume and shoes and I have yet to meet the first unwilling or unpleasant shop assistant. Admittedly all these shops were in one of the major cities. Things may be different in rural areas. Then again, they may not. Why not find out for yourself? Getting 'dressed' is a lot more fun if you actually have somewhere to go to. Not every chain is as well represented as the other, for instance the **BIJENKORF** has only eight department stores, and **HEMA** has more than two hundred, but there's always one of them near you. If you don't have the nerve or the time to spend an afternoon or two shopping at your high street favourites, mail-order companies are the perfect solution. There are five major ones for clothes, all of which are originally German, and one for make-up, which is French. All publish catalogues and websites (in Dutch).

MY LISTINGS

KLINGEL +31-(0)10-447 9800. mail: Klingel, Postbus 499, 3000 AL, Rotterdam. www.klingel.nl. Not for the young and wild, but for anyone past their teens with a taste for style. Best feature: They're the first mail-order company to have discovered that a lot of girls have big feet. Most of their shoe-collection now goes up to size euro 43 (UK 10), some of it to 46 (UK 13).

NECKERMANN. +31-(0)115-640 024. mail: Neckermann, Antwoordnummer 8022, 4530 RB, Terneuzen. www.neckermann.com. Everyday fashion. Nothing too fancy, just practical clothing. Also: furniture, curtains, household appliances, electronic equipment and computers. Best feature: slightly cheaper than the others.

OTTO. +31-(0)13-4666 666. mail: Otto, t.a.v. Carla Depman, Antwoordnummer 5000, 5005 AA, Tilburg. www.otto.nl. For all ages, tastes and budgets. Best feature: the 'Exclusive' collection, which consists of a wide range of fashion to die for. It will make you look smashing. Very nice, very feminine and very much worth the extra money. On the down side: most of their shoes available in max. size euro 41 or 42 (UK 8 or 9).

WEHKAMP. +31-(0)38-426 4264 (orders) or 426 4364 (info). Mail: Meeuwenlaan 2, 8011 BZ, Zwolle. Website: www.wehkamp.nl. Much like Neckermann, nothing spectacular but all very affordable.

QUELLE. +31-(0)115-626 466, fax +31-(0)115-626 490. Mail: Postbus 186, 4560 AD, Hulst. Website: www.quelle.nl. Affordable everyday fashion, again much like Neckermann and in fact sometimes overlapping with Neckermann in clothing brands.

YVES ROCHER +31-(0)35-609 1122, fax +31-(0)35-609 1101. Nieuwegracht 4, 3763 LA, Soest. www.yvesrocher.nl.

Wide range of make-up and perfumes. Their foundation and powder are good enough to cover a beard shadow and their lipstick and nail-varnish are easy to remove. Best feature: monthly special offers which allow you to buy expensive stuff at half price. On the down side: the nail-varnish tends to chip off a little too easily.

LANDELIJKE KONTAKTGROEP TRAVESTIE & TRANSSEKSUALITEIT (LKG T&T). Postbus 11571, 1001 GN, Amsterdam. +31-(0)6-2543 5865. E-mail: lkgtent@xs4all.nl. www.lkgtent.nl. National support group run by TVs & TSs. If you're looking for advice, a listening ear or a safe night out they offer it all. The people behind the group have all 'been there' themselves. The group publishes a bi-monthly magazine in Dutch for members called 'Transformatie'. Monthly meetings (all from 8 pm. onwards, except Middelburg which is from 9 pm) in the following cities: Amsterdam, 1st wed. +31-(0)6-1008 6671 (call between 4 & 6 pm); Eindhoven, 1st sat. +31-(0)40-286 9404 or 251 8144; Groningen, 4th wed. +31-(0)50-526 2481, Hengelo 4th Sat 31(0)622383820, Hoorn, 3rd wed. +31-(0)20-512 3210; Middelburg, 2nd fri. +31-(0)118-612 280; Rotterdam, 2nd sat +31-(0)10-420 5055; Nieuwegein, 3rd sat. +31-(0)348-564 318. For directions to the venues, phone the appropriate numbers. Eindhoven is the busiest night with a regular crowd of up to 80 people. The meeting in Amsterdam is held in a pub, all the others are in community-centres or an otherwise closed environment. Last year I mentioned the group was thinking of changing it's name, but in the end they didn't.

MARIPOSA TRAVESTIE LOUNGE & SHOP Cornelis Krusemanstraat 9, Amsterdam. +31-(0)20-667 0345, mobile +31-(0)6-1140 1498. www.travestie.tv. Ask for: Mary or Ilse. Mariposa has moved! Mary & Ilse have taken their business to a new address closer to the city-centre, where they will concentrate on selling clothes in their new shop called First View. They are the sole importers of a classy fashion range called Hexeline. The shop is open tuesday's till saturdays from 10 a.m. onwards. The tranny-lounge has the same opening-hours but only for members. Non-members are welcome on thursdays and saturdays, with the last saturday of the month traditionally being the longest and busiest night.

Dear Vicky, dear readers,

In October I enjoyed a visit by three friends from England.

Louise Wood, who had her profile in last year's Tranny Guide, contacted me after having read my profile to see if we could meet (This proves the usefulness of the Tranny Guide personal profiles).

And so on a dreadfully cold Friday night in October Louise, her friends Zara and Jo, with my friends Jun, Natasha and Renate and myself set out for a night in Amsterdam. Louise, Zara and Jo had already spent the day shopping and we all arrived quite late because we had to get dressed en femme and drive to Amsterdam after work. When we joined them we started with supper at *THE SAOW* Thai Café (see listings), then continued to dragbar *DE LELLEBEL*. Both places were packed, but we had a good time. After an hour or so at De Lellebel we continued to *CLUB 'IT'*, which is just around the corner and has recently re-introduced tranny-friendly nights. (look out for their "Golddiggers" theme nights) Because we were trannies we all got in for free, but it may also have had something to do with the fact that there was hardly anybody there. We had a good time regardless. By 2.00 a.m. Louise, Jo and Zara went back to the apartment they'd rented (they'd been in their heels for over twelve hours by that time) and we all said our goodbyes. If anyone else needs a guide on a visit to Amsterdam or The Hague just send me an e-mail. If I can't be there I can almost always find someone else who'll be happy to do the honours. **monica.dreamgirl@tiscali.nl**

Last year saw the birth of yet another new party for the T-scene, *THE KITTEN CLUB*, organised by '*TRAVESTIE.ORG'* and dragbar De Lellebel. It was held in March and November in the '*PALACE*' discotheque in Amsterdam just around the corner from *DE LELLEBEL* and attracted around 60 people each night, which made for a busy place. Entertainment was provided by

A Personal Report

The 'portal' to everything tranny on the Internet

Holland ■ *A Personal* Report

There is a door-charge for the lounge. The new place is quite close to Amsterdam's most famous shopping-street, the P.C. Hooftstraat. It's fairly easy to find a parking space in the area. Paid parking until 7 p.m. From the Central Station take tram 16 to stop 'Valeriusplein'.

TRAVISAGE Postbus 150, 3640 AD, Mijdrecht. +31-(0)348-692 045 or +31-(0)6-3014 6166. www.travisage.nl. Ask for: Ad or Truus. Dressing-service and tranny-shop run by a cross-dresser and his wife. This is a trusted and trustworthy place if you're taking your first steps in the outside world. They stock all the necessary goodies and they gladly help you achieve the look you want. Visits by appointment only.

DE LELLEBEL Utrechtsestraat 4, 1017 VN, Amsterdam. +31-(0)20-427 5139. Just off the Rembrandtplein, in the middle of the city centre. This is the country's only tranny pub. Attracts trannies and admirers. Entertainment by their resident stars Desiree dello Stiletto, Esther van Cartier, Sugi LaRi, Felicia Six and others. It's small, but it's a good and safe place. Parking in the area is a disaster. It's best

to leave your car at the city hall (Stopera) parking, which is less than ten minutes away in heels.

CAFE DE GIJS Lindengracht 249, 1015 KH, Amsterdam. +31-(0)20-638 0740. This is a typical neighbourhood pub in the area of the city centre called the Jordaan. It's named after it's friendly owner, Gijs, who wants his pub to be a place where people of all genders can meet and learn to understand each other. This is where the local branch of the national support group LKG T&T meets every 1st Wednesday, but you're welcome to visit every other day of the month. Upstairs is a small changing room where you can leave your bag if you're going into town. Use of the room is free, but call in advance to announce your arrival and please be polite enough to spend a few euros and leave a big tip as a 'thank you'.

CARAMBA Lindengracht 342, 1015 KN, Amsterdam. +31-(0)20-627 1188. Mexican restaurant opposite De Gijs. The local LKG T&T group sometimes have their supper here before their Wednesday-night meeting, so the staff are used to trannies. They serve decent food at decent prices and you can usually show up without a reservation, although on Fridays and Saturdays it's better to be safe than sorry.

'T SLUISJE Torensteeg 1, Amsterdam, +31-(0)20-624 0813. E-mail: sluisje@dds.nl, www.sluisje.nl. Small pub/restaurant with tranny waitresses and entertainers in the heart of the city. Nice place with good food which is very welcoming of tranny costumers. It's very popular so reservations made at least a week in advance are very necessary, certainly if you want a table at their nine o'clock seating. You can only reserve by phone and you can only pay in cash. The menu can be viewed on the website, which is also in English. If you're in Amsterdam this place is definitely worth a visit.

SAOW THAI CAFE Oudezijds Achterburgwal 160, Amsterdam. +31-(0)20-422 3023. Small cafeteria-type restaurant in the red light district where all the staff are Thai 'katoi'. After supper they change their waitresses-dresses for show-costumes and do a lip-sync-show of about an hour. The food is good and cheap. Get there by taxi, as the red light

district is not a completely safe place for a woman on foot, alone or in a group. (Unless you want to find out your 'street value'.)

MAC The famous make-up brand now has three sales counters in the Netherlands, at the department-stores of De Bijenkorf in Amsterdam (Dam 1, +31-(20)-625 6006), Rotterdam (Coolsingel 105, +31-(0)10-282 3700, ask for the MAC-counter) and Maastricht (Achter het vleeshuis 26, +31-(0)43-3285800, ask for the MAC-counter). They sell the whole range of MAC-products and do on the spot make-overs.

The 'portal' to everything tranny on the Internet

illustrious scene-queens such as 'Saphira' aka the Dutch Tina Turner, 'MayDay', 'Sugi' 'LaRi', 'Felicia Six', the 'Chicks with Dicks', 'The Working Girls' who are currently the top in tranny-entertainment, and it's always a real pleasure to watch their shows. Every one partied until the early morning. I've noticing more and more trannies are bringing their wives/girlfriends to these parties. They are good occasions to show off clothes, wigs and style, not just for the tranny, but for the partner too. In November I was with three friends, and we'd decided we wanted to have supper in a good restaurant, but because one of us couldn't get away from the children early enough we ended up with only just enough time to grab a bite at a Burger King. Bad for the calorie-count, but good for everyone's confidence. None of us had ventured into the neon glare of a fast food restaurant before while en femme, and though we didn't pass, we all felt good enough to return the stares we received with friendly smiles. After this boost to our confidence the party felt all the better.

In May 2003 Amsterdam hosted the second International **TRANSGENDER FILM FESTIVAL** (the first was in 2001). The festival was held at '**DE BALIE**', a venue just off the popular Leidseplein, it ran for five days and showed a host of short and long films and documentaries. The opening film was 'Georgie Girl', a well made documentary on the extraordinary life of Georgina Beyer, the worlds first ever transsexual MP who holds a seat for Labour in the parliament of New-Zealand The theme of the festival was 'Transmasculinities" and so a fair number of the films on offer were about FtM-transsexuals, which was interesting because that's a side of the T-scene one doesn't usually encounter. Seeing and meeting FtM's was an enriching experience. Certainly the funniest film about FtM's was 'Unhung heroes', in which five 'guys' dream about how they're going to come up with the quarter of a million dollars each needs for a penis-transplant. One night was drag-queen night, and showing were 'Wigstock', the documentary on the drag-festival that took place in New York during the 1980's & 1990's, and 'Trash', the film that made Holly Woodlawn famous before Lou Reed immortalised her in his song 'Walk on the Wildside'. Holly Woodlawn, Wigstock-organiser Lady Bunny and Wigstock film-director Barry Shills were all present to light up the festival with there dazzling personalities. Shills is presently working on a documentary on the life of Holly

A Personal Report

STRAVERS LUXE SCHOENEN Main branche: Slotermeerlaan 117a, 1063 JN, Amsterdam. +31-(0)20-613 5285. Also at: Overtoom 139, 1054 HG, Amsterdam. +31-(0)20-616 9973. website: www.stravers-shoes.com. Shoe-shop with a wide range of ladies shoes in sizes up to euro 47. The staff are used to trannies They are very friendly and helpful.

CYNTHELLE Main branch: Van Woustraat 50, 1073 LM, Amsterdam. +31-(0)20-671 9375. Also at: Utrechtsestraat 47, Amsterdam. website: www.cynthelle.nl, e-mail: info@cynthelle.nl. Shop which sells cosmetics and affordable wigs and is welcoming to trannies.

ROSANNA HAIRMASTERS Gedempte Gracht 603, 2512 AM, Den Haag. +31-(0)70-363 0650. Tranny friendly wig shop which sells the major brands (Gisela Mayer, Ellen Wille, Raquel Welch etc.) The shop is tiny and quite hard to find but you'll find friendly service. It's best to make an appointment by phone.

UGEKA Stadhouderslaan 4, 3583 JH, Utrecht. +31-(0)30-251 3599. This is a shop which has taken it's collection to several gatherings of the national support group, so they're used to trannies and will be happy to help you find your perfect hairstyle. They sell not only synthetic wigs, but also real human hair. A friend of mine bought a real hair wig here and it is by far the best wig I have ever seen. Why? Because it doesn't look like a wig, it looks like her own hair.

TRATTORIA CASA DA TONI Prinsestraat 36, 2513 CD, Den Haag. +31-(0)70- 364 3097. Small Italian restaurant in the middle of the city run by a lovely couple, Flavio & Monica, who are very welcoming to trannies provided you look your best. They serve excellent food & wines. It's very popular and you'll need to book at least a week in advance, certainly if you're with more than two. Park your car in the parking garage at the Torenstraat, which is five minutes away in heels.

RESTAURANT LA FONTAINE Deltaplein 623-625, 2554 GJ, Den Haag. +31-(0)70-325 9757. e-mail: lafontaine@kijkduin.net. www.restaurantlafontaine.nl. Close to a large parking, this is a nice beach-club and restaurant on the boulevard of Kijkduin, the far most southwestern tip of The Hague. La Fontaine is in the middle of a row of beach-clubs. It's popular, so book a table well in advance, especially if you're going on a Friday or Saturday. Make sure you ask for a table overlooking the North Sea for a spectacular view.

BODEGA DE SPIEGEL Laan van Meerdervoort 52/V, 2517 AM, Den Haag, +31-(0)70-365 1778. Small café-style restaurant run by the same people who own café Duinstee (see below). They're not trying to achieve Michelin-stars here, but the food and the atmosphere are good.

CAFE DUINSTEE Halstraat 10, 2513 AJ, Den Haag. +31-(0)70-365 3145. Small mixed/gay pub with a friendly atmosphere in the middle of the city. Attracts some local trannies. It's a good place if you want to go for a drink between supper and the disco.

STRASS DISCOTHEEK Javastraat 132, 2585 AX, Den Haag. +31-(0)70-363 6522. Small gay disco on the edge of the city centre with a relaxed atmosphere and a fun loving crowd. Attracts some local trannies. Saturdays are the busiest nights, but Friday's are more fun because there are more girls present, who are far more likely to be interested in a chat or a flirt than the gay guys. The fun doesn't start until after midnight. Parking is not too bad and free.

GAY PALACE Schiedamsesingel 139, 3012 BA, Rotterdam. +31-(0)10-414 1486. www.gay-palace.nl. In the centre of Rotterdam, possibly the hippest gay-disco in the nation. They employ drag-queen dancers & emcees and are accepting of tranny customers. The music is mainly up-to-date techno.

SILHOUETTE BOOTS & SHOES Karel Doormanstraat 467, 3012 GH, Rotterdam. +31-(0)10-413 0516. www.silhouette.nl. Ask for: Nel or Sandra. Family-run business with over 30 years of experience. Come in drag or in drab, you will always be given a warm reception and good advice. Fashionable, sexy, high quality shoes & boots in sizes up to euro 42 and a small selection up to size euro 46. You can order online, but frankly a visit can be a real treat. They have special night-openings for T-girls twice a year on thursdays. They are also a pre-sale point for tickets for tranny and fetish-parties. Highly recommended. If

you're lucky enough to have small feet (max.size euro 41/UK 8) you can also try their branches in Schiedam, Haarlem or Zoetermeer.

VOILA DAMESMODE Karel Doormanstraat 362-364, 3012 GR Rotterdam. +31-(0)10-411 9473. Back in the listings since I've had some good reports on them recently. Diagonally across the street from Silhouette, this is a large shop which sells up market suits and evening wear for girls of all sizes. Exclusive and thus expensive, but with a friendly service.

DE ZEEUW SCHOENMODE Slinge 584a, 3086 EX, Rotterdam. +31-(0)10-480 4790. Shoe shop with fashionable, classy styles in sizes up to euro 45. Friendly service. On the corner of a busy shopping square and next to a parking garage, it is easy to reach by car, bus and underground. The neighbourhood is not as good as it used to be, but I'd still rate it safe enough to go en femme.

The 'portal' to everything tranny on the Internet

Woodlawn, and the festival-visitors were lucky enough to be shown a 25-minute preview of the film so far. By the time this edition of the Guide has come out it should (nearly) be finished, and judging by that preview the entire film is going to be an absolute must-see. Other films included "Gaudi afternoon" by director Susan Seidelmann (Desperately seeking Susan), based on a novel by Barbara Wilson, "Mutti, der film" (Mommy, the film), an over the top comedy starring two drag-queens from the Berlin scene and the Norwegian documentary "All about my father", in which the director portrays his tranny father and the effect his father's openness, about his Transvestism, has had on their family. Most of the films on offer were mainstream enough to be shown on television, and one can only hope that they will be shown. The audience for most films was a good mix of tranny boys and girls and genetic men and women. The festival also included a party on the Saturday-night where the music was provided by an all-butch rock band and a tranny DJ.

Obviously I didn't just go to the films; I also went shopping in Amsterdam, which was another good experience. I found friendly service in every shop I went into, and encountered no problems on the streets. The thing is, in the part of the city-centre surrounding the film-venue at least half of the people are tourists, and they seem to consider seeing a tranny just another part of their Amsterdam-experience.

The first weekend in August, Amsterdam played host to *GAY PRIDE*, which has become a four day event full of lectures, forum-discussions, parties and on Saturday the Canal Parade, which attracts gay and transgendered people from all over Europe and spectators from all over the country. Under a blistering sun characteristic of last year's summer 85 boats and floats sailed the Amsterdam canals under the watchful eyes of several hundreds of thousands of people. I went with a small group of friends to admire and be admired, and we had a great day. We followed the parade for a while and then continued on our own little parade which ended at a friendly pub '*DE GIJS*' (see listings). We ended up being the focal point of another annual event. 'De Gijs' is visited each year by a group of costumers of a pub in a tiny village north of Amsterdam. Once each year, the owner of this pub sends a coach load of his regulars to Amsterdam to visit 'De Gijs'. These people have never before seen a tranny (unless

A Personal **Report**

Holland ■ *A Personal* Report

CALAND SCHOEN Nieuwe Binnenweg 14, 3015 BA, Rotterdam. +31-(0)10-436 6317. www.calandschoen.nl. Fashionable ladies shoes up to size euro 46/UK 13. The attitude of the staff tends to be one of indifference rather than friendliness, but they sell good quality footwear at prices to match.

LAURA DAY +31-(0)6-2261 4150. e-mail: Lauradaytv@hotmail.com Laura is a wonderful girl who runs a dressing service, gives make-overs & make-up lessons and will escort you shopping. She also sells boobs and wigs. Furthermore she knows what's happening in the scene in the south of the country and in Belgium. Once a month she hosts a tranny night in Club Mystique (see below).

FUN4TWO Middelweg 18, 2841 LA, Moordrecht. +31-(0)182-378 724 or 0900-386 4896. www.fun4two.nl. Situated just off the A20 motorway near Gouda with a huge private parking lot, this is really a sex-club for couples, but with T-parties twice a year on Thursdays. The dates are announced on their homepage and on www.travestie.org. Don't be put of by the fact this is a sex-club. Nudity is only allowed on the 1st floor and if you're not interested you simply stay downstairs. Just have a good time dancing, talking and eating. It's a classy place and the owners are nice people. Changing room is available and all drinks, food, entertainment and a personal locker are included in the admission.

CLUB MYSTIQUE Zundertseweg 84, 4715 SC, Rucphen. +31-(0)165-343 280. website: www.parenclub-mystique.nl. This is another sex-club for couples, in the country-side between Rotterdam and Antwerp, which holds T-nights every 2nd Thursday, hosted by the lovely Laura Day. It has private parking and room to change. Food and drinks are included in the admission. The place attracts trannies and admirers, and because of that the atmosphere is more erotic than in Fun4two. Since Thursday is a regular day for the club you'll also find straight couples present.

VOGUE Veldbleekstraat 4, 7551 DD, Hengelo, +31-(0)74-250 8308 / 250 8410. website: www.vogue.nl. Hip straight disco in the east of the country which is accepting of gays and trannies. You'll never be the only tranny, since their resident T-girl Chantal, who is both beautiful and friendly, is always there, either behind the bar or on the floor.

T-CAFE GRONINGEN Gedempte Zuiderdiep 64.9711 HK, Groningen +31(0)503142052. Restaurant in city centre of Groningen run by T-girl Katja who also performs her own comedy & Musicshow. Katja welcomes other T-girls.

WWW.TRAVESTIE.ORG This is only a virtual place and it's only in dutch. Their website offers news on the national and international tranny-scene, a contact-service and a chatroom which is used by lots of people. Log on and you'll never be

Photos on this page with thanks to Pamela from Belgium

lonely again. You're bound to find people who will be able to show you around and give you the 'ins and outs' on any of the major cities. The people behind this site also co-host the parties at Fun4Two and the Kitten Club at The Palace in Amsterdam, both of which are held twice a year.

BEAUTY-LINE Nieuwe Binnenweg 348b, 3023 ES, Rotterdam. +31-(0)10-425 7272. www.beauty-line.nl. Ask for: Ingrid. This is a hairdresser and beautician who will style and cut your hair in a feminine way. She has several tranny-customers. Call first for an appointment and to discuss your wishes and expectations.

MEDI SKIN CARE Pegasusstraat 16, 1131 NB, Volendam. +31-(0)299-404 571. Two friendly ladies run this company. They provide professional laser treatment at their own practice and at the monthly meetings of the support group LKG T&T in Nieuwegein (see above). They are not as expensive as most other laser treatment people.

POUR TOUS Maliestraat 18, 3581 SM, Utrecht. +31-(0)30-233 2843. e-mail: info@pourtous.nl. www.pourtous.nl. Laser treatment for men, women and transgenders.

BEAUTY CENTRE PHYSICAL De Venser, Berthold Brechtstraat 1, 1102 RA, Amsterdam Zuidoost. +31-(0)20-699 9512 or 695 3095. Ask for: Dolly de Hond. E-mail: beautycenterphysical@hotmail.com. www.twistedpair.nl/physical. Laser treatment, make-up lessons, manicure, pedicure, make-overs for a day or a night out. Treatment only by appointment.

VROLIJK GAY & LESBIAN BOOKSHOP Paleisstraat 135, 1012XL, Amsterdam Tel: 020-6235142 www.vrolijk.nu email: info@vrolijk.nu A good place to go. It has a large section with transgender books upstairs (mainly in English) and also a nice selection of transgender/travesty DVDs see www.vrolijk.nu/films/speelfilm-t.html

they went on the trip before), and so are full of misconceptions and questions, and they are all very eager to learn about us and drink with us, which definitely makes for a fun filled afternoon for all involved.

This year Travestielounge '*MARIPOSA*' moved to new premises, closer to the centre of Amsterdam and in a much nicer, very stylish old house. They now have a shop on the ground floor where they sell an exclusive line of Polish clothing called 'Hexeline' and the lounge on the first floor. The place was officially opened on the last Saturday of November with a small get together for all the members and other regulars. Two weeks earlier Mary & Ilse had opened the doors to the neighbourhood, to explain what goes on in the first floor lounge. The responses from the neighbours were invariably accepting. In the old neighbourhood the taunts and harassments from the local Morrocan community towards the owners and the customers had become unbearable, up to the point were it became almost impossible to leave without being verbally abused. This is very disconcerting, especially if you're just coming out of the closet. Talking to the elders of the community only proved a short term solution, and so the decision was made to leave.

In the profile I wrote for last year's Guide I said I was considering laser-treatment to get rid of my beard. I have since started undergoing the treatment, although I'm not quite sure whether 'treatment' is the right word. Torture is more like it. Even with the machine at a low intensity it still feels like my chin is being assaulted by a mad accupuncturist. My skin reacts quite violently, taking more than two weeks to recover and lose the red rashes and pimples. Nevertheless the effect on the hairs is almost immediately visible too. So I suppose I'll continue. Beauty requires suffering, right?

In the listings I've given short descriptions of addresses which I've already mentioned in previous years to make room for new shops and services. I couldn't have made this update without the help of **Conny, Chris, Laura, Renate, Ayla, Jun, Natasha, Sonja & Paula.**

I know this list is far from complete. So if you have visited The Netherlands or if you are Dutch and you feel you have something to contribute or If you are planning a visit and you need advice or a guide drop me a line at:

monica.dreamgirl@tiscali.nl.

Have a wonderful year and be fabulous,

Monica

A Personal Report

The 'portal' to everything tranny on the Internet

Ibiza Spain ■ A Personal Report

GETTING THERE

The first thing you need to use is a good tranny friendly tour operator, we used **RESPECT** Contact number 0870 770 0169. The company is great, you don't get any hassle or bother, except in flight, as you can't choose who catches the plane with you. Most flights are available locally although you will need to use a taxi on arrival as they only arrange transfers for Gatwick. Flight times are good, not much waiting around, and the beauty with Respect is you have a courtesy room if you do have to wait. They are a gay tour operator and are very competitively priced.

WHERE TO STAY

Trannies need to stay in Figuretas or Ibiza Town. I would recommend Figuretas, it has everything you need until you become adventurous enough for Ibiza Town. Here's what I know from what Respect offer accommodation wise.

SUD STUDIOS Everyone starts here for the first time. It's central in Figuretas, with fab sea views, close to the beach. Side apartments do have a little street noise.

CENIT This has a pool and is a bit further away from the beach but closer to Ibiza Town`

CENTRAL PLAYA This is located over the supermarket, next to the taxi rank, close to the beach and is ideal for all needs in Figuretas.

HOW TO GET AROUND

Taxis are the best form of transport, when you can get your hands on one. The preferred form of transport is on foot. So wear comfortable footwear as you may have a little walking to do if you want to get into Ibiza Town where the action is. A taxi from the airport to Figuretas will cost approx 12-15 euros about 10 quid.

BARS IN FIGURETAS

MONROES This is on the main road (Ramon Muntaner) and is the first bar you come to if you are staying in the Sud. Its the oldest gay bar on the island and looks a bit like a green shed from the outside, but has the mod cons inside i.e. air con. Camp music plays out all day and night with quiz and bingo nights in the week.

BAR KITSCH Directly opposite Monroes on the other side of the road. The bar has a nice spill out terrace with leopard skin covered chairs.. You can watch the world go by here. The toilets are down a spiral staircase look for the stiletto heel nailed to the door.

CAFÉ MAGNUS This bar/restaurant is right on sea front and ideal for people watching on the promenade. Slightly dearer on your euros but very trendy. Its an ideal meeting place and everyone's friendly. Respect hold their welcome meeting here.

IBIZA TOWN

This place is a Mecca for everyone who is cool, whatever your nationality (and you won't find many British). It is an oasis for all the beautiful people and very accepting of anyone who is different, stylish and not afraid to show it.

Ibiza Town is split into 3 areas, Street of Virgins, Sa Penya and D'alt Villa (inside the castle walls).

To get there from Figuretas you literally walk down the main road (Ramon Muntaner) and take a right into Avenue de Espana (the main road leading to the town). It takes approximately 15 minutes at a fairly slow mincing pace, and you wont get hassle down any of it, you might get a few second glances and gaping mouths but if you throw enough shade and don't freak out you'll be fine (honest). There are no lager louts, mouthy hen parties or frightening grannies here, so chill.

Ibiza Spain ■ by Cathy Kissmet

STREET OF VIRGINS You will know when you are there because you can't go any further forward without getting wet. It's the back end of the town (no pun intended). The town itself is not for the claustrophobic - there are tons of cobbled streets with walls so close together you wonder if they are going to topple over. Everyone one of them is full of shops, bars, restaurants, and above all that are people's homes. Any bar down the street of virgins is fine to have a drink in, and the more adventurous can drink elsewhere within the town. A few I would recommend on this street are **THAI'D UP** (nice cocktails), **FOCIFUM** (good people watching spot right in the middle), **CAPRICHO, CLUB CARGO** (chairs can be a bit awkward to sit on), **LA NADA** (German and very friendly). If in doubt just look for the gay rainbow symbol.

As a TV you will be adored, drooled over, pointed out and treated like the celebrity you are

SA PENYA The most prominent, bar here is Angelo's. If you look left just before you enter the walled part of the town you will see it in the distance. As a TV you will be welcomed here with open arms. The bar is lovely with the largest gay terrace on the island and is a good stop off before going on to Anfora. The toilets are a must see and are located through one of the many bar areas and down the stairs with no stair rail (so watch your step) Unisex toilets, very Ally McBeal, but a terracotta style with many lavish decorations.

D'ALT VILLA Very beautiful surroundings within the castle walls. Its especially European up here but don't let that put you off, the atmosphere is very chilled out. Anfora disco is here within the walls and is the only full on gay night-club that we found. They put on themed nights and don't bother turning up early as its not open until midnight

TO SUM UP

Look, just go to Ibiza, book yourself with Respect (Kevin will look after you), dress to impress and hit the bars in Figuretas and Ibiza Town. It's a must and we will be going again in 2004. We are not on a commission honestly but would just love other TG girls to benefit from the incredible Ibiza experience. See you on the beach girls!

Photo by www.1ofthegirls.com

My name is Cathy Kissmet and I love to be out and about around the UK on the Tranny scene.

Last year myself and my partner decided that it would be fun to try out a whole week in the sun with myself fem full time. We chose Ibiza and specifically Figurates/Ibiza town as we had heard some very good things about the area. We had an amazing time and could not believe that such a chilled out and funky place really existed. Its perfect for trannies as no one seems to give a f*** how you dress and what you get up to. Just as long as you are sexy, stylish and love to party.

Ibiza town is crammed full of to die for cutting edge clothes shops, relaxing restaurants (where you can sit and watch the world go by) and tranny friendly bars all playing incredible music. Figurates is very gay, with its own beach and special atmosphere. I spent much of the time just lying in the sun on the beach in my little bikini, gazing out over the ocean, or with my nose in a book under an umbrella.

If you want to experience a week in Spain as your female self this is the place to go. The area is a total melting pot for so many nationalities and groups of people that usually would never meet each other and the flavour you get from all these cultures colliding is unique. We met hippies, Jamaicans, drag queens, gay boys (young and mature), Italians, French, Germans and even the odd UK resident. Not forgetting the beautiful Spanish people. The things that we did not find were bars full of English thugs, kids and places flogging fish and chips (in other words the things we were trying to escape from)

My very efficient girlfriend has put together a little list about the area and we hope it will help others as we had problems finding specific information that would be of use to the TV on holiday when we were planning our trip.

A Personal **Report**

The 'portal' to everything tranny on the Internet

PUERTO RICO:

CHEZ FUNNY BOY" is the best Drag and TV show I have ever seen and gets better every time I go over which is about 5 times a year. They change the acts very often and come up with new ones all the time. The show is on every night of the week, starts at 10.30pm and is a 2 hour long show. There is a different show every night. The bar is open from 9pm and it's a good idea to go early to get a good seat, and you can watch English comedy programmes on the large screen before the show. There is no cover charge and trannies are made especially welcome. The costumes are fantastic and the show features the best impersonation of Shirley Bassey, Liza Minnelli, Tina Turner, Madonna and many more. Definitely not to be missed. The bar has English speaking staff and is air-conditioned which is great for these girls with wigs. A taxi from Playa Del Ingles takes about 15-20 mins now because of the new motorway and costs about 16 Euros. Buses go every few minutes. The bar is situated in the Commercial Centrum on the 2nd floor, 4th Phase above the Tterdisa supermarket. The ideal thing to do is to go up early and have a meal in any one of the fabulous restaurants there and make a night of it.

PLAYA DEL INGLES

JERRY SHOW is on the top floor of the Yumbo Centre. A visit there is a must for every tranny. Jerry is a tranny herself and makes everyone very welcome especially trannies. Her bar is where the best known Spanish trannies and she-males and drag queens go. The place doesn't really get going until after midnight. The bar closes about 4.30am sometimes later. There is a show on every Friday and Saturday starting at 12.30am and features Jerry herself, Batusi, Fabiola and Angelo.

CAFÉ LA BELLE is on the ground floor of the Yumbo Centre. It has an English Drag show every night which is very good.

RICKYS CABARET BAR is also on the ground floor of the Yumbo, cabaret show on every night also.

KLAMATTE is downstairs in the basement in the Cita Commercial Centre. Show on every night. Beautiful she-males Lourdes and Sami and stunning TV Gina appear. Show starts about 10pm, no cover charge. It is a small intimate bar and definitely tranny friendly.

MARINA BAR is beside Marietta apartments. Show on every night with the main star Moelia, a beautiful TS. No cover charge and show starts at 9.30pm. Worth a visit and tranny friendly.

WESTFALIA is situated on ground floor of the Cita Commercial Centre, you can't miss it, it's quite a big bar with Drag and TV shows every night from 9pm – 12.30am. No cover charge and tranny friendly.

Natalie from the Gemini Club

Every year Natalie and the girls from the Gemini in Dublin travel to Gran Canaria for Carnival, 10 days of non-stop dressing and partying. It is featured mainly in the Yumbo Centre which is a big shopping centre with lots of gay, tranny and drag bars. Carnival Las Palomas is held either February or March, dates can be checked through the Spanish Tourist Board. The area is highly recommend for a "Tranny Break" (See the Ireland Section of this book for Gemini Club contact details)

Fidel owner of Chez Funny Boy

A Personal Report

185

Italy ■ *A Personal* Report *by Vicky Lee*

A recent Google search resulted in the discovery of what may be more than a coincidence... While planning the re-launch of our WayOut Wine Bar concept every Friday in the City of London - I did some routine searches and came across this web site.

The fact that there was another place called The WayOut Wine Bar was not a surprise. The fact that this little bar had wayout@hotmail as an email address seemed pretty strange and at first I did not notice any further coincidence.

Then it was pointed out to me ...

This WayOut Wine Bar is located in **ATRANI** near Amalfi Italy.

The web site reads like many of our listings - so here it is.

THE WAYOUT WINE BAR is located in the square of Atrani, which has become more and more the going out place for Amalfi and the surroundings, and it is the place for people who want to have a taste of quality italian wines without spending too much money.

Wayout Wines and Spirits is a chill out wine bar for young people from all over the world, a perfect place to taste the best regional and italian wines with some nice crostini and a high quality cheese and snacks selection.

Come and have a glass of wine with us, You won't regret it!

For further information and booking: Wayout is in Piazza Umberto I

84010 Atrani - Phone +39 089 873516

Email: wayout@hotmail.com

"Will you be the first Tranny to visit Atrani ? Give them all at The WayOut Wine Bar my Love ! " The race is on.

The UK is difficult to reference because it is split into so many small counties, some of which have just a few entries.

This is why we split the country into seven sections plus a Nationwide section for the businesses whos services can be accessed anywhere.

UK Personal Reports

UK The Listings

UK Profiles

M8
M56/62
M6
M1
M5
M4
M2
M3

Photo by ullirichter.com (URP London)
Tel: +44 (0) 7980 920580
Makeup & Styling by Lorraine@annodom.com
Model Jo@annodom.com

"What are these events like?"

Some events offer lessons and formal discussion. Others are designed to be informal and spontaneous.

They are generally non-profit enterprises, run by dedicated people who put in a great deal of effort to provide, very good value for money, opportunities to be with others, often for an extended time period.

Whether you are closeted or 'out' these events offer a safe place to mix with a large number of people, 'en femme', for a day, a night, for whole weekend or even longer.

The organisers are always keen to hear from new participants and will be glad to talk to you on the phone to answer any queries. Most have an information pack that they will be happy to send you.

In previous editions of The Tranny Guide I have featured articles describing some of these events. Details of these articles are on page 116 and back issues are still available.

April 3rd 2004 - Drag Olympics at the WayOut Club, to enter 07778 157290 or www.wayout-publishing.com
April 17th 2004 - The WayOut Club's Birthday
April 17th 2004 - Trans-Nation Midlands at ClubDV8 Birmingham www.trans-mission.org.uk
April 23rd 2004 - Transliving Tight Lacing 01268 583761 stacy@transliving.co.uk www.transliving.co.uk
April 30th - 2nd May 2004 - Spring Bank Holiday Weekend at Preston. Contact Janett Scott 01582 732936
May 8th 2004 - Roses/Angels do "Hedwig and the Angry Inch" in Brighton www.repartee.tv
May 9th - 16th 2004 - Kentisbury Revival Holiday On camping site in West Quantoxhead, North Somerset 01984 632515
May 12th 2004 - Miss Tranny Grange at House of Drag www.trannygrange.co.uk
May 28th 2004 - Transliving Bring and Buy Sale Tel:01268 583761 stacy@transliving.co.uk www.transliving.co.uk
June 2004 - Ascot Trips By various dressing services including www.theboudoironline.com, www.pandoradepledge.com, www.hideandsleek.co.uk
June 12th 2004 - Angelic at Pink Punters, Milton Keynes www.theangels.co.uk Tel: 01908 377444
June 18th - 20th 2004 - Midsummer House Party Weekend of elegance, charm & grace celebrating the bygone age at Mill House Hotel, Kingham, Oxfordshire www.millhousehotel.co.uk
June 12th 2004 - Angelic at Pink Punters, Milton Keynes www.theangels.co.uk Tel: 01908 377444
June 19th 2004 - Trans-mission 2nd Birthday held in Manchester www.trans-mission.org
June 19th 2004 - Angels UK Debutante's Ball www.theangels.co.uk Tel: 01908 377444
June 25th 2004 - Transliving Stacy's Birthday Party 01268 583761 stacy@transliving.co.uk www.transliving.co.uk
July 10th 2004 - Thames Boat Party www.repartee.tv
July 14th 2004 - 4th Birthday of House of Drag www.houseofdrag.tv
July 23rd 2004 - Transliving Summer Frocks and Trade Stall 01268 583761 stacy@transliving.co.uk www.transliving.co.uk
August 27th 2004 - Transliving Maids Night 01268 583761 stacy@transliving.co.uk www.transliving.co.uk
September 2004 - TV Wedding Festival in Bournemouth Contact: D. Daniels PO Box 11, Swanmore, Hants SO32 2ZU Tel/Fax 01489 893451 ddan282739@aol.com
September 18th 2004 - Angelic at Pink Punters, Milton Keynes www.theangels.co.uk Tel: 01908 377444
September 22nd 2004 - Miss of House of Drag Contest www.houseofdrag.tv
September 24th 2004 - Transliving Glitter 'n' Glamour 01268 583761 stacy@transliving.co.uk www.transliving.co.uk

October 2nd - 11th 2004 - *Kentisbury Revival Holiday* On camping site in West Quantoxhead, North Somerset 01984 632515

October 1st - 4th 2004 - *Skin Two Rubber Ball* www.skintwo.com Tel: 0207 627 3332

October 7th - 11th 2004 - *Edelweiss Belles North Wales Weekend* at Colwyn Bay. Contact Sam Mclaren 01978 843087

October 16th 2004 - *Alternative Miss London* Contest at the WayOut Club. to enter 07778 157290 or www.wayout-publishing.com

October 22nd 2004 - *Transliving* Halloween Ball. 01268 583761 stacy@transliving.co.uk www.transliving.co.uk

October 30th 2004 - *Transfandango Halloween Ball* held at the London Marriott Hotel, Grosvenor Square/Duke Street, London W1 Website www.transfandango.co.uk

October 29th-31st 2004 - *Miss TV Scotland Weekend* Tel: 01592 891344 or www.hideandsleek.co.uk

November 5th-8th 2004 - *Miss Rose 2004 Harmony Weekend* at Scarborough. For details send SAE to Martine Rose, 208 Holmley Lane, Dronfield S18 3DB or email martine@repartee.tv

November 19th - 21st May 2004 - *Rotherham Weekend* Contact Janett Scott 01582 732936

November 26th 2004 - *Transliving* Supergirl Contest 01268 583761 stacy@transliving.co.uk www.transliving.co.uk

December 2004 - *Angelic* at Pink Punters, Milton Keynes www.theangels.co.uk 01908 377444 - Date to be confirmed

December 1st 2004 - *Muse Worlds Aids Day Party* at House of Drag www.clubmuse.co.uk

December 3rd - 5th 2004 - *Southern Girls Weekend* in Bournemouth Contact: D. Daniels PO Box 11, Swanmore, Hants SO32 2ZU Tel/Fax 01489 893451 ddan282739@aol.com

December 10th 2004 - *Transliving* Christmas Party 01268 583761 stacy@transliving.co.uk www.transliving.co.uk

March 2005 - *Spring Glitz Weekend* in Blackpool, Joyce/Angela 01782 620930

March 26-28th 2005 - *TV Wedding Festival* in Bournemouth Contact: D. Daniels PO Box 11, Swanmore, Hants SO32 2ZU Tel/Fax 01489 893451 ddan282739@aol.com

April 2005 - *Edelweiss Belles North Wales Weekend* at Colwyn Bay. Contact Sam Mclaren 01978 843087

April 9th 2005 - *Drag Olympics* at the WayOut Club. to enter 07778 157290 or www.wayout-publishing.com

April 16th 2005 - *The WayOut Club's 12th Birthday* www.thewayoutclub.com Tel: 0208 363 0948

Steffan Whitfield's

Alternative Miss London
2004/5

Dedicated to the memory of
Ron Stome
The 12th Year
of this stunning
contest at

The

Club

16th October 2004
£2000 worth of prizes

Entry is open to anyone
with a sophisticated outfit
and a sexy outfit who
registers before 12pm

Drag OLYMPICS

3rd April 2004
9th April 2005
at
The *WayOut* Club

£300 worth of prizes

*"One of the funniest things
I have ever seen"*

Entry is open to anyone
with four inch heels
(or higher) registering
before 12pm

more details
of both events
www.wayout-publishing.com
www.thewayoutclub.com

Transfandango
Charity Ball
2003
"A Fairy Fantasy"

Over the last two years this amazing
event has raised over £60,000
For Manchester Children's Hospital

Richard O'Brien's Transfandango

"Halloween Charity Ball"

Black Tie, Halloween Costume or Posh Frock

Saturday 30th October 2004
at The London Marriott Hotel
Grosvenor Square, London W1K
6JP

*Champagne reception,
3 course meal, tombola, celebrity auction,
Cabaret and Dancing*

To Book Tickets,
Contribute Sponsorship
or Contribute Prizes
Please contact Charmaine Owen
administrator / fundraiser at
**Wallness Children's Charity
Sorrel Bank House,
25 Bolton Rd,
Pendelton, Salford M6 7HL**
Tel 0161 737 1203
Email wallness@care4free.net
Reg Charity 518086

For History of this event,
pictures of previous years
and a multitude of detail
including accommodation,
suggestions and information
on this years event.

the five stars appeal
Wallness Children's Charity

www.transfandango.co.uk
Frequently updated as we lead up to the event

Lianne - I was dressed as a woman and so was my passenger -This policeman was completely professional and open minded (I just wish the rest of the world's population were the same)

Julia Maddison - I had the need to call our local 'Homophobic advice Officer' after verbal abuse and stone/egg throwing incidents at my home in Northampton. He was most helpful, and a couple of days later our local beat officer came to see me at home. This was around mid to late 2002 I think. I wasn't fully en femme at the time but the PC was polite and helpful, and we had the best result when, as we stood in my kitchen looking at the damaged window, another stone was thrown by passing kids who were arrested, taken to the station and warned. Most of the group was about 11 or 12, and the Police asked their parents to collect them. Surprisingly I've had no repercussions and the abuse has got much less/ non-existent now.

Paula - one of the people behind Travestie.org, is a Dutch policeman. She writes, "Transgenderism has never been an issue in my training, but neither were homosexuality or extreme kinds of sex. All of these things a policeman will encounter, but we are expected to deal with them in a normal and professional way just like we would deal with anyone else. Personally, in my work I meet a lot of TGs who work as prostitutes. My colleagues never make derogatory remarks in their presence and treat them as they would anyone else. But as soon as the T-girl in question is out of sight some of them will make 'funny' remarks. Only a few do, however; most of them don't really care."

Kenni Joanne - President, Crossroads Chapter. - I live and pass as a female most of the time, I was stopped by the Michigan State Police one night for having a burnt out headlight and he was most courteous and professional. After I informed him that it had just burned out that evening he ran the license, and registration check. Everything came back OK so he told me to have a good time, and be careful. About three months later I was a witness and bystander to a car accident and when the same officer approached me he said he was glad that I fixed my headlight.

Elvia - is a recently trained Dutch police-assistant. She says "There is no special treatment for transgendered people that I'm aware of. I was taught to treat everyone with courtesy and respect, regardless of what they wear or look like."

Janie Jones - I live in Edinburgh - I was pulled over for a random tyre check and one tyre was a bit iffy. The two officers were very courteous and professional and didn't bat an eyelid. (Not to mention the fact that I got off with the price of a new tyre and no penalty points...). I was pleased to see the Mardi Gras parade in August headed up by the police Gay and Lesbian Association (in uniform).

Barbara Curry - Connecticut Outreach (USA) Fantasia Fair, Each year, a representative from the Provincetown Police department comes to the Monday morning orientation breakfast to advise fair participants that they won't tolerate two things: illegal parkers, and secondly they do not tolerate intolerance and urge ANYONE in town citizen or visitor to feel free to dial their 9-1-1 emergency services if they experience even the slightest bit of harassment or intimidation. Their philosophy is that if a perpetrator feels they can get away with it, it can easily escalate to something more severe. So they encourage people to ask for assistance.

Jenny - 15 years ago when I was reverting to male mode wriggling back into a pair of trousers while parked in a side road a tenacious bobby politely asked me what I was doing, where I had been etc. There were no problems and I was simply wished good night. Several years later and a great deal more confident, I was stopped and warned of the local speed limit, no problems, rudeness or facetious comments, just a warning to keep my speed down. More recently, as an almost full time woman, I organized a visit to our local TG gathering, from the local police community liaison officer. He was very pleasant and even wrote an article for our local support group magazine. So, I have nothing but praise for the boys in blue.

Charlotte Belle - (Charlee) Trans-Action (UK) Co ordinator - The local police liaison officer has come to the our meetings. Notts police, as well as South Yorks police are very committed to LGBT issues. It is with the Notts LGBT consultative panel, that I have been invited too join.

Bella Jay - from Repartee mag - I have been stopped while 'dressed' on two occasions. First time about 10 years ago when I had just started going out and was still very nervous. I tried to explain my reason for being dressed the way I was, but the officer made it clear that the way I was dressed did not matter to him, told me what he wanted to say and sent me home. Second time was much more recently in London with Tiffany Tuesday and Leah True in the car. Two officers came over to the car and were very nice and polite and I felt we were treated no differently from the couple of other occasions I have been stopped in 'male mode'.

Continued page 194

A few years ago I wrote about the little kids that stopped on their pedal bikes outside my house and asked ... Are you a man a woman or ... a WWF wrestler. Well they came back this year ... on motor scooters, kicked the sh*t out of my car and smashed the window on my front door - in addition to regular verbal abuse to me and my partner.

I know that my area, like most areas in the UK, and around the developed world, has a policy of treating focused hatred as a crime and resources, (an LGBT liaison officer), is available to me to ensure understanding and at least an equal response.

My local police have been very understanding and helpful and the harassment has stopped (at the moment). However I did come across many 'glitches' in my local communication systems and I feel that if I had not been "well connected", I may have fallen into the "frightened tranny" trap. Instead, now I have a cctv system, I know my rights and I have strong personal contacts with local officers who could not be more understanding. Most importantly I do not feel isolated. One very interesting point: My local ward officer showed great empathy, explaining that he had also suffered harassment, vandalism and even bullying, because ... he is a police officer. He said "I would never wear my uniform home that would be asking for trouble".

Of course we are ALL at risk of bullying and vandalism. All my neighbours, including black, Asian, gay, elderly, single woman, have concerns about these young 12 to 17 year old "bad boys & girls". We all deserve an equally supportive response from the authorities.

We are also ALL capable of getting into trouble with the law, (if only for a blown tail light), but again we all deserve equal respect and care during such confrontations with authorities.

I have been working to help ensure that this is the case for trangendered people - but up to this point, despite meeting 100's of TGs weekly and a year with the LGBT advisory committee for the Metropolitan Police, I had heard very few personal stories, good or bad, about hate crime aimed at transgendered people or inequality of response, to the needs of transgendered people. Still - both I, the police, and the LGBT community, take the need for improvement in these areas very seriously.

This made me think how ARE we doing?

There are over 3000 contacts in my email address book and if my correspondents sent me good and bad experiences with the police - this would be a very interesting "snapshot" survey of the relationship between police and transgendered people (internationally).

I related my own experiences and I asked my correspondents - What is our relationship with the police? Do you avoid them? Do you welcome their help? Do they treat you better or worse than non transgendered?

My summary

After receiving nearly 100 replies I was pleased that almost all reported good relationships in individual contact with police officers. Furthermore there was a good number of reports of involvement with advisory groups or police liaising directly with TG groups. Very few of these responses mentioned more than motoring incidents - though this may indicate a continuing reluctance to report more serious incidents either as witness, victim or perpetrator. Those that offered negative stories on investigation turned out, after a little investigation, to be incidents at least five years old indicating that authorities are now more aware and ARE improving.

One interesting point that arose was that it is thought that "the media" lets down, both TG people and the police. It is the media that are lagging behind - hanging on to sensationalism and re-running out of date behaviour even in new productions.

Here are a few snippets of the replies I received. I have posted an un-cut version of this report on the free article section of www.wayout-publishing.com

Have YOU been a victim of transphobic hate physical or verbal ? Have you requested help ? Have you received it ? As a witness or in routine enquiries - what are your experiences with the police?

Email me vicky@wayout-publishing.com

A Personal Report

UK ■ *A Personal* Report

Danielle - I have been stopped twice en femme (Hampshire Police). In neither case was anything said about me being cross dressed (although it petrified the wife) ; I was upfront and told them I was a TV immediately.. They did their checks and sent us on our way. I have also been taken home by the RAC - same experience

Karren - made a very good point - My view is that if I needed police help I am reasonably sure that I would get fair and compassionate treatment. My reason for saying this is that I have a stammer and on the few occasions when I have been stopped whilst driving, in male clothes, they have always been thoughtful towards my speech impediment and very polite which is better than the usual snigger I usually get in shops etc. For the record I live in Birmingham, have been out driving whilst dressed many times and I also go out during the daytime on shopping trips occasionally too so my chances of running into the police are not that low.

Frederic - Washington DC police force has a gay and lesbian unit, which has investigated hate crimes and arrested people who harass transgendered people. The police department also has an advisory committee made up of gays, lesbians and transgendered that is advising the police on transgendered issues. This includes the safety of TG sex workers, & the protection of T girls going about their lives. The police here are very concerned about the safety of transgendered girls.

Patrick - Gay.com / PlanetOut.com Network - The year 2003 has been the most deadly on record for San Francisco transgender people, with more victims of anti-transgender killings reported this year than in any year prior. Thirty-eight transgender people have been reported killed so far this year, twice the number reported just two years ago, according to experts who monitor anti-transgender violence. Last year, 27 such killings were reported. "It's brutal and it's gut-wrenching," said Shawna Virago, a transgender activist at Community United Against Violence, a San Francisco agency that provides support to gay, lesbian, bisexual and transgender victims of hate and domestic violence. Virago said that domestic violence is also a factor in many anti-transgender killings that is rarely discussed. "That also has to do with transphobia: the belief that trans people don't have legitimate relationships," she said. "Because we are only often seen as sex workers, the domestic violence piece is far too often left out."

Kelly Stevens - after a trip to the USA - New York City, about 10 pm, Midtown Manhattan. I was dressed and walked up to two beat cops and asked for directions. They answered as though i was just another visitor to New York. San Francisco, about 6 pm, driving a rental car. Young cop stopped me to tell me my trunk lid was bouncing open as I hit bumps. I thanked him. He asked for a driver's license "for a routine check". He examined it for a few seconds. It had my male identity on it of course. He said, "Thanks, Ms Stevens", and sent me on my way.

Tamara X - Traffic accident Dec 2002. I was involved in a minor accident in London whilst dressed. There was just minor damage, but the other driver felt that the police needed to be called. Three policemen arrived on the scene and were very annoyed with the other driver for calling them. They were incredibly polite and considerate towards me and rebuked the other driver in front of me and apologized that I had to go through unnecessary hassle. A thoroughly encouraging experience of correct treatment towards a member of the transgender community I feel.

Catherine - writes - I'm watching an episode of 'COPS' as we speak and I find that hard to understand what jurisdiction they are following (it's currently 7:50 eastern standard time on November 25th and the program is on the cable FX network) but they are referring to the transgendered woman that had her purse stolen as 'he' and 'him' rather religiously, even going so far as to 'correct' themselves when they start with 'her - or I mean his' Just my $0.02

I replied - Excellent point - To be fair the program may have been recorded a few years ago. But even recent cop shows here in the UK misrepresent our community and the police while trying to make television for "every day joe" who they think will not following their plot or losing empathy through political correctness. Of course these out of date television representations have far more impact on the general public than all the hard work of the real authorities.

Steve - says - My experience of dealing with the police is that there are some obviously well meaning people and initiatives being tried, but so often the personnel change too quickly for long-term relationships to build, and we have to start over again. This is especially true of local community homophobic abuse officers. On the whole however, it is moving in the right direction.

194
The 'portal' to everything tranny on the Internet **www.wayout-publishing.com**

What is your name and what is your background?

Niamh Holding (Niamh K) from West Wales, a post-op bisexual living with both my partners and running a medical equipment company whilst doing a bit of BDSM lecturing and nude modelling in my spare time. Naturally all this is with the permission of my Owner.

Are you happy to be called a tranny and what does this name mean to you?

It depends who's using the term as to whether it comes across as derogatory, I'm sure plenty of people have had it shouted in the street abusively, but then when used by someone transgendered it is no more than an abbreviation. Even then I no longer see it as applicable to me, as I see trans-sexualism as something I've been through rather than a permanent condition.

How old are you and how young can you remember thinking about or actually cross-dressing?

Early 40s, cross-dressing as such was an on & off thing that never really worked for me, more significant now are the once buried memories of, as a child, praying to wake up in the morning as a girl.

Where do you buy clothes?

Everywhere from designer outlets to BHS, Dorothy Perkins etc. Not forgetting bike shops for proper protective gear.

What leads you to choose the styles you wear?

Can any lady answer that?! But the bottom line is to be eye catching and desired.

Do you have one look or many images?

Many, from nude through slutty, business suits to glamourous evening wear, not forgetting heavy leathers.

Is make-up and hair important to you and if so how do you achieve your look?

Yes, I always strive to look my best, so the hairdresser visit is a monthly thing even though I'm still growing my hair (about half way down my back right now). Make-up is second nature now, though I won't go out the door without doing a full job including eye liner and mascara.

To what degree do you practice hair removal, and other body feminisation?

Obviously I'm on HRT for the rest of my life,

and as to the rest... my Owner doesn't allow any body hair at all.

Who knows that you dress?

Just about everyone I know it's the way that I wear clothes, though there are a few people who see me undressed more often than dressed.

How often do you dress and if you go out where to?

Most mornings, and weekdays it's normally to work.

How much of a sexual turn on is trannying for you?

Being female is wonderful and the sex life is great, whether with another woman or with a man.

What is your definition of feminine?

A state of mind more than a physical thing.

To what degree do you feel gender?

Been through it is my feeling; once I transitioned I felt euphoria at my gender.

To what degree would you consider permanent hair removal, hormones, surgery?

Done the lot of them, never regretted it.

What one piece of advice would you give to someone that has just found they are not the only tranny in the world?

Get out there and live life to the full, you only get one shot at it.

are "trannies" because the word includes us all what ever our way of presenting ourselves and our reasons for doing so. Trannies have a lot to give the world, uniquely, and we are stronger together. When we are out on our own we can choose whatever name we like. I'm Mandy, a very special individual.

How old are you and how young can you remember thinking about or actually cross-dressing?

"As old as I look and as young as I feel" – No, I'm about to hit one of the big decades – you'll have to guess which. I've been dressing regularly for 20 years now. I probably first thought about it as a kid.

Where do you buy clothes?

I buy clothes in the sort of women's clothes shops which specialise in flashy bargains. Despite what people think the assistants are OK about men buying women's clothes. I've talked to them – they've seen it all. I'm quite shameless anyway. It's the same with shoes. But if I see a bargain I'll get it anywhere – and TK Maxx is great for bargains by the way. Otherwise I have things made for me by friendly dress-makers and outfitters. I love spotting or inventing new ideas for outfits. Cheap items can make great outfits. One of my smartest outfits is a pair of pyjamas from WhatShoppes which cost less than £10. Sleepwear can make great going-ut gear. I use Mail-order when I can't get to the city where the shop is. Trashy Lingerie in L.A. and Frederick's in Hollywood have great on-line catalogues. But watch the shipping charges!

What leads you to choose the styles you wear?

For going out at night - the more 'glamour' the better. I'm out to be noticed. Things have to suit my height and body-character. At home it's comfortable and feminine.

Do you have one look or many images?

Many, many images. I never like to wear the same look twice. I go from sophisticated to film star to vamp to tramp to cocktail demure to dance-diva to Mardi Gras show-off.

Is make-up and hair important to you and if so how do you achieve your look?

Hair and make-up are crucial and I spend lots of time over both. I have about 18 wigs at any one time and spend regular time looking after them. I've a small crate of make-up and am always experimenting with looks, shades, emphasis. If I see some-one when I'm out or in a picture with a look that I covet I'll try to remember the details for when I'm next in front of the mirror. And some of my best looks have come about by accident, not what I intended but altogether better.

To what degree do you practice hair removal, and other body feminisation?

I shave my legs, arms, armpits and torso with a wetshave in the bath. I put my tits away each night, and what I do with my privates is…. private.

What is your name and what is your background?

Mandy Romero. I live in the North-West of England – Liverpool. I'm unattached but have many great friends with whom I socialise around the area. I'm currently involved in a number of performance projects.

Are you happy to be called a tranny and what does this name mean to you?

When I'm "acting up" on stage or at an occasion, and dressed up to the nth degree I like to call myself a drag queen, and I'm happy to be referred to as a TV or cross-dresser, but if I'm associating with my sisters and transgender friends we

Personal Profile ■ Mandy Romero

Who knows that you dress?

Most of my friends and acquaintances know that I dress. Either I told them, or showed them, or we met while I was out and, mainly, I (re-)introduced myself to them.

How often do you dress and if you go out where to?

I'm a part-timer but a busy part-timer. I go out with friends, and on my own – to places where I know I'll be in friendly company – pretty regularly. But I am intrepid – I did go round the world in drag. (see the 10th Tranny Guide for report) But I also don't take silly risks, and I do try to find out something about where I'm going (and the best way home) if I'm in an unfamiliar city or country.

How much of a sexual turn on is trannying for you?

It makes me feel sexy but I'm not in it for the sex alone. I need and expect to be adored and admired and I want to be respected as an individual. Gay men, the occasional sensitive bi-curious, and even experienced straights are great but sex comes after respect, and that's even when I'm being a tramp. In fact without respect – in the true sense of the word – tranny sex is, in my opinion, a sad waste of time and energy.

What is your definition of feminine?

Other people make you feminine – it's how people relate to you. You make the gestures, achieve the looks, feel the force of your self-expression, but it's nothing without acknowledgement. So am I just as feminine as others' (maybe) limited and clichéd version of it? Well, deep down, like all of us, I'm a uniquely individual human being in whom femininity is just one, but a very important, layer of my being.

To what degree do you feel gender dysphoric?

When I'm dressed my brain goes into a different gear, but some things stay constant, and I'm glad they do. Male and female aren't simply body alternatives, they're active impulses and they proceed from the same sources of our energy.

To what degree would you consider permanent hair removal, hormones, surgery?

Hair Removal would make my life a lot easier but I've not seen enough evidence of success to make me think it worth a lot of money to have it done. I've thought about breast implants and may have them done one day but the rest, hormones, other surgery, would be more loss than gain for me, I feel.

What one piece of advice would you give to someone that has just found they are not the only tranny in the world?

Get active and connect with the scene, network, meet people like you. Be brave and join the party. It's fun.

197

Being the Tranny-in-residence at the Bluecoat Arts Centre in Liverpool has started one of the most interesting times of my life. It all began in 2002 when I got involved with a big performance installation at the Centre,

This eventIt was being directed by the famous Mexican performance artist Guillermo Gomez-Pena, and I provided the DJ soundtrack and my own drag presence to the "exhibits" which were like living dioramas which the audience could interact with. I was up on a scaffolding tower with a view over it all and I changed appearance several times during the three hours, starting with my famous peacock dress and blue hair and ending up like a sort of Amazon porn-goddess. It all got me so excited that I decided I'd get out and about more as a performer. So I went along to the Liverpool Tate Gallery later that autumn at the opening of an exhibition called "Shopping" and just stood around in various poses surrounded by empty shopping bags while everybody passed me by thinking about what I meant. It certainly got the Gallery people confused.

Then I applied to be a Bluecoat Associate Artist and they said yes, so I started planning what I would do. The first thing I planned was to take the Mandayana stories out of my "Dragging Round The World" book and have them read onstage while I was reading them

in a book. This involved creating a Mandy-style boudoir, with the help of my friend Tabitha, and then I got my friends Lorraine and Sarah to provide live music, and my friend Sunni to dance during one of the stories, (and getting the stories recorded was also an adventure) and I used pictures from my Round-The-World trip to project on the wall, and it all lasted over two days, the whole 18 stories, with me turning up in 18 different looks, one for each of the stories, and it was a wonderful time. I have some great entries in the "Mandayana" Visitors Book to prove it.

That was in October, but before that I took part of my "Dragging Round The World" show to the Manchester Green Room and since then I've been back to the Tate to do an "intervention" at their Performance Art exhibition, where I made everybody a Performance Artist for the night, and I've been a rubber-clad dominatrix searching for raw meat (and looking after live maggots!) in an empty reservoir in a show called "Finale" by the Pacitti company. That was in December and even in rubber that place was so cold!!!

Now I'm busy with a repeat showing of my "TV- Jukebox", where I perform to one-minute pieces of music which the audience pick from my specially-created CD, and they see the results on a TV screen. I'm thinking of taking this to Barcelona and doing it outdoors on the Ramblas. And I have so many other plans.

Being a Performance Artist (though they call us Live Artists these days) has been so good for my imagination and my confidence. I've found that there are so many other ways of being a tranny and so many more ways of being seen. It's let me say things about the way the public see us, and make comments about this gender-thing which I never could before. And so much dressing-up, so much finery.Thanks to the help of many of my friends it's been an adventure which I want to take on further, as far as it will go. So thanks to the Bluecoat for believing in me!

Watch this space.

Performance artist ■ Mandy Romero

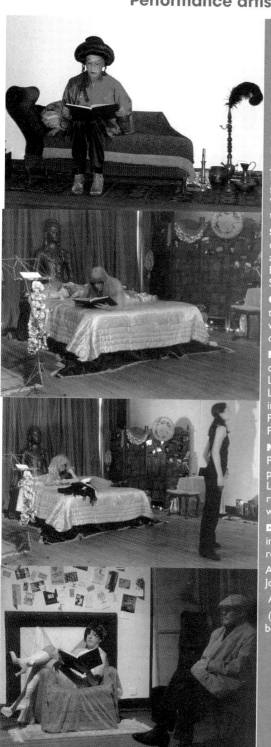

What a year!

March – Offered one of three bursaries as an Associate Artist in Live Art at the Bluecoat Arts Centre in Liverpool

April – visit to San Francisco to meet with artists and activists – lots of ideas and plans

March-June – big gap while a campaign is planned and ideas are shaped

June – Bluecoat commissions "The Mandayana", an installation based on stories from the unpublished "Dragging Round The World" – work starts on preparations for this

September – Performance of short version of the "Dragging Round The World" show at the Manchester Green Room Platform Event "Emergency" followed by spot at Superstar Boudoir in Liverpool

October – "The Mandayana" presented at the Bluecoat in its full "two-day, 18-story, with projections and with live music and dance in specially created boudoir" version

November – Unofficially encouraged to create interventions for the opening of the Liverpool Tate exhibition of documented Live Art, "Art Lies and Videotape" – two interventions made, "I Am A Famous Performance Artist" and the "Do-It-Yourself Performance Art Kit"

November-December – worked with the Pacitti Company on their show "Finale", performed in the Toxteth Reservoir, Liverpool, in December –presented as a rubberclad dominatrix role feeding maggots with raw meat in a greenhouse!

December – Premiere of "TV-JB" an interactive installation at the Bluecoat, to be repeated in January.

And contributions to Liverpool Tate and John Moore's University Live Arts seminars

And there will be more in 2004

(Most of the above available for booking....!)

A Personal **Report**

In our listing we give the preferred methods of contact.

Generally we do not list opening times and prices as these can change so easily.

We always give a phone number, email and website ...
... if we can.

We recommend that you use these to check and get more details before visiting anyone listed.

To help you find your way around the guide, you will find a description of the report ... or the first and last area, on the top of each page.

At the back of the book is an advertisers index.

Omission from these listings is in no way a criticism.

Please let us know of updates and new entries.

UK NATIONWIDE LISTINGS

ACADEMY CLUB
Mail Order - PO Box 135, Hereford, HR2 7WL Tel: 01432 343100;
Email: guy@tawse.com www.academy-inc.com . . .
04 - Sells a large selection of booklets, video tapes, audio tapes and CD's. It is home to Miss Prims Muir Academy for adult boys girls and special girls (TV's). An academy for maids and

ADRIA UK
Mail Order - email@adriauk.com . . . . 04 - Fetishwear company selling adult clothing and accessories. Also sell bridal wear.

ALTER EGO
PO Box 10TG, Bramhall, Stockport SK7 2QF Fax only 0044 161 440 9938;
Email: enqs@alter-ego.com; Website: www.alter-ego.com . . . .
04 - Feminine Fashions for the Taller figure - indulge your feminine side in over the top glamourous luxury fabrics that will enhance and caress your beautiful body!

ALTERNATIVE LOOK
FREEPOST NWW 8035A, Poulton-Le-Fylde, FY6 7ZZ, Tel: 0870 444 5997
Website: www.alternativelook.co.uk . . . .
04 - Full range of wigs and an understanding of TG needs.

ANGELS (UK)
Website:www.theangels.co.uk . . . .
04 - The Angels website has been designed to support the transgendered community and inform those interested - a leading network. .

ASGARD ESCORTS
Nationwide Tel: 0207 207 6972; Email: info@asgardescorts.co.uk; Website: www.asgardescorts.co.uk . . . . 04 - TV/TS and gay male escorts in the UK and beyond. Free site. Full stats & pics.

ASSQ (TV-TS VIDEOS)
PO Box 23893, London SE15 2WQ . . . . 04 - A range of TV-TS videos available from their free catalogue.

ASTROLOGY SERVICES
Nationwide Tel: 0780 361 4883; Ask for: Mike; . . . .
04 - Mike offers you a personal chart for only £15 for 20 pages of character profile. Or you may wish to have a relationship chart to find out your compatibility with another.

BAD INFLUENCE
Ask for David & Donna Email: bdinfluence@earthlink.net www.bad-influence.com . . . . 04 - Lowest prices for quality designer Fetish fashions. Sell High Heels some upto 7 inch heels. Also GIO authentic Full Fashioned Stockings in size 11 (will fit 6'2"). Corsets, long leather gloves.

BANANASHOES
Nationwide mail order Ivy Cottage, Mooregate Grove, Moorgate, Rotherham, S60 2TR Tel: 01709 364588; Email: sales@bananashoes.com; Website: www.bananashoes.com; Ask for: Sharon Herrera; . . . .
04 - Online catalogue catering for the TS-TG-TV community with footwear, fetish, lingerie & clubwear.

BEAUMONT TRUST
BM Charity, London WC1N 3XX Tel: 07777 287878 (7-11 Tues & Thurs)
Email: bmonttrust@aol.com; http://members.aol.com/bmonttrust .
04 - Educational charity running a helpline two nights a week & providing info & speakers to those interested in all aspects of Gender Identity.

BLUE MOON
P.O Box 186, Barnsley, South Yorks, S73 0YT Tel: 01226 754 252;
Email: bluemoon@repartee.co.uk; www.repartee.co.uk; Ask for: Bella Jay; .
04 - This mail order business works in association with Roses Club & Roses Repartee. They sell a range of clothes & accessories.

FREDERIKE DE JONGE PHOTOGRAPHY

TEL: +44 7745 853399
deadringers@hotmail.com
www.deadringers.com

ay and Lorraine's

BIRTH
BOAT

Max Factor
Lasting Colour Lipstick
Colour hour after hour
£6.50
Overall rating ★★★★

Rimmel
Lasting Finish Lipstick
Long lasting, vibrant colour and shine
£3.99
Overall rating ★★★★

A Few Lipstick Tips

The proper and most economical way to apply lipstick is with a brush and this should be done after first outlining with a lip pencil.

No one has the perfect lip shape and there are various ways you can make up your lips to give an illusion your natural lip shape. If you have large lips then pencil just inside the natural line to slim them down. If you have asymmetrical lips then usually one side of the top is narrower than the other. In this case evenly balance with lip liner and fill. For thin lips, if the mouth is too small or either upper or lower lip is too thin then use lip liner to draw in the correct shape, just outside the natural line. But be careful not to over compensate and end up looking like a clown.

Foundation and powder can be used to block out the shape of the mouth as much as possible so the correct shape can be pencilled in when applying lipstick. A lip-gloss, applied after the liner and lipstick has always be used to accentuate the lips.

You should try and make sure your lips tone with what you are wearing. There are warm colours then just red. Brown is an unusual choice but can look stunning. Burgundy and plum colours are good in winter and look lovely in summer.

INTERNATIONAL
REPARTEE
TRANSGENDERED AND CROSS-DRESSING LIFESTYLE

44

Lots of Colour Photos and Special Features

in this issue:

- TV Holiday Week
- Beard-cover tested
- Chicks In The Sticks
- Police Diversity Training
- In The Media

Being an Angel!

Boat
PARTY

features

- Reader's Letters
- Reader's True Stories
- The Joy Of Femininity
- News • What's On
- UK Guidelines
- Girlie Gossip
- Contact Ads
- Girl Talk

Autumn 2003   £10

ISSN 0967-7682
44>
9 770967 768022

A Rose's Publication

BLUES VIDS
Tel: 07940 742442 Website: www.BluesVids.co.uk. . . .
04 - London based dealer of TV/TS videos. Buy Direct
or Mail Order service. £10 each video (16 Euros).

BODY4REAL.COM
P O Box 27250, London, N11 3YR.
Tel: 0870 7443361/fax 08704601741;
Email: info@Body4Real.com; www.Body4real.com . . . .
04 - Sale of health / beauty products and wide range of
hair removal and treatment products.

BRITISH ASSOCIATION FOR COUNSELLING
BACP HOUSE, 35-37, Albert Street, Ruby,
Warwickshire, CV21 2SG. Tel: 0870 443 5252 fax 0870
433 5161; Email: bacp@bacp.co.uk; www.bacp.co.uk. . .
. 04 - This association will be able to set you on the
path to properly qualified counsellors They will send
you the list of local counsellors if you send an s.a.e.

BUTTON, BOOT & SPATTERDASH
Freepost, Robinson Grove, Hibaldston, Nr Brigg,
Humberside DN20 9BR. Tel: 01652 650651
Email: button@weddings.co.uk;
Website: www.weddings.co.uk/button . . .
04 - A fabulous colour catalogue will introduce their
wide range of corsets made to original patterns. This
company is a great find. Highly recommended.

C & S CORSETS
Nationwide - C&S Constructions, P O Box 2459,
Westbury, Wiltshire, BA13 3WA.Tel: 07020 953508;
Email: tightlacers@madasafish.com Website:
www.candscorsets.com; . . . . 04 - Information Pack.
Call for a price list with a measurement chart.

CATHERINE ROBERTSON
P.O. Box 86, Falkirk, Scotland, FK1 5YG. Tel/Fax 0131
476 4638; Website: www.catherinerobertson.co.uk
Email: sales@catherinerobertson.co.uk. . . .
04 - Manufacture of 'Masquerade' & 'Serenity' padded
girdles. A specially designed & hand finished foundation
garment. These padded curve forming panty girdles give
hips and a bum to be proud of. Mail order only.

CROSS TALK
The Northern Concord, PO Box 258, Manchester M60
1LN Email: jennyB@northernconcord.org.uk; Website:
www.northernconcord.org.uk Ask for: Jenny Baker . . . .
04 - Highly readable magazine with media watch,
articles, news and views from Jenny Baker at Northern
Concord. Mail order by subscription only.

DACAPO JEWELLERY
Tel: 01634 221131 Mobile: 07961 047846; Email:
dacapojewel@aol.com; www.pinkcottage.co.uk or
www.dacapojewellery Ask for: Theresa; . . . .
04 - Transsexual jewellery, beautifully feminine, made to
fit any size finger, neck wrist & ankle. Phone for a
colour brochure.

DELECTUS BOOKS
Mail Order & Internet 27 Old Gloucester Street,
London, WC1N 3XX Tel: 0208 963 0979 Fax: 0208
963 0502; Email: mgdelectus@aol.com; Website:
www.delectusbooks.co.uk. . . . 04 - Purveyors and
publishers of quality erotic literature including many
transvestite titles including 'The Petticoat Dominant',
'Frederique' and many more.

DIRECTWIGS.COM
P.O.Box 1006, Swindon, SN3 6BE. Tel: 01793 632152;
Email: orders@directwigs.com; www.directwigs.com . .
04 - Ladies & men's wig's-toupees-pieces. Mail order.

DIVINE
Divine, King Street, Earls Barton, Northants, NN6 0LQ
Tel: 01604 812550 Fax: 01604 812511; Email:
sales@loveisdivine.co.uk; www.loveisdivine.co.uk. . . .
04 - Fantasy footwear & clothing. Footwear from sizes
3 up to 13. Thongs to dresses in hand picked glowing
leather & PVC. Catalogue 40 page full colour £5 inc
p&p. Video catalogue full range of erotic fantasy
footwear & clothing £5 inc p&p.

ELOISE
Mail Order Website: www.eloise.co.uk 04 - Breast
forms and bras etc sizes AA to 40 and A to 42 in some
cases then up to DD

EVANS (MAIL ORDER)
Nationwide mail order ; Website: www.evans.ltd.uk . . .
04 - The Evans chain - Mail Order Service. Everything
for big girls from top to toe in sizes 16 to 32 including
all the accessories, larger size tights, underwear and
shoes for all occasions up to size 11 in wider fittings.
The catalogue is generally better than uninspiring shops
because it uses beautiful fuller figured models who
show you what can be achieved. You can always drop
into a shop to feel the quality then order by post.

FACE FACTS (MAIL ORDER)
Jews House, 1 Steep Hill, Lincoln, LN2 1LS Tel: 01522
544727 fax 01522 538714; Email:
facefacts@theinternetpages.co.uk; Website: www.face-
facts.co.uk Ask for: Beryl Holland . . . . 04 - With 25
years experience & the finest selection of wigs plus a
full range of beard cover foundation, by mail order this
could be a good place for girly boys to get image
advice.

FANTASY FASHIONS - TVFASHIONS (MAIL ORDER)
PO Box 36, Chesterfield, S40 3YY Tel: 01246 551196;
Email: rose-marie@fantasyfashions.co.uk; Web site:
www.fantasyfashions.co.uk Ask for: Rose-Marie; . . . .
03 - Maids outfits, schoolgirl uniforms, party dresses,
ball gowns and petticoats. Any costume made to order.
Quality clothes at affordable prices. Credit cards
welcome. Please send SAE for free information

FANTASY FICTION MAGAZINES
Fantasy Fiction & Fashions (Dept. TG), PO Box 36,
Chesterfield S40 3YY Tel: Tel/Fax 01246 551196;
Email: info@tvfiction.com; Website: www.tvfiction.com
Ask for: Kate Lesley; . . . . 03 - TV/TS fiction books and
magazines, including Tales of crossdressing, Tales of the
Maid, and Tales of Sissy School. Stories including 'fem-
dom' tales involving enforced feminisation, maid
training, sex-change and she-males. Some stories now
available for download as eBooks. Please send SAE for
free information pack. Credit cards welcome. Available
in some adult shops and newsagents.

FANTASY FUZION
Unit 12, Gosforth Industrial Estate, Christon Road, Newcastle-upon-Tyne, NE3 1XD Tel: 0191 2130955; Email: tyneway@tyneway.co.uk; Website: www.phaze-clothing.com. . . . 04 - Sexy clothing manufactured by Phaze includes corsets. Mail order service . See their brochure or website.

GALOP
PO Box 32810, London N1 3ZD Tel: Shoutline: 020 7704 2040; Email: galop@onetel.net.uk; Website: www.galop.org.uk. . . . 04 - A voluntary sector, anti-violence & police monitoring charity for lesbian, gay, bisexual & transgendered people. They run a helpline - Shoutline, they also lobby, influence policy, liaise with statutory agencies, do outreach to other groups and provide training for the police, local authorities and community organisations. Minicom 020 7704 3111, Admin Line 020 7704 6767, Fax 020 7704 6707

GAY TO Z
41 Cooks Road, London SE17 3NG Website: www.gaytoz.com . . . . 04 - Comprehensive guide to gay bars in the UK. Available on the web or write for a printed directory with payment of £3.

GENDER ASTROLOGY BY SANDRA
Nationwide West Midlands Tel: 01384 898728; Ask for: Sandra; . . . . 04 - Experienced astrologess TV. Sandra offers suggestions plus reflections to help you understand your deeper self. Detailed hand written analysis available on request or telephone consultation.

GENDER TRUST NEWS (GEMS)
Community Base. 113 Queens Road, Brighton, East Sussex BN1 3XG Tel: 07000 790347 or 0120273 234024; Email: info@gendertrust.org.uk; Website: www.gendertrust.org.uk Ask for: Rosemary Turner or Meg Heyworth; . . . . 04 - The magazine of the gender trust - the first stop for anyone considering themselves transsexual is to receive a copy of this publication. News, views, experiences, network contacts. Available by subscription only.

THE GENDER TRUST, BM CHARITY
London WC1N 3XX Tel: 07000 287878 Helpline (Tue & Thu 7-11pm)Email:info@gendertrust.org.uk Website: www.gendertrust.org.uk . . . . 04 - UK registered charity offering information & support for transsexual, friends, partners, family. Also information for professionals dealing with gender related issues in the workplace. Membership organisation with magazine.

GENDYS NETWORK
BM Gendys, London, WC1N 3XX Tel: 01773 828973; Email: gendys@cwcom.net; Website: http://gender.org.uk/gendys/index.htm. . . . 04 - A network for all who encountered gender identity problems personally or as loved ones & associates, transsexuals, transgendered & gender dysphoric people of either sex, & for those who provide care, both professional & lay. Produce a quarterly journal. Also check out "About Gender" pages on their website.

HONOUR (MAIL ORDER)
Honour, Unit 3, 158 Coles Green Road, London NW2 7HW Tel: 020 8450 6877; Website: www.honour.co.uk

04 - A very friendly company with a range including PVC clothes in sizes right up to 20 plus an extensive range from other designers in leather & rubber. A terrific selection of sexy footwear is also available in a good range of sizes. Many items including books & videos. Catalogue only £5

HOUSE OF DRAG (AGENCY)
P.O Box 70 Enfield EN1 1DA Tel: 079766434302; Email: steffan@houseofdrag.com; Website: www.houseofdrag.tv Ask for: Steffan; . . . . 04 - Steffan Whitfield entertainer and co host of The WayOut Club lwebsite is an agency for Drag Performers MCs and DJs as well as photographic and catwalk models. To present yourself to the world on this site there is a small fee. But if Steffan likes your pictures and feels that you might get work he will put it up at no charge but will take an increased percentage of any work obtained. HOD artistes are featured in WayOut Publications, showcases at The WayOut Club and at worldwide House of Drag parties.

KARN PUBLICATIONS GARSTON
63 Salisbury Road, Garston, Liverpool, L19 0PH Tel: 0151 427 6640; Email: PBFarrer@aol.com; Website:www.members.tripod.com/~PBFarrer/KARN/ KARN.html Ask for: Peter Farrer . . . . 04 - Fascinating books. Using clips from historical documents & magazines, Peter highlights cross-dressing between 1920- 1950. . New titles keep coming. Mail order.

KAYS COSMETICS

Kays Cosmetics, PO Box 50, Mirfield, WF14 9XJ Fax Order Line: 01924 503322 Email: sales@kayscosmetics.co.uk; Website: www.kayscosmetics.co.uk . . . . 04 - Suppliers of Dermablend at sensible prices.

L & G SMITH LINGERIE

P. O. Box 94, Romford, Essex, RM1 4PG Tel/Fax: 01708 760781; Email: lgs@box94.fsnet.co.uk Website: www.box94.fsnet.co.uk Ask for: George or Linda; . . . . 04 - This company makes ladies lingerie in 100% nylon simplex, in 8 colours. All items are made to order, write for a free catalogue & a sample of nylon simplex.

LADYBWEAR

Cheshire Tel: 0161 975 5380 fax 0161 975 5399; Email: lady@ladybwear.com; Website: www.ladybwear.com Ask for: Glen; . . . . 04 - A unique UK based store designing, making & selling its own label of sexy clothing, footwear & lingerie in female & male cut, in sizes UK6 upto UK36 & with free delivery worldwide.

LAURA'S CORSETS & GIRDLES

Mail order Merseyside Tel: 01704 551296; . . . . 04 - Laura keeps a stock of all kinds of underwear; new & part-worn. She has corsetry from the 1940's & occasionally earlier. She also has videos on the subject Send 4 x 1st Class stamps for master list.

LEATHERWORKS (LONDON) LTD

77/79 Southgate Road, London, N1 3JS Tel: 020 7359 9778 fax 020 7226 6745; Email: office@leatherworks.co.uk Website: www.leatherworks.co.uk Ask for Andrew . . . . 04 - Supplies beautiful leather boots & shoes by mail order. Send £10 for a colourful brochure. Feminine fetish clothing in leather & rubber is also sold.

MAGNUS (MAIL ORDER)

2 High Street, Harpole, Northampton, NN7 4DH. Tel: 01604 831 271/ 831751. . . . 04 - Specialises in large sized shoes inc. flats to high heels in everyday & smart evening styles in large sizes & width fittings plus large size tights & stockings. Mail order service. Ladies sizes go up to a size 11. are available. A shop at above address & in other locations - help to trannies varies shop to shop. (Ask for a catalogue and if styles interest you ring your local branch & ask of their latest policy) NOTE open every 1st Saturday morning each month from 9.30 - 12.30

MARTINE ROSE'S FAMOUS BOOBS

Blue Moon, P.O.Box 186, Barnsley S73 0YT Tel: 01226 754252 . . . . 04 - These bra fillers are special heavy duty balloons with a paste filler, to give just the right weight, feel & bounce! At just the right price!

MELANIES TV ZONE

Email: mel@melanies-tv-zone.com; Website: www.melanies-tv-zone.com Ask for: Melanie . . . . 04 - UK operated website featuring resources, articles, tips, features, free live chat, contact ads, erotic & glamour pics run by T Girl Melanie.

MERMAIDS

BM Mermaids, London WC1N 3XX Tel: 07020 935066; Email: mermaids@freeuk.com; Website: www.mermaids.freeuk.com . . . . 04 - Support group specifically for children & teenagers up to age 19 with gender identity issues (&/or their families, friends, professionals).

MIDNIGHT FASHIONS

Unit M, Kingsway Ind Estate, Luton, Beds LU1 1LP Tel: 01582 391 854; Email: sales@midnightfashions.co.uk; Website: www.midnightfashions.co.uk . .04 - Leather, PVC, Gothic, Lingerie, Bondage, Adult Toys.

MORGANA CLOTHING

Wakefield Tel: 01924 291069; Website: www.morganaclothing.co.uk. . . . 04 - Made to measure clothing upto size 30. Goth clothing and great footwear.

ONE OF THE GIRLS - PORTRAITS

Nationwide Tel: 01792 815670 (office hours); Email: studio@1ofthegirls.com; Website: www.1ofthegirls.com . . . . 04 - Professional Photographer - Tranny friendly business. One of the Girls Portrait Photography.

OTTO BOCK UK LTD

32 Parsonage Road, Englefield Green, Egham, Surrey TW20 0LD Tel: 01784 744900 Website: www.ottobock.co.uk Email: bockuk@uk.ottobock.de . . 04 - Manufacturer of products. They make Prosthesis.

PHOENIX LACE

Website: www.PhoenixLace.co.uk . . . . 04 - Introducing a brand new website catering for cross-dressers needs

PILLOW TALK (MAIL ORDER)

Unit 11, Laker Road, Rochester Airport Ind. Estate, Rochester Kent ME1 3QX Email: sales@pillowtalksexshops.co.uk Website: www.pillowtalksexshops.co.uk Tel: 01643 864295; . . . . 04 - Mail order company & 12 shops supplying erotic fantasy wear, uniforms, stockings, shoes, basques, dresses, videos and specialist magazines. TV's welcome.

PRESS FOR CHANGE

BM Network, London, WC1N 3XX Email: letters@pfc.org.uk; Website: www.pfc.org.uk Ask for: Alex Whinnom . . . . 04 - Is the UK campaign for equality and respect for all trans people. Founded in 1992, is a political lobbying & educational organisation which seeks to achieve equal civil rights and liberties through legislation and social change. Staffed entirely by volunteers and welcome new members. Newsletter available on request.

ROSALIND WOODS (MAIL ORDER)

Dept TL3, P.O. Box 20 Congleton, Cheshire, CW12 1UP Tel: 01260 226 399 fax 01260 226 575; Website: www.boutique.co.uk Ask for: Rosalind . . . . 04 - They design and make their own dresses & underwear for sale through their own mail order service. They also operate their own 'made to measure' service for male clients. Huge selection of knickers in exciting fabrics and colours. The Catalogue is £5 (refundable).

ROSE'S CLUB

P.O Box 186 Barnsley, South Yorks, S73 0YT Tel: 01226 754 252; Email: roses@repartee.tv; Website: www.repartee.tv Ask for: Bella Jay . . . . 04 - Roses club was founded by Martine Rose who publishes 'Repartee', one of the best magazines for cross-dressers in the world, Bella Jay also works full time on all the Roses's activities & is your first point of contact. This is a major international support group which is very involved in the growth of understanding & acceptance of cross-dressing & the transgender community. Roses works closely with others like The Beaumont Society & The Gender Trust. The club has nationwide organisers in various parts of the country. In most cases these are TVs and their partners who can give advice & support & a pick up point for mail. The Clubs newsletter, Rose's Xtra, is available on subscription with Repartee.

ROTHWELL & TOWLER HOLIDAY INSURANCE

66 High Street, Honiton Devon EX14 1RT Tel: 01395 516555 / fx: 01395 516556; Email: enquiries@rothwellandtowler.co.uk; Website: www.travelfirst.co.uk Ask for: Martin Rothwell . . . . 04 - The first name in travel insurance. Specialists in UK and Worldwide travel They offer a full range of single-trip and annual multi-trip policies for anything from 1 day to a year away.

SEDUCTIVELINGERIE.CO.UK

Tel: 01702333116 Website: www.seductivelingerie.co.uk, ... 04 - On Line store for seductive lingerie. Has Plus sizes available.

SKINGENESIS

Tel: 0845 0700939 Website: www.skingenesis.com . . . . 04 - A non-invasive, non-surgical skin rejuvenation group of clinics. Hair removal treatments that don't involve lasers. Many tranny clients. Spme other treatments include Acne Solutions, Scar removal, Thread Veins treatments, Remove lines and wrinkles and naturally boost collagen/

SOUL MATES

c/o 'Roses' Sheffield . . . . 04 - In association with 'Roses' Real Ladies offering understanding support for female partners struggling with transvestism. 01736 850533 Helen (Avon) 01454 412088 Michelle (Dorset) 01202 519051 Jane (Nottingham) 0115 9456598. Strictly no trannies to ring these numbers please.

SSSH

PO Box 122, West Haddon, Northampton, NN6 7DS . . . . 04 - World recognised society for the fascination for fully fashioned Nylon Stockings with stiletto heel shoes, associated corsetry and foundation wear. Members receive a free newsletter, detailing events, availability of hosiery, videos & journals. Highly recommended.

SULIS

Westfield Industrial Estate, Midsomer Norton, Bath BA3 4BH Tel: 01761 410107; Website: www.sulis.co.uk 04 - Mail Order - Top quality Silk Lingerie, nightwear, Underwear & blouses.

SWINGTIME COLLECTION

14 Oval Waye, Ferring, Worthing, West Sussex, BN12 5RA Tel: 01903 243 392; Ask for: Phil or Zoe; . . . . 04 - Dreamlike '50s style fashions. Satin & lace circle skirts & dresses. Feminine lacy blouses. Enormous selection of bouffant petticoats & crinolines. Lace trimmed panties (20 colours). If this is you send in an A4 size S.A.E. marked TG for free mail order catalogue. Personal callers are also welcome (by appointment only).

THE BOUDOIR SHOP.COM

PO BOX 1422, Ilford, Essex IG2 3HF Tel: 020 8365 7075; Email: info@theboudoirshop.com; Website: www.theboudoirshop.com . . . . 04 - A high quality mail order company for the transgendered. We sell Make-up, corsetry, body shaping garments, tuitional videos,

MAC make-up
ALL RACES ALL GENDERS ALL AGES

OUTSIDE LONDON

BIRMINGHAM
Caxtongate, Cannon St B@
021 631 2062

HARVEY NICOLS BIRMINGHAM
31-32 Warfside St, The Mall, B1
0121 616 6000

HARVEY NICOLS LEEDS
Victoria Qtr, 107-111 Briggate LS1
0113 246 9703

HOUSE OF FRASER, BLUEWATER
Greenhithe, Dartford, Kent, DA9
01322 374000

BRIGHTON
6 Dukes Lane, BN1
01273 720026

CARDIFF, THE CAPITOL CENTRE
Queen St, CF10
029 2064 0690

FRASERS, GLASGOW
45 Buchanan St, G1
0141 221 3880 x2014

KENDALS, MANCHESTER
Deansgate, M60
0161 832 3414

SELFRIDGES, TAFFORD CENTRE
1 The Dome, Trafford Park
0161 629 1133

DEBENHAMS, BELFAST
Castle Court Shopping Centre
028 9043 9777
For 'London' see
London UK section

www.maccosmetics.com

CD Roms and much more. New products being launched regularly. Part of The Boudoir Dressing Service success. This services comes highly recommended by many.

THE BOW BELLE SORORITY
BBS, PO Box 11, Swanmore, Hants SO32 2ZU Email: Ddan282739@aol.com; .... 04 - The Bow Belle Sorority is a nationwide organisation for all those who love to dress in party frocks and ball gowns. The Sorority organises occasional little girl parties and other pretty-pretty events. This does NOT involve any form of CP.

THE EONIST DIGEST
P.O.Box 11, Swanmore, Hants, SO32 2ZU Email: Ddan282739@aol.com; .... 04 - Mail order magazine for TV's. Send 6 x 1st class stamps for sample copy. Produce 'hour glass' for corset lovers and 'bow belles' for lovers of party frocks and ball gowns.

THE FORUM SOCIETY
PO Box No 418, Cardiff, CF24 4XU Tel: Info Line 0906 613 3314; ... 04 - Association of about 50 swinging groups with hundreds of members. Activities include postal friendship, exchanging literary fantasies. They also have a monthly newsletter.

THE GENDER TRUST
PO Box 3192, Brighton, BN1 3WR Tel: 07000 790347; Email: info@gendertrust.org.uk; Website: www.gendertrust.org.uk. ... 04 - UK charity supporting transsexual people, partners and families. Membership organisation, quarterly magazine, booklets, leaflets, Info for employers and professionals on gender related issues.

THE HOURGLASS 2004 SOCIETY
HG2000, PO Box 11, Swanmore, Hants SO32 2ZU Email: Ddan282739@aol.com; .... 04 - The Hourlgass Society is dedicated to those who love corsetry and all associated aspects. A quarterly magazine, the HourGlass Wire, is part of annual membership.

THE SAMARITANS
See Local Phone Directory For Nearest Branch, Head Office - 46 Marshall St W1V Tel: 08457 909090; Email: jo@samaritans.org.uk; ... 04 - An organisation that supports any one who is suicidal or is going through a time of crisis. We offer a confidential non -judgemental service that is available 24 hours a day. If you should feel the need to contact us to discuss via email or use our national help line. Our mailbox is read every day of the year by a group of trained volunteers - all using the pseudonym "Jo". Callers are offered absolute confidentiality and do not lose the right to make their own decisions (including the decision to end their own lives). Your messages (and our replies) will be kept for 30 days at most.You may ask for earlier deletion of a message.

THE SEX KITTEN SHOP
Mail order Tel: 07906 046843; Email: info@sksfantasia.com; Website: www.thesexkittenshop.com. ... 04 - Large internet mail order service, specialise in clothing, boots and shoes in a wide range of styles in sizes 3 - 13 & products for TV's, TS's, & cross dressers as well as bondage, S&M & toys. Family run business offering a very discreet service.

THE TRANNY GUIDE ON VIDEO
WayOut, P.O.Box 70, Enfield, EN12AE Tel: 07778 157290; Email: vickylee@wayout-publishing.com; Website: www.wayout-publishing.com Ask for: Vicky Lee; .... 04 - This 80 min video was made by 'Image Right Television'. It takes you to dressing services, shopping trips, clubbing, group discussions & then in the studio presenter Laura asks Vicky Lee all the questions that trannies & their partners or friends want to ask. Available by mail order at £20.95 + VAT inclusive of delivery. Also available at £19.95 from Vicky

TOUCHABLE
Box 100, Eastwood, Notts, NG16 5FW Tel: 01773 711999 Fax: 01773 711999; Email: sales@touchable.co.uk; Website: www.touchable.co.uk 04 - Designing & retailing since 1994. The on-line & paper catalogue shows Basques, 1950's style made to measure, designer light reflective fabrics. Fine fully-fashioned stockings & extensive hosiery ranges. £3 for catalogue redeemable on purchase.

TRANSFICTION.CO.UK
Website: www.transfiction.co.uk. . . . 04 - A commercial site selling tranny fiction.

TRANSFORMATION - MAIL ORDER
Worldwide Tel: 0161 772 3111 Fax: 0161 773 6358; Email: orders@transformation.co.uk; Website: www.transformation.co.uk . . . . 04 - This is a mail order service. Catalogues in English, German, French, Spanish & Japanese plus Customer service girls who speak all these languages fluently. Free quarterly catalogues.Discreet packaging.

TRANSLIFE
Tel/Fax: 0207 348 0864 Website: www.translife.co.uk Email: sales@translife.co.uk. . . . 04 - Website with all you need to create your perfect look. Wigs, make-up, breast forms, shoes, boots, corsets, lingerie, hosiery, evening & day wear and foundation garments.

TRANSWIGS
P O Box 2361, Bournemouth, BH1 1XU. Tel: 01202 747177 fax 01202 747953; Email: transwigs@msn.com; Website: www.transwigs.co.uk Ask for: Lynn . . . . 04 - This girl team run a discreet & exclusive mail order wigs for TV's/TS's. £3.00 for brochure or check out the online catalogue.

TRENDCO MAIL ORDER SERVICE
Sheridan House, 116 Western Road, Hove, Sussex, BN3 1DD Tel: 01273 774977 Fax: 01723 720116; Email: trendco@fstdial.co.uk; Website: www.wigsattrendco.co.uk . . . . 04 - Mon - Sat 9am - 5.30pm. Trendco moved their head office and mail order centre in 97. From their new home they offer a newly expanded range of wigs and hairpieces for those that can't visit their London shop or this visitors centre. Write for a free catalogue you will not be disappointed. (See also London Hair and Beauty).

TRUST COLOURLABS
Room 333, PO Box 1018, Doncaster DN11 8RT Email: info@trust-colourlabs.com; Website: www.trust-colourlabs.com. . . . 04 - Explicit confidential photo processing service. Your photos are handled with care and returned in plain discreet packaging the same day. APS and B&W film welcome.

ULTIMATE SHOES
P.O.Box 572, Norwich, NR1 2SD. Tel: Telephone 01603 661652 Fax: 01603 622116 Email: lisa@ultimate-shoes.com; Website: www.ultimate-shoes.com Ask for: Lisa . . . . 04 - High Fashion Footwear (in sizes 3 - 13), breast forms and accessories, now including an exclusive range on our label, made on a mans last for perfect comfortable fit. Free catalogue.

VOLLERS
6-9 The Approach, Claybank Road, Copnor, Portsmouth, Hampshire PO3 5LL Tel: 02392 660150 /0468 555935 Fax: 02392660958; Email: info@vollers-corsets.com; Website: www.vollers-corsets.com . . . . 04 - Classic corsetry in many styles. Excellent catalogue worth it just for the pictures.

WAYOUT "HOME" VIDEOS
WayOut, P.O.Box 70, Enfield EN1 2AE Tel: 07778 157290; Email: vickylee@wayout-publishing.com; Website: www.wayout-publishing.com Ask for: Vicky Lee; . . . . 04 - The events and the shows at The WayOut Club are often recorded and compiled into the "home" video collection. These tapes are excellent for those who can't visit the club. Each has 1.5 - 3hrs of material. The recordings are on home camcorder by amature operators but they are presented nicely in boxes that build to make a collection. At time of research the collection is up to edition seven and planning a special 10th anniversary edition. Available on PAL system video and now on DVD by mail order only. Write for full details of the contents of all the videos. The price of each tape is £ 17.95 + VAT inclusive of delivery.

WESTWARD BOUND (MAIL ORDER)
2 Tavistock Place, Plymouth, Devon PL4 8AU Tel: 01752 221415 Fax: 01752 221417; Website: www.westwardbound.com Email info@westwardbound.com Ask for: Steve & Sarah; . . . . 04 - Mail order business. Shoes to size 11, lingerie, wigs, plus the whole fetish spectrum. Call for a free catalogue.

WWW.TGCOSMETICS.CO.UK
TGC Trading, Unit 106, 9 St. Johns Street, Colchester, Essex, CO2 2EZ Email: sales@tgcosmetics.co.uk Website: www.tgcosmetics.co.uk . . . . 04 - New web based cosmetic company.

WOMEN OF THE BEAUMONT SOCIETY (WOBS)
BM WOBS, 27 Old Gloucester Street, London, W1N 3XX Tel: Co-ordinator/Eastern 01223 44124; Email: wobsuk@aol.com; Ask for: Diana Aitchison . . . . 04 - Support & advice for significant others of transgendered people. Is sisters to the Beaumont Society. London/ Southern 01892 783443 Midlands and West 01684 578281 Scotland 01389 380389

XDRESS.COM (UK)
9B Meadow Works, Court Street, Trowbridge, Wilts, BA14 8BR Tel: 01225-769486 Fax: 01225-774452; Email: services@bdyaware.demon.co.uk; Website: www.xdress.com . . . . 04 - A mail order service offering high quality, own label, lingerie & fantasy outfits designed, proportioned & made especially to fit the male physique.

UK CENTRAL

A D 2
74 Lower Parliament Street, Nottingham, ND1 1EH Tel: 0115 9502727 Fax: 0115 9117887; Ask for: Graham Cullen; . . . . 04 - Friendly club playing mostly commercial music. Open every night till 12, DJ from 9.30. Drag every Sunday, occasionally a theme night.

A Personal **Report**

My name is Charlotte Belle. I am founder and co-ordinator of Trans-Action (UK) and organise and run the Nottingham Group. I am 38 years old. I am a pre op TS. I have been transitioning since November 2000. For many years, since the age of fifteen, I lived in the knowledge I was different and was a closet TV for a long time. My ex wife found out about my feminine side as I confessed to her my inner feelings. She even picked my name and helped with make up and dress, style etc. From January through September 2000 I became more convinced I wasn't a TV but something else . By September I realised I was in-fact TS and began the very traumatic and painful steps toward transition. In November I transitioned leaving my family, house and former life behind. The rest of my life, as they say, is history.

Jackie Daniels is the manager of Trans-Action (UK) Net Group. Jackie is a TV and is 36 years old. She lives in Oxfordshire but still manages to make most Nottingham Group meetings. We met via the MSN Chat rooms and we have become really good friends since. Jackie is well known on the scene and yet has only been going out since October 2002.

TRANS-ACTION HISTORY

Trans-Action (UK) started out as a group of friends who got together as a means of social and mutual support. Living in North Nottinghamshire at the time, there was no other nearby venue to go. We were out and about trannies in any case. We often ventured out to Les Femmes in Sheffield and went into Nottingham to The Central pub. The group was created as Trans-Action back in **October 2001**. Three of us formed a social group to encourage others through a community to gather together trannies near by and in the East Midlands to get together and help them to get out. At the time Sutton-In-Ashfield was a haven for trannies. We often went round for coffees and on a Sunday would take it in turns to cook a meal and have friends around for Sunday dinner. Dressed or not.Trans-Action had no real direction and no basis to drive it forward. It was a social group with about a dozen or so members and no agenda was set up and no regular, formal meetings ever took place. One prominent member sold her house and "tranny" van and bought a boat before sailing off around the world.

By **March 2002**, I had moved house and Trans-Action had fallen by the way-side. A new group, "The Black lacy nightie Party " had formed and replaced the Trans-Action group. As a group we met up once a month or so and went to a venue. Les Femmes was a favourite. We would often take the new girls into the Motor-way cafes for breakfast after a late night out in Sheffield. Other venues we visited were Manchester, Birmingham and of course Nottingham.

Also in March 2002 a tragic event happened which shook the tranny community with which I was a part of. A TS friend committed suicide and it completely changed my view of life and my own transition. 13 months on I vowed that it should never happen again.

There was wrangling within the various aspects of being transgendered TVs TS's etc. In September 2002 North-Notts Trans-Action was formed. A group where TGs could come and socialise and have mutual support but this time with regular meetings and an agenda.

An MSN Group was set up using the MSN internet messaging services and an On-Line group was created along with the growing real group which grew in size from an average of 5 or 6 girls in Sept 2002, to 7 or 8 girls per meeting by March 2003. The Net Group grew for an initial membership of 56 in September 2002 to over 100 my March 2003.

Continued page 213

WHAT IS TRANS-ACTION (UK)?

Trans-Action explores all issues relevant to the transgender community, providing an ever growing range of helpful information. The objective is to foster a greater understanding of all aspects of transgenderism...transvestism, cross-dressing and transsexuality.

Trans-Action a self-help social and support group for TV,CD, TS and all others who identify themselves as transgendered.

We promote transgender awareness and positive image to the public at large.

Trans-Action holds monthly meetings in Nottingham.

1st Wednesday of the month - Coffee evenings 7pm till late.

3rd Thursday of the month - "Better out than in!" Pub nights at a venue in Nottingham 7.30pm till late.

We are always looking to hear from members interested in hosting other regional meetings - Glasgow and Bristol being recent developments in this area.

We do all we can to identify the people and businesses that seek to exploit the fear and stigma that often exists within the transgender community.

We help and support members who wish to build confidence through social activities outside the confines of group meetings. (Shopping trips, visits to pubs and bars, cinemas etc.)

We publish a quarterly newsletter, available for free at our meetings and in downloadable pdf format via the website. It can also be ordered through the post by subscription.

Trans-Action has around 250 members and is expanding rapidly. The website contains many photo galleries with 100's of pictures of members. There is also an archive of hundreds message posts - indicative of how actively involved with the group the members are.

Trans-Action seeks to keep members informed of issues affecting TG's, to help them understand their situation and assert their rights. This includes topical news, political comment and changes in the law relating to transgendered people.

We offer help and social support at practical levels. From beauty advice, skin care, electrolysis to reporting homophobic or transphobic incidents.

People can join Trans-Action via the internet, at our monthly meetings, through referral from LGBT helplines, or by responding to contact information to be found in articles, publications and NHS GIC (Gender Identity Clinic) welcome-packs. As well as an active message-board, the net group also offers a chat facility.

We are fortunate to be able to call on several professional consultants to provide topical advice at our monthly meetings. The type of themes you may find featured include:

Assertiveness counselling.Transgender issues within the family.

Corrective make up techniques,

The selection of wigs and beauty products.

Nails - polishing, painting and nail art.

Advice on temporary and permanent hair removal.

Police LGBT liason advice relating to transphobic crime.

Speak like a woman! - the role of speech therapy.

Join Trans-Action by visiting the website at:

http://www.groups.msn.com/Trans-ActionUK

If you need to contact one of the organisers to discuss transgender issues, please email or phone Charlotte: mobile: 07800 926427
email: charlottebelle65@hotmail.com
phone Jenna: mobile: 07816 348069
email: jenna@electrabeauty.com

A Personal Report

ALTERED IMAGES
Ask for: Tia Tel: **0773 4007672** Website:
www.alteredimages.4t.com Email: alteredimages@go4.it
or alteredimages@tarts.fsworld.co.uk. . . . . 04 - Hair,
Wigs, Makeup and beauty. Postbox and changing
facilities. Escorted shopping trips.

ADVANCED SKIN CLINIC
Pontefract, West Yorkshire Tel: 01977 699944 Email:
advancedskinltd@aol.com .... 04 - Specialise in IPL
Laser hair removal, IPL N-Lite acne treatment,
Electrolysis, Crystal clear dermabrasion, botox,
Jevederm face fillers, Chemical tattoo removal, semi
permanent make-up.

BAR ZEUS
6 Lower Warrengate, Wakefield Tel: 01924 201705; . . .
04 - Friendly & welcoming bar/club.

BUTTERFLIES SUPPORT GROUP
PO Box 417, Leeds LS1 5PN. Tel: 0845 3316106
Mobile: 07932 905120. Email: butterflies@mesmac.co.uk
04 - A support group for Transsexuals, their partners
and family. Information service. Meetings are held on
the1st Monday of the month at the Yorkshire Mesmac
building (see below) from 8.00pm till 11,00pm Props:
Heather Beaumont and Val Deville

CAMELEON (WATFORD)
Cameleon Centre, 34 The Avenue, Watford WD1 3NS
Tel: 01923 242565; . . . . 04 - Laser hair removal from a
company that advertises to trannies. Open 6 days.

CAMPANILE HOTEL & RESTAURANT
40 Penn Road (opposite Pink Punters), Fenny Stratford,
Bletchley, Milton Keynes MK2 2AU Tel: 01908 649819
Fax: 01908 649818 Email: mk@envergure.co.uk . . . .
04 - 80 comfortable double or twin rooms, remote
control TV' with satellite, bar & restaurant, buffet
English breakfast.

CHAMELEON GROUP
Wollaton Grange Community Centre, Tremayne Road,
Bilborough, Nottingham Tel: 0115 9283610 . . . . 04 -
Phone Thursdays from 8pm to 11pm only. This support
group holds a meeting every Thursday from 8pm to
11pm at Wollaton Grange Community Centre.
Changing facilities are available.

CINDERELLA & ROCKAFELLA'S
Blackheath, West Midlands Tel: 0121 559 3003 Ask for:
John 04 - A progressive salon for hair and beauty.
Treatments include waxing, wig preparation plus a fully
kitted out professional digital photo studio and photolab.

CRISTIANOS LASER CLINIC (ALTRINCHAM)
Bank Chambers, 2 The Downs, Altrincham, Cheshire
WA14 2PU Tel: 0800 085 0661 Email:
info@cristianos.co.uk Website: www.cristianos.co.uk/tg
Ask for: Chris Hart . . . . 04 - by appointment via her
Altrincham address Chris Hart can now offer the same
service and price as her Manchester and Leeds clinics
and in her Earls Court clinic which shares the same
building as Dr Russel Reed.

DESIRE
619 Attercliffe Road, Sheffield, Yorkshire, S9 3RD Tel:
0114 2442626; Ask for: Kevin or Linda . . . . 04 - Shoes

& boots to size 12. Wigs, lingerie, corsets, waist
clinchers, plus leather & PVC clothes. Also a range of
adult baby wear. A range of fetish & TV mags & videos
is also on offer. The shop is open Mon - Fri 9.30am-
8pm Sat 9.30-6pm, Sundays 11am-4pm with an eight
hundred square Foot. showroom.

DIVAS DRESSING SERVICE
Yorkshire Area Tel: 07769 624517 Website:
www.divas.uk.com Email: bev@divas.uk.com . . . .
04 - A new discreet, exciting and fun dressing service.
You will be pampered in style and made to feel
glamourous, feminine and sexy.

DRESS WITH STYLE
Tel: 01827 830670 before 8pm Website:
www.dresswithstyle.co.uk Email:
caroline@dresswithstyle.co.uk . . . . 04 - Dress maker
that makes made-to-measure clothing.

FOR YOUR EYES ONLY
Midlands Tel: 0121 328 2878 . . . . 04 -
"Accommodation Address" service. For safe delivery
& receipt of mail (private, personal, business, etc).
Affordable prices. Phone anytime from 12 midday to
10pm for details.

HAY WAY SHOES
Unit 1, Abbey Court, Corporation Road, Leicester
LE4 5DW Tel: 0116 2663444 fax: 0116 2668729;
Email: hayway@hayway.demon.co.uk; Website:
www.hayway.demon.co.uk . . . . 04 - Manufacturer
offering exclusive footwear from sandals to thigh
boots, sizes 3-14 , up to 5" heels. Make for TV, Fetish
& Glam. Highly recommended. Est 25 Years. Phone
for free catalogue.

HORIZONS COUNSELLING
Worcestershire Tel: 01299 271957 Mob: 07803
533154; Email: kyates@uk.packardbel.org; Ask for:
Kay Yates BA(Hon) PG Dip(Couns) BACP . . . .
04 - In partnership with West Midlands Gender
Councelling and hypnotherapy for people with gender
dysphoria.

JESSICA GREEN BEAUTICIAN
West Midlands Tel: 0121 451 1018; . . . . 04 - Jessica is
a beautician who offers her electrolysis skills to TSs &
TVs. She is qualified with M.B.A.E & B.A.B.T.A.C,
using Diathermy & Blend techniques. Jessica can also
help you with wigs, make-up, ear piercing & waxing.
20 years experience.

KAREN BACK
Oxfordshire Area, The Barn, Warmington, Banbury,
Oxon OX17 1BU Tel: 0771 201 8469 . . . . 04 -
Premier wig collection available from an independent
specialist. Confidential home visits within Oxfordshire.
Send £2.50 for full colour brochure.

KAREN PARKER PHOTOGRAPHY
Milton Keynes Tel: 01908 566 366; Email:
karen@karenparker.co.uk Website:
www.karenparker.co.uk Ask for: Karen. . . .
04 - Award winning photographer specialising in
commercial & alternative portraits. Make-up is not
offered but digital enhancement allows wrinkles to be
faded or removed, eyes/smiles brightened - the only

Continued from page 210

As **2003** shaped up so did Trans-Action. The net group grew to over 150 members and the turn out of the monthly group meetings increased to an average of 8 or 9 per month.

In March I travelled to Glasgow to run a meeting for the Scottish girls of Trans-Action.

The Net Group also accepted US and Euro members as well as UK girls nation wide making it a world wide group.

Trans-Action(UK) was re-launched in Sept 2003 after a 2 month cooling off period and celebrated its first anniversary at the new location of my current house in Nottingham. A new logo and an On-Line membership of well over 180 was achieved. The monthly group meetings now swelled to 9 or 10 per meeting and a new Bristol group was in the making.

As of November 2003, the Net group boasts over 217 members. The Nottingham Group has 9 or 10 girls per meeting on the 1st Wednesday of the month, whilst the Bristol Group meets on the 2nd Wednesday of the month with an average of 7 girls per meeting.

Trans-Action (UK) has had a great deal of support from the girls who are involved with the group both on-line and at meetings. It is their group and it would not have happened with out them. Nottingham GAI project have been supportive too as well as the Nottingham Gay and Lesbian switchboard who both have details of the group on their data base.

The group has come along way in two years. The group exists because the girls feel they have somewhere to go to to be themselves. A haven of acceptance. Our motto says it all, "Better out, than in!"

I have come along way in two years too. It helps me to see others happy. My life is so much richer knowing so many friends and people in similar and differing circumstances have benefited from Trans-Action(UK). It has not been easy and it has taken a lot of my time and resources but it has been worthwhile. For each success there are two or three failures. But that is life and I will continue to help and give my time to helping those who need Trans-Action(UK).

www.groups.msn.com/Trans-ActionUK

If you are transgendered - whether you are CD, TV or TS we would welcome you to join in and get out there with us.

A Personal Report

The 'portal' to everything tranny on the Internet

UK ■ Central

limit is the imagination! Private dressing rooms, complimentary tea/coffee plus caring personal service. Call for free advice about how you can achieve a look that until now you've only dreamt of......

LASER IMAGE
Sheffield Tel: 0114 272 9337; Ask for: Caroline .... 04 - Laser hair removal, tattoo removal. Recommended by tranny clients.

LION BAR
Birchills Street, Walsall Tel: 0192 261 0977 .... 04 - Junction 10 of M6. Tranny friendly pub.

MEDDISSA SHOES
115 Queen Street, Morley, Leeds, LS27 8HE. Tel: 0113 253 0369; .... 04 - This shop offers a large range of shoes - sizes upto 12.5 ladies and AA fittings as well.

NEWS FOR NOWHERE
96 Bold Street, Liverpool, L1 4HY Tel: 0151 708 7270 . 04 - Radical & community bookshop committed to social change. Stockist of transgender, lesbian & gay books & magazines.

PAPILLION - ISOBEL MARTIN
Berkshire/Buckinghamshire/Oxfordshire Mobile: 07958 464032 Fax 0118 945 3947 .... 04 -. Isabel is a highly qualified and experienced beautician, masseuse, electrolygist and body piercer. There is also a dressing service, make-over and make-up lessons. Isabel is also a counsellor for male and female sexual problems. Overnight accommodation can be arranged.

PINK PUNTERS CLUB
2 Watling Street, Fenny Stratford, Milton Keynes, North Bucks Tel: 01908 377446; Web site: www.pinkpunters.com. . . . 04 - Gay club which is very tranny friendly. Last Mon of each month they have a Totally Tranny night. The Club runs 7 days a week, good for a quiet drink earlier in the week then karaoke on Thurs thru the club nites on Fri & Sat. Discreet location & own taxi service.

REFLECTIONS GROUP
at Victoria Centre, Park Road, Wellingborough Tel: 07779 490173 Email: verina.tv@ntlworld.com .... 04 - Held on 2nd Thursday of month

RICHARD'S WIGS
Unit 82, Row D, Kirkgate Market, Leeds, LS2 7HP. Tel: 0113 246 8304; Ask for: Collette; .... 04 - Collete is waiting to help you find your style with wigs for £3 to £750 Only one person in the shop at a time. Appointments can be made. Mail order available. Shoes and boots to size 13. Open everyday except Sunday, 9am to 5pm (wed 9am to 2pm).

SHOPHOLLYWOOD
7&8 Willow Gate, Stoke Lyne Road, Stratton Audley, Bicester, Oxon OX27 9AU Tel: 01869 277211 Fax: 01869 278036; Website: www.shophollywood.co.uk Email: sales@shophollywood.co.uk; .... 04 - Fabulous range of elegant and sexy lingerie, clubwear and dancewear including Shirley of Hollywood. Beautiful colour catalogue available.

THE MAKE-OVER ROOM
16-18 Newington, Unit 4, 1st Floor, Liverpool, L1 4ED (off Bold St/Renshaw St) Contact: Gordon, Tel: 0151 706 0765 Mobile: 07949 353 470 Email: gfawce@colourstyling.freeserve.co.uk .... 04 - Offers make-up, hair and wig advice, along with a colour and image consultancy service. Centrally located, under the Egg Café.

TOTALLY TRANNY
Milton Keynes Tel: -07931 419323 Email: jaybee_ohno@yahoo.co.uk Ask for: Johannah .... 04 - Group that meets at the Pink Punters club on the last Monday of the month.

TRANS-NIGHT
at Downtown 46 Upper Kirkgate, Wakefield Tel: 01924 299662 .... 04 - Held on 1st Friday of month from 9pm - 2am.

TRANS-SHROPSHIRE
Room 10, Leegomery Community Centre, Leegomery, Telford TF1 8EX Tel: 01952 240099 .... 04 - Serving the Trans community, family and friends with support group and support phone line, a buddying scheme, a clothes rail and once a month police surgery to get confidential advice on issues trannys may be facing in the community. Resource Library. Looking for volunteers.

TRANS-YORKS
17-21 Chapel Street, Bradford, BD1 5DT. Website: www.trans-yorks.org.uk .... 04 - An informative resource website including events listings..

TRENDS (SHEFFIELD)
337 Glossop Road, Sheffield, S10 2HP Tel: 0114 2768676 .... 04 - Wigs & Hairpieces. Appointments advisable. A private fitting room is now available.

BIRMINGHAM

AMRIT VARMA'S 'TEMPTATIONS'
Wilton Market, Unit 51-56, Ground Floor, High Street, Erdington, Birmingham, B23 6RJ Tel: 0121 373 2624; . . . .04 - Help with underwear - look no further help is at hand bra, corsets, swimwear, partywear for any size & I mean any - specialist in bras bigger sizes.

ANGELS CAFÉ BAR
- 0121 622 4880, 127 Hurst Street, Birmingham B5 6SE. Has a large glass frontage. It's a licensed café bar, in a continental style! Coffee and pastries are lovely. The staff are friendly, and are genuinely interested in you.

ARCADIAN CENTRE
Very handy for nearby secure parking. Kudos Video Dance Bar - 0121 666 6806, 28 Horsefair, Birmingham B1 1DD. A fantastic place that'll make you glad you walked up the small hill. Huge video screens, chirpy attitude free staff, great atmosphere and music with links to London clubs such as Trade and Heaven. Missing - 0121 622 4256, 48 Bromsgrove St Birmingham B5 6NU. Has kept Brummies singing for ages. Karaoke nights range from strangled cat to the next Kylie

214   The 'portal' to everything tranny on the Internet **www.wayout-publishing.com**

BIRMINGHAM BIZZARE BAZARRE
Birmingham Tel: 0121 602 1316 Email: info@brumbazaar.co.uk Website: www.brumbazaar.co.uk,. . . . 04 - Fetish Market every 3rd Sunday,11-5pm. £4.00 Entrance. Very friendly, good facilities & changing. Always and After Bazarre Party/Event.

CINDY'S TV SERVICE (BIRMINGHAM)
Birmingham Tel: 0121 454 8257; . . . . 04 - This mature lady can help you achieve your desires. Everything can be supplied to take you from man to woman in luxurious discreet surroundings. Full wardrobe including fetish, make- up, wigs. Optional maid and sub training.

COMPULSION AT SUBWAY CITY
Subway City, 'CompLivery Street/Water street, Birmingham (under the railway arches) www.clubcompulsion.bravepages.com/Events.htm 04 - A full night of hedonistic experience! Staffed by people in the scene, we welcome Trannies BDSM, Goths, Fetish, Rubber etc. Dress code strictly enforced .

DV8
0121 666 6366, 16 Kent Street, Birmingham B5 6RD. One of Birmingham's newest gay venues, with a huge dance floor. Attracts a large and diverse crowd who get into a frenzy, as the bass rattles your bra fillers out. I've found that the crowd are always interested in 'how you did your make-up'.

THE GREEN ROOM CAFÉ BAR
0121 605 4343, Unit A28, Arcadian Centre, 70 Hurst Street, Birmingham B5 4TD. A friendly mixed pink/straight Café bar

ENIGMA BAR
0121 622 4710, Hurst Street, Birmingham B5 4BD. A Modern stylish basement bar a few doors down from the Hippodrome theatre. They put on singers and strippers various nights of the week.

ST MICHAEL'S TV/TS SUPPORT GROUP
Birmingham Tel: 0121 559 3181 Help; . . . . 04 - This group has been in operation for over 11 years and caters for people in the Midlands who welcomes members from anywhere. This non-commercial group holds drop-in meetings every Tuesday, Wednesday and Thursday from 7pm to 10pm. With Saturday socials with buffet and bar 6pm to late. Ring helpline between 7pm and 10pm Tues, Wednesdays and, Thursdays.

SUBWAY CITY
0121 233 0310, Livery Street, Birmingham B3 1HL. MEMBERS ONLY: Membership is £2.50 and can be obtained by Harry (0121 236 1522). Large gay night club. Four bars, two discos, restaurant. Situated underneath railway arches under Snow Hill you get a distinct industrial feel. Bass is so loud here you may want to wear body armour. It can get VERY hot too I suggest that you take one of those fans that the Victorians were so fond of.

THE NIGHTINGALE CLUB
0121 622 1718, Essex House, Kent Street, Birmingham B5 6RD. One of the longest running gay night clubs. It's just massive. Also a fantastic 'BIZZARE BAZAAR' (SM/fetish fair) during the daytime every 3rd Sunday of month that has loads of stalls with tranny stuff.

TRANSFORMATION (BIRMINGHAM)
62/64 Oxhill Road, Handsworth Wood, Birmingham Tel: 0870 741 6655; Email: orders@transformation.co.uk; Website: www.transformation.co.uk . . . . 04 - Open: 9am-8pm Mon-Sat. This well known UK chain which offers a broad range of goods and services to cross-dressers.

MANCHESTER

ANYTHING THEATRICAL
84 - 86 Olham Street, Manchester, M4 1LF. Tel: 0161 236 5266; Website: www.anythingtheatrical.co.uk Email: anytheatrical@aol.com Ask for: Dave Morrell; . 04 - Danskin Dance tights, make-up and fancy dress for those special theme parties. Wig's, eye-lash's, etc.

BLUES CLUB
211- 215 Stamford Street, Ashton-Under-Lyne, Lancashire Tel: 0161 330 3212; Email: blues@club6913.freeserve.co.uk; . . . . 04 - This long established welcoming venue (21 yrs with current owner). Blues bar is open 7 days a week till 2am weekends except Sundays til 12.30.

BODYWISE
12 Market Street Ashton-Under-Lyme, Nr Manchester Tel: 0161 339 3886; . . . . 04 - The friendly folk at Bodywise offer beauty treatments to cross-dressers including waxing, electrolysis and make-up lessons.

To get to the Bullring is simplicity itself just follow the signs as you drive into Birmingham to one of the numerous car parks.

Mine and Kitty's favourite is the one off Small Brook Queensway as it's directly below the centre. A Lift takes you up to the main shopping area.

There are three floors to choose from. The largest shop here is the one that may have caught your attention if you'd seen it in the press is **SELFRIDGES** it looks space age from the outside as the curvaceous 'rump' is covered with 15,000 aluminium discs. It's even better once you walk in.

There are loads of smaller concessions such as **AGENT PROVOCATEUR** scattered around the levels. You can buy anything from a greetings card to a diamond-studded mobile phone!

I have to say that if shoes are your thing, then you won't be disappointed by the choice here. **OFFICE SHOES** (www.officeholdings.co.uk) have a very spacious shop, and their staff (especially Rob) were only too willing to help me find a new pair of heels. One piece of good news is that the shoes I tried on all seemed quite generous in their sizing across the toes; also I couldn't help noticing, that a few styles are now being offered in a size9. Office have many varied styles, colours and heel heights, and you'll be glad to find something other than plain black courts to wear.

The other major shoe shop here is **SCHUH** (www.schuhstore.co.uk) and they have very cool fashionable boots, shoes and trainers- some going up to a size 9. The staff here are cool, and I have bought both online, and in the shop in blokey mode. Some people look at you, but think of your ultimate goal. Worth it? I think so.

Oh no! You've forgot your nail polish! Quickly head off and find **BOOTS** (www.boots.com) and look at their latest offerings. Friendly staff are on hand to help you out. I particularly liked the new range of chrome effect polish – so space age! The staff are all very sympathetic to 'tranny needs' so you can get good advice if you can't find the 'Immac' any longer (It's called Veet now by the way).

After a long day shopping, you'll want a break. 'Costas' make fantastic coffees (and even better chocolates – what diet?) Kick off your heels and just chill out for a while. The waitresses are great, and can recommend any pastries to compliment your drink. The mugs are generous – I was pleased to have enough room for cream on top of my chocolate. Mmmmm!

The Bullring is a stones throw from Hurst Street, and it's pink clubs and bars. I dropped into 'Route 2' but I only had a Coke and ice, as I was driving home shortly afterwards.

Come and visit I know you will be impressed.

Photos with thanks to The Bullring shopping centre Birmingham and photographer Juli Edwards.
Stacey Christie's full Personal Profile is in the
11th Edition of The Tranny Guide.
see more colour pictures from this report on page 52 & 54

SHOPPING IN
BIRMINGHAM
NO BULL !

WELL IT'S HERE !!!!

After years of planning, re-development and considerable traffic problems we have our new shopping complex THE BULLRING! So, just how good is it ? 'Bloomin fantastic!

Nearly all the major shopping brands have set themselves up here. Just how the place has changed ! The area has been returned to the pedestrians, and the newly renovated St Martins church sandstone has been cleaned and stands between the two halves of the complex.

I approached the management for permission to take photographs for this article – and was pleasantly surprised to find total co-operation from both the shops located there and the Bullring owners.

I'd been there a few times since it had opened, so I knew where I was going, but be warned –IT'S BIG!!! There are interactive touch screens so you can see where you are, and how to get to where you want to be. You could of course look at the web site(www.bullring.co.uk)

I hope that many of you will come and have a look at our new Birmingham masterpiece. I know that you'll be pleasantly surprised by what you find. All the staff and security made me feel very welcome and safe.

If you are discreet. i.e. as long as you don't go dressed in 6" stilettos and sparkly dress, you'll fit right in. Remember Staceys Number one rule though – NEVER park on any open 'waste' space, you'll be clamped! Hope to see you soon.

Thanks to a very kind and lovely lady photographer Juli Edwards for her time and to Adam who carried all our coats and bags throughout our 'expedition'.

staceychristie@blueyonder.co.uk

A Personal **Report**

What is your name and what is your background?

Hiya I'm Kaya, a tranny from Manchester, UK, Iwork, in a semi skilled manufacturing plant, with a typical bunch of rowdy lads. I am currently single (but always looking!). I love all the usual big boys toys, cars, bikes, computers etc., but I also love being a bit of a showman, or showgirl, singing, dancing etc..

Are you happy to be called a tranny and what does this name mean to you?

I don't mind the word tranny, I prefer T-girl but I can't stand the word transvestite, it just sounds perverted and creepy to me, and we all know that's not the case. To me the word tranny is someone who enjoys being more elegant, femme clothes or not. I have always liked glamour, clothes and uniforms that are a bit special and its nice to look glamourous isn't it?

How old are you and how young can you remember thinking about or actually cross-dressing?

Currently just coming over the big thirty hill! The first time in a skirt was just for a laugh but that was in my early youth.

Where do you buy clothes?

I'll buy clothes anywhere really, usually shopping around with a girlfriend. Sure sometimes it feels awkward, but I'm sure that passes in time. "For my girlfriend" is a line I use a lot. There are also a lot of good mail order places but I don't use them much as I wanna see what I'm going to buy.

What leads you to choose the styles you wear?

That's a hard one. Anything really. I pretty much know what I like and if it will suit her, but I'd say I'm trying to stay a young looking as possible. Singer's etc, they give me lots of ideas definitely. Britney spears, Kylie etc. I like their style, young, fresh, fun and sex.

Do you have one look or many images?

I suppose in a way I have many images, I'm pretty new to this so I want to try out different styles but not the extreme slutty stuff. I've done the usual, schoolgirl thing and I'd love to go out as a playboy bunny girl. I've always thought they looked stunning. I go out looking the best I can as a normal trendy girl. PS. I'm blonde now and more convincing. (I hope)!

Is make-up and hair important to you and if so how do you achieve your look?

Make-up is so important, and so is hair, it transforms my psyche as well as my face visually. I used to go through catalogues, FHM and other magazines and try and match my features to the glamour girls and copy the make-up. It's an on going thing really. You can never stop learning to do make-up better. I don't just plonk the hair on. I style it, make it come alive! I am very lucky as a very close friend is in the drag scene, so I learnt lots from him, but I can't do all that he's shown me yet!

To what degree do you practice hair removal, and other body feminisation?

That's an easy one, Danskin dance tights. I only shave the bits that will show, chest, face etc. I also use Immac cream on my face as I get awful razor burn which lasts for ages, but with Immac I have clear skin. - It works ok for me on my skin but I don't advise you to try it without caution.

Who knows that you dress?

That's another easy one, Everyone really. I just got fed up of being secret, scared and all, it was bringing me down. There was me thinking I was the only tranny in the world - boy how wrong was I ! I mentioned how I felt to a mate of mine (after a few beers), he was totally cool about it, and since then it's kinda gotten around to everyone. The support has been fantastic. "Is that all!" or "cool!" is often said.

How often do you dress and if you go out where to?

I don't really dress to just to sit at home but I do to try a new style or do make-up practice. I go out with friends, but I'm not the type to sit in a bar on my own all dressed up. So I (that is Kaya) doesn't really get out too much, but when she does she makes up for it! Manchester's gay village is a great place for (fellow) trannie's to go, I never seem to get trouble, apart from the admirers trying their luck. Which I kinda like, it's the stamp of approval and I like that feeling.

218

How much of a sexual turn on is trannying for you?

It feels fabulous to feel sexy, but hard to get turned on when your "tucked" innit?

What is your definition of feminine?

Feminine to me means being more open, more caring and daring, to look as good as you can - make-up or not. It is to see the best in people. Too many guys bottle stuff up and have this macho bullshit thing going on. That's not good! If we all had to spend a year 'enfemme' by law. Maybe then we'd have more respect for each other!

To what degree do you feel gender dysphoric (i.e. that your brain is feminine)?

To me I don't feel anything at all like that, I'm a guy but ok sure I'm a bit femme as well. I'm just being me. I personally feel I have achieved a good balance as a person with this extra bit, but I'm not gonna hurt my head thinking about it too much.

To what degree would you consider permanent hair removal, hormones, surgery?

I would love to have my face and chest done permanently, I hate shaving and besides it would save me a fortune in creams and blades

What one piece of advice would you give to someone that has just found they are not the only tranny in the world?

You know yourself and you owe it to yourself (and others) to be honest. You can't hide away from something that's already there. Accept it and understand it. It's what you are, now do something positive and embrace it. People are generally more supportive than you might think – they're probably doing it as well! Don't leave it too late, go for it when you're young and can get away with less make-up.

Blooms
New York
Napoleons
Showbar
(Northern
Concord)
Rembrandt
New Union
Metz

MANCHESTER

Deena Gomersall

The village in Manchester has long been established as a leading UK gay scene. As so often happens, the Transgender community has latched on making the village their home too - enjoying it's freedom, friendliness and vibrant club and pub life. Although society as a whole is now, slowly, becoming more acceptant towards Trans people, the area around the village is still second to none in regards to it's tolerance and pleasantness towards those of us wanting to express our feminine side to the max. Every club and bar in the village is manned by it's own door security who will give you a warm greeting, open doors for you and wish you to 'have a good evening, ladies'. Inside you will find you are treated as any 'ordinary' customer, without stare or ridicule, either by staff or customers. That is something which is most refreshing, putting you at ease and allowing you to really enjoy your night out.

CANAL STREET

Runs the entire length of the gay village along, would you believe it, the Manchester canal. This is possibly the liveliest area in the whole of central Manchester and is said to include some of the best bars in Europe. It is certainly bright, glitzy and very busy. The street 'heaves' on hot summer days. Canal Street was the original home of Manumission and Manto and was made famous by being the setting of the television series 'Queer as folk'. Other than the ones featured in this guide, Canal Street also offers:

QUEER 4 Canal street 0161 2281360. High ceilings and a wooden floor are the main features of this mixed clientele bar.
BAR 38 10 Canal Street 0161 2366005. A friendly fun type bar that offers good music and unisex toilets so there can be no argument as to what a tranny should use.
GLOBE! 34 Canal Street 0161 2379117. This bar is hidden out of sight, opposite the Rembrandt hotel. The small entrance gives way to a fantastic basement bar.
MANTO 46 Canal Street 0161 2362667

BLOOM STREET

If you asked a gay what the best street in the village was, they would almost undoubtedly say Canal Street, ask a TV the same question and chances are they would say Bloom Street. This is because on Bloom Street is The Hollywood Showbar where the Trans Community first began stepping out; the Northern Concord being based there which provided a meeting place for transvestites along with changing facilities for those with the nerve to venture further afield. Also on Bloom Street is Napoleons, reputed to be the largest TV venue in Europe and certainly very popular with the Trans Crowd. Stretching from Aytoun Street to across Princess Street where the Manhattan showbar sits on the corner; like Canal Street, Bloom Street acts as a border area to the Manchester Gay Village. It does not boast as many venues as Canal Street but, as well as the above, there is to be found: Paddy's Goose, Berlins and New York New York as well as a string of take-away food places. Bloom Street is still a very busy and popular street in the village, particularly during Mardi Gras time. Trans people will visit the village any evening of the week but it is Wednesday and Saturday evenings that are established as being 'Tranny nights' when our girls come from all around the North and beyond to sample and enjoy the village' hospitality. It is then that you will find such streets as Bloom Street and Canal Street littered with Trans folk making their way to the multitude of venues on offer. But the village isn't just about it's bars, you will find a number of good restaurants in which to dine before commencing your evening, fast food outlets after your night is over and there are some top class and fairly priced hotels where you can stay to avoid travelling back home after your night out. If you are a tranny and you haven't yet tried the village why are you waiting?

PADDYS GOOSE 29 Bloom Street, Manchester M1 3JE Tel: 0161 2361246. Paddy's Goose is an old fashioned traditional style pub with a nice Irish flavour. The pub is more for the older generation but sees a regular influx of trannies on Wednesday's and Saturday's. With plenty of modern pubs and bars beating out strong music and flashing lights, Paddy's provides a nice alternative. One large main room with a television, cheap bar prices, ladies loos at the far corner which has mirrors! and two stalls. Paddy's is a friendly pub where someone will always come over and chat to you, if only to tell you how nice you look. There is parking opposite the pub along the barrier to the old coach station but beware because over zealous traffic wardens give out tickets like confetti... even if you are not illegally parked.

THE INTERNATIONAL HOTEL 34 London Road, M1 3PF (near

the Supertram Station) Tel: 0161 2361010. The preferred place to sleep over in Manchester now is the Hollywood International. Twin rooms cost between £40 and £45 though basic single rooms are available from as little as £15.00

REMBRANDT HOTEL 33 Sackville Street. M1 6HS Tel : 0161

236 1311. Once owned by the documented Transsexual Julia Grant, the Rembrandt is a comfortable pub and hotel that boasts to be the only truly gay run venue in the village, offering good food and inexpensive accommodation. The venue was highly popular during the time of Julia's reign in the village but sadly, since she sold up, the hotel is no longer as friendly as it once was and not as popular a place for over- night accommodation. Prices £45 en suit inc. breakfast. Reputedly the middle bar still welcomes Trans visitors (the lower bar is used by bears) but very few still visit... hence no internal photos at this time.

THE HOLLYWOOD 100 Bloom Street, Manchester M1 6HZ.

Tel: 0161 236 6151. Another establishment once owned by Julia Grant, the Showbar once had a Gay Only door policy but now is quite a mixed bag clientele. The downstairs bar has a stage where DJ's play their stuff to the packed dance floor, cabaret acts and top stars regularly perform here. The upstairs (Piano Bar) is much more relaxed with plenty of soft seating, two bars and a resident pianist who plays and sings all the popular songs or accompanies those who wish to get up on stage and try out their vocal chords for themselves.

MCTUCKY'S Chorlton Street. Good variety of Chicken and chips meals, plus Pizzas, Cheese Burgers, Fish burgers and Vege Burgers. Jacket Potato, Corn on the Cob & Apple Pie.

Tea, Coffee, Cappuccino, Hot chocolate or cold canned drinks.

SAFAD Restaurant & Take-Away. 47-49 Bloom Street. Tel 0161 237 3339. Middle East Cuisine. Pizza's from £2.80. Variety of Kebabs small / large Fatayer. Burgers from £1.80. Mezze

Napoleans

Yorkshire

Upstairs

Speed Queen

A Personal **Report**

A Personal **Report**

VILLAGE FAST FOOD Nice, inexpensive take away serving Kebabs and burgers, chips, pizzas plus extras.
KRUNCHY CHICKEN Chicken Burgers, Vege burgers, Spicy Chicken wings and boxed meals.
MAXWELLS CHIPPY Bloom Street, between Paddy's & napoleon's. Maxwell's has changed hands a number of times over the last few years and is no longer the 'traditional' British Fish & chip shop but it still remains as popular as ever. A tasty favourite (of mine) is chilli and chips which can be bought in large or small trays or the less expensive Curry and chips. Also available is an assortment of burgers, Giant sausage, peas and fried chicken, plus, of course, fish & chips. The staff are very good and ensure that you are served quickly and conveniently.
VIA FOSSA 28 – 30 Canal Street Tel: 0161 236 6523 www.viafossamanchester.co.uk. One of the village's busiest bars, this large establishment features a fantastic Gothic design and has a ground level bar, upper drinking area reachable by stairs and a balcony running along the left hand side of the pub and a basement bar. There is regular entertainment and most weekends features Karaoke Not highly popular with the Trans crowd because it gets so packed on an evening though the venue did host the main dinners for the 2003 Transfusion Birthday party that was held throughout the village. One downside to Via Fossa, if you are needing to relieve yourself in a hurry, is the toilets are not easily accessible and there is normally large queues.
SPICE 29 31 Sackville Street, Manchester. Tel: 0161 237 5555. One of the really great things about the village in Manchester is that there are so many places in which to buy a meal. Most of the more popular bars such as Velvet, Taurus, Spirit, slug and lettuce, Eden and the Gaia have terrific menus of tasty food or there is the large variety of fast food take-away outlets to choose from. Isn't it nice though to have a meal in a proper restaurant away from noisy drinkers? Spice, just down the road from Bloom Street on Sackville Street is a really nice, clean restaurant that has an open Menu, all meals laid out in large pans where you just help yourself, filling your plate to your hearts content. If you still feel empty… go and get some more… change the meal that you had; it's entirely up to you, and all for a very reasonable price. The upstairs dining area in the Spice Restaurant, help yourself to rice, vegetables, poppadums and a tasty variety of spicy dishes.
TRIBECA & B.E.D. 50 Sackville Street Tel: 0161 236 8300.

Tribeca is described as a 'deliciously lazy' bar serving a large variety of drinks: Cocktails, Spirits, Shooters, wine, Sangria and pitchers to share with your tranny friends. Bar open till 2.00am. Below stairs is the Bed weekend club open 10.00pm till 2.00am with Hip Hop, Funk and Soul on a Friday and 'Breathe' Soulful dance music on Saturday. Dining available in both bars. Slightly away from the 'main' bars of the village, Tribeca is well worth a visit.

NEW YORK NEW YORK 94 Bloom Street, Manchester Tel:

0161 236 6556. This is probably one of the most famous Gay club's in the country having been around long before Gay's came out of the closet and started being accepted by society. The bar is very lively and the resident DJ keeps the younger clientele on the small dance floor in front of the bar. The venue is very T* friendly even though it does not see too many Trannies visiting, in spite of being given free entry from the usual bar charge. On one occasion when a large number of trannies were visiting en-masse the doormen joked 'You're not leaving again'. A lower area by the toilets features a few items of New York trivia such as authentic traffic lights and phone booth.
THE THOMPSONS ARMS 23 Sackville Street, (around

corner from the coach station) Tel: 0161 228 3012. This is the topmost venue in the Gay Village and right around the corner from the new coach station. Thompson's is tremendously popular with the younger crowd and they arrive in droves to this friendly and spacious venue with a one room lower bar and an upper bar often made 'girls only' (no sorry, that means genetic). There is a friendly atmosphere here but you do tend to get buffeted about a bit as large groups of partying youngsters arrive or leave; a bit tough on those four inch heels you are trying to stand up in. Toilets are up the stairs, there is a fair sized dance floor on the far left as you enter. Give it a try.
EDEN Amazon house, Canal Street, Manchester. Tel:

0161 2379852. This venue is slightly different in that it is on the opposite side of the canal to all the other venues on Canal Street. The Eden's bar is now open until 2.00am Monday to Saturday. A fun place full of friendly people. A great feature of the Eden, for those hot Summer nights is a moored barge that is docked on the Canal and used as an extra seating area
VELVET 2 Canal Street, Manchester Tel 0161 2369003

www.purpleturtle.com Mon to Thurs 12 noon till 11.00pm Fri / Sat 12 noon till 1.00am Sun 12 noon till 10.30pm. Because this bar is at the 'far' end of Canal Street and the Village, not too many Trannies have ventured up there but, recently, more and more girls have been exploring some of the remoter bars and Velvet has come out as a favourite. Upon entering, the friendly doorman will greet you with a 'Good evening Ladies', you walk down the steps and over an inbuilt fish tank to be greeted all over again by the friendly bar staff. A standard range of drinks is available at the bar. Food here is excellent and the mixed bag of people that frequent the venue are always friendly and ready to talk, parties of young girls often prompt our girls to put their drinks down and dance with them or to get in amongst the photographs. There is two stalls in the ladies loos which is on the Canal street end of the room (opposite the bar) A good starting point for an evening in the village.

NEW UNION 111 Princess Street, Manchester M1 Tel: 0161 2281492. Manchester's original 'traditional style' gay pub, not elaborately furnished but keeps busy and provides additional accommodation. The prices for accommodation are between £30 - £45 at weekends.

TAURUS 1 Canal Street, Manchester Tel: 0161 2364503 www.taurus_bar.co.uk. Mon to Thurs 12pm till 11pm, Fri/Sat 12pm till 1.00am Featured in 'Metro Life' revealing that Taurus is one of Manchester's food and drink scene success stories. The venue which has a ground and lower floor, is very friendly and relaxed. There is a private dining room, cocktails served from 4pm till 7pm daily. Food wise there is a varied and excellent menu to be had for those girls arriving in the village early and wanting some sustenance before going on around the pubs and the clubs. The bar staff are always friendly and helpful and the customers always ready to have a chat with our girls. Try it. The loos are down the stairs.

SPIRIT Canal Street, Manchester Tel 0161 237 9725. A  modern four level pub that has a large dining area, three bars that are constantly busy and an open balcony on the 2nd level, with steel seating that offers the best possible view of the rest of the village. Trans girls are always made welcome by both the staff and the other users. www.spiritmanchester.com.

NAPOLEANS 35 Bloom Street, Manchester M1 3LY Tel:  0161 236 8800. Whereby all the other venues featured in this guide are gay or gay/straight mix that are Trans friendly or tolerant, Napoleons is known as the Trans bar in the village where you would expect to find TV's and TS's. In fact, Naps is reputedly the largest TV/Cd venue in Europe. Many 'established' Trans-people visiting the village now often avoid 'ending up' in Napoleons as they try to separate themselves from the main crowd and, instead, try to situate themselves in the many other bars. But Napoleons still remains a very popular place for the Trans community, including those on their first time out. One problem now with Napoleon's is that it has become a Trans pick-up joint for all the tranny fanciers, who thinks, a guy in a dress, does so because they are wanting to be picked up.

ROCKINGHAM is on Harter Street at the bottom of Waterloo Street that turns off Princess Street. Inside the main bar are marble pillars with bronze lamps in the shape of Torches. The venue is smart and decorative. Toilets are at the far end to the bar.

CHURCHILLS 37 Chorlton Street, Manchester. M1 Tel:  0161 236 5529 Churchill's had a major face-lift in 2001 changing it from a rather dingy bar to the modern establishment that it is now. Highly popular amongst those that frequent the village regularly, there is regular entertainment on the stage, which on a Wednesday evening is conducted by Drag hostess / singer Dana Brookes and her pianist or there is disco playing music to cater for all tastes. For those of us requiring more secluded, comfortable settings the upstairs landing provides just that, accessible up an ornate metal railed stairwell. As with all other venues in the gay village, Trans people are welcomed with a smile by the pubs staff though Churchill's does attract large parties of 'straights' who may give the odd curious look your way.

GAIA 46 Sackville Street, The Village Tel: 0161 228  1002 Being slightly away from the more popular venues in the village, Gaia's often overlooked by the Trans crowd and even the majority of the gay community. This does have it's benefits as this means that there s often a little more space to relax in for a while. There is a spacious dining area on the main floor, along the front windows so that you can watch the village in full swing as you eat. There is also a lower bar area with large dance floor at Gaia, known as the Jinx lounge. Here 'dirty and decadent' music is mixed by the resident DJ. Regular drinks promotions are served in the lounge on Saturday evenings. gala.manchester@virgin.net

DSDC

Tel: 0161 202 3831 Fax: 0161 202 5246 Website: www.dsdc.co.uk Email: info@dsdc.co.uk .... 04 -A company that specialises in graphic design, advertising & photography.

FRILLYS

230 Market Street, Droylsden, Manchester M43 7AX Tel: 0161 371 5174 Mobile 0797 1328 827; Website: www.frillys.co.uk; Ask for: Julie; .... 04 - Full dressing service from French Maid to the blushing Bride. Stock range of clothes including PVC in all sizes, wigs, shoes, dresses, underwear, corsetry. Alterations and made-to-measure service. Make-up tuition with Julie. Help with voice pitch control. Accommodation available and an Escort service available.

FFW TV AND FETISH SHOWROOM

Unit 82, Cariocca Business Centre, 2 Hellidon Close, Ardwick Manchester M12 4AH http://fleshfetishwear.mysite.freeserve.com Email: fleshfetishwear@hotmail.com Tel: 0161 273 5446 Mobile: 07790 626 008. .... 04 - TV owned and run business selling a wide range of Rubber, PVC, AB and Sissy wear, uniforms and TV media. Open Sat 10-4pm or weekdays and evenings by appointment. changing facilities available. Emma opens showroom any day or eve, Why not come over on a Wed eve before your night out in the Village?

HOLLYWOOD SHOWBAR

Phoenix Shopping Centre, Bloom Street, Manchester, M1 6DD .... 04 - Cabaret Show Bar in the centre of the Manchester Gay village, hosted by the well known Julia Grant. Also the Northern Concord group meet every Wednesday from 6.30pm until 11.30pm. Doors open after till 2am. This stylish venue has a full licensed bar, hot & cold food, improved changing facilities & stylish décor.

HUDSONS (MANCHESTER)

Lloyds house, 18 Lloyd Street, Manchester, M2 5WA Tel: 0800 4586151 Website: www.hudsonsuk.com Ask for: Sue or Lisa; .... 04 - Hair replacement specialist using the latest wigs, hairpieces, including over 300 fashion styles. Discreet service always by appointment. Send for free brochure.

IMPECUNIOUS HOUSE B&B

Northwick Nr Manchester Tel: 01606 79947; .... 04 - This lovely couple were founding members of the Northern Concord. They will give you a warm welcome at this homely, safe B&B with great food. They will also tell you all about the close by lively Manchester tranny scene.

KELLY

Central Manchester Tel: 0161 236 5938; Website: www.kellypeckoo.co.uk .... 04 - Kelly, who is a TV, & her lady helper have been providing a full dressing service, including dress making, make-up lessons & maid training. Overnight stays. Escort available. Also imported from USA breast forms & hip & bum pads £100-£120.

EDEN BAR & GRILL

Tel: 0161 237 9852; .... 04 - A cosy refuge on the canal side with a light touch on the tape deck. A good spot to start your evening. A very mixed crowd.

NAPOLEON'S

35 Bloom Street, Manchester M1 3LY Tel: 0161 236 8800; ....04 - Open: Monday to Thu 10.00pm til 2.00am. Fri & Sat 8pm - 2am. Wednesday to Saturday upstairs Disco and Bar. Wednesday nights with FREE tata-hash (a delicacy served by Ernie). TV's are welcome and are given free entry every night.

NATURAL IMAGE WIGS (MANCHESTER)

In Debenhams Plc, Market Street, Manchester, M60 1TA Tel: 0161 832 8666; .... 04 - See Hot Hair Croydon, for details.

NEW UNION PUB & HOTEL

111 Princes Street, Manchester Tel: 0161 228 1492; .... 04 - The New Union is a gay pub & hotel which is a popular meeting place for TVs, particularly on Wednesdays & Saturdays from 10pm. The hotel welcomes you to stay or to take a room to use as a base for a night out.

NEW YORK, NEW YORK

98 Bloom Street, Manchester Tel: 0161 236 6556; www.newyork.free.online.co.uk .... 04 - This two level bar is friendly and stylish. Packed at weekends. Regularly have Drag DJ's & is very popular with TV/TS crowd.

NORTHERN CONCORD

P.O. Box 258, Manchester, M60 1LN Meeting every Wednesday at The Hollywood Showbar, Corner of Bloom Street and Prince Street, Manchester. Ask for: Jenny Baker jennyb@northernconcord.org.uk ; .... 04 - Support group that meets at the showbar's first floor 'Piano Bar'. The strength of the Manchester scene owes much to this well run & entirely voluntary group which has been in existence since 1965. Between 50-100 girls, partners & friends attend at 7.30pm - midnight. This is the perfect venue for your first time out, as they make any newcomers feel at ease. Changing facilities are available. Some may go on to a pub or night-club. Special events such as an open night at a local shop are arranged from time to time. The group encourages partners, families and friends to join them. They can arrange for one of its girls to meet individuals and take them to the meeting. The group run weekend long events produce an excellent quarterly magazine, 'Cross Talk' available by membership or subscription. This organisation sets a standard for self help groups around the world.

PADDYS GOOSE

Opposite the bus station on Bloom Street, Manchester 04 - Trannies are still very welcome at this traditional city pub.

REMBRANDT HOTEL

33 Sackville Street, City Centre, Gay Village, Manchester, M1 3LZ Tel: 0161 236 1311 Fax: 0161 236 2457; Email: rembrandthotel@aol.com; Website: www.rembrandtmanchester.com Ask for: Duncan/aka/Sharran; .... 04 - Accommodation in the heart of Manchester's gay village, 2 bars & a Bistro , 20

bedrooms, 14 en-suite, bed & breakfast from £35 standard room, £45 en-suite room . Price includes Full English Breakfast & VAT. Mention The Tranny Guide and you will get a 10% discount when booking a room!

SALON MAIER
52 Bridge Street, Manchester, M3 3BW Tel: 0161 834 0860; . . . . 04 - This friendly shop with 35 years experience helping cross-dressers. Has wigs from stock plus custom wigs and hairpieces, styling to suit your needs.

STAR PHOTOGRAPHY
Tel: 0161 861 8441 Mobile 0790 187 6518; . . . . 04 - We will photograph you professionally, en femme. This is a totally confidential service.

TOTAL FITNESS LASER CLINIC (MANCHESTER)
Wilmslow Way, Handforth, Manchester, Tel: 0161 4402615; Website: www.totalfitness.org . . . . 04 - Laser hair removal for men & women. Advanced Alexandrite laser (F.D.A approved) with integrated dynamic cooling. Phone for a information brochure.

TRANSFORM MEDICAL GROUP
St.Johns Chambers, 2 St.John Street, Manchester, M3 4DT Tel: 0161 839 8687; . . . . 04 - This private medical practice offers a range of cosmetic surgical procedures. Nose reshaping, Adam's Apple reshaping etc, etc. They have a few other branches around the country.

TRANSFORMATION (MANCHESTER)
428 Bury Old Road, Prestwich, Manchester Tel: 0870 741 7766; Email: orders@transformation.co.uk; Web site: www.transformation.co.uk . . . . 04 - Open: 9am - 8pm Mon - Sat. The original shop in this well known, internationally advertised chain offers a full range of goods & services to cross-dressers.

VELVET (MANCHESTER)
2 Canal Street, Manchester. Tel: 0161 236 9003; . . . . 04 - Bar/Restaurant.

VIA FOSSA
28-30 Canal Street, Manchester. Tel: 0161 236 6523; . . . 04 - Bar/Restaurant.

VILLAGE CARS - TAXI
41 Bloom Street, Manchester Tel: 0161 237 3383; . . . . 04 - A licensed taxi service providing a good courteous service to TVs (& others). 4 & 7 seater vehicles are available.

VINTAGE TO FETISH
Afflecks Palace, 52 Church Street, Manchester Tel: 0161 835 4078;Email: v2f@afflecks_palace.co.uk . . . . 04 - Fetish & Antique clothing for the discerning few. PVC, rubber, limited editions, underwear, hats & accessories. They have everything to make you sparkle.

UK NORTH

AFTER EIGHT
46 Earlsdon Street Coventry CV5 6EJ Tel: 024 7667 3939; Contact Mrs York; . . . . 04 - A tranny friendly eveningwear sale and hire shop. With a permanent sale room with gowns from £15 to around £150 as well as full price gowns, accessories, cosmetics, handbags, etc

ANGELA STEVENS
Durham Tel: 07951 634947 or 0191 5842095; Ask for: Angela; . . . . 04 - Durham area in private house, make-overs for TV/TS customers, accommodation available and escorted outings to pubs, clubs, cinemas & shops if required. Goods available include silicone boobs, corsetry, underwear, shoes, uniforms. Dermablend official consultant or mail orders.

BACKSTAGE DANCEWEAR
Grimsby Tel: 01472 361704; Ask for: Jill; . . . . 04 - Designer / Dressmaker providing mail order &

225

Downtown Girls

As the Yorkshire girls get out and about more often, so more and more venues are becoming available for our use and, slowly but surely, the general public are also becoming more aware of us and, to a large extent, are tolerant and friendly towards us. A number of changes have occurred in venues and meeting nights since the report in the 11th edition of The Tranny Guide.

In York, **THE BAY HORSE** has changed hands and is no longer used by the local girls who now meet at **THE YORK ARMS** each third Wednesday and, in addition, **IDOLS** at **TOFFS NIGHTCLUB** on alternate Sundays.

The regular monthly meeting at Wakefield's **DOWNTOWN BAR** is now held on the first Friday of the month rather than the third and this change has proved to be very popular with an ever-growing attendance that includes many girls travelling up from the Midlands.

In Leeds the gay night scene has been further boosted by two new venues: **MISSION**, and **ARCH 54** opening last September. Meanwhile the ever-popular **OLD RED LION** on a Tuesday continues to attract Trans girls, and boys, from far and wide. There is an increasing number of groups of trannies visiting Leeds to sample it's night life as an occasional alternative to Manchester's gay village. In nearby Bradford the **S29** night club has been taken over by '**CLUB LIFE**', unfortunately the number of local girls getting out on a night has dwindled so there isn't as much trans-awareness happening.

1993 sadly saw the closure of **TRANS YORKS**, formerly an internet contact and support group which had achieved much for the local TG community. In it's place has now arisen **YORKSHIRE GIRLS PLUS+** (YG+) which, like Trans-Yorks, has members much further afield than Yorkshire (Hence the 'Plus') and, at the time of writing, it has a

membership of over 150. This new support group welcomes for ALL 'girls'; TS's, TG's, GG's, RG's, TV's, CD's, Wives and Partners, you name it, in fact anyone who presents as female. The group is based in Yorkshire and the northern counties, but those further afield in other counties (and countries) are most welcome to join. YG+ is a help and support group and a means by which our girls can keep in touch with each other. It is a non-sexual help and support group and it is not a sex contact group. YG+ endeavours to keep its members aware of all Trans activities taking place in the region. YG+ website: http://yorkshiregirlsplus.org.uk To Join the group:
http://groups.yahoo.com/group/yorkshiregirlsplus
YorkshireGirlsPlusowner@yahoogroups.com
Pauladawn@wildroseuk.com

BRADFORD

THE SUN INN 124 Sunbridge Road, Tel: (Richard) 01274 737722 Friendly gay pub outside the city centre, formerly used as a monthly meeting place for Trans-Yorks members before it's closure. Drag DJ and regular entertainment. Small groups of T*girls still visit regularly. Pub hours with the opportunity to move onto the close by 'Club Life' nightclub afterwards.

CLUB LIFE 12 – 14 Fulton Street Tel 01274 725899 Open Wednesday to Sundays; Wed & Thurs 10 till 2.00am Fri & Sat 10 till 3.00am. Reasonable sized dance floor and DJ. Admission £3.50 (sometimes reduced for Trannies)

BARNSLEY

CHICAGO ROCK CAFE Island Corner, Wellington Street Tel: (Julie) 01226 733181Fun gay venue with live entertainment from 8.00 till 1.00am Disco plays hits from 1957-1995 The restaurant is open until 1.00am with a discount on party bookings

BLUE MOON SHOPPING SERVICE & ROSES REPARTEE MAGAZINE PO Box 186 Barnsley. Tel: 01226 754252. Run by Bella Jay of Rose's Repartee. Array of wigs, Jewellery, Cosmetics, hosiery and Lingerie available through mail order. Write to above for details or see Ad. in Rose's Repartee Magazine.

BRIGHOUSE

ALTERNATIVE HAIR 19 Park Street Tel: 01484 715365. Good range of wigs and with help and advice from friendly staff. Private fitting done upstairs.

DONCASTER

THE VINE Kelham Street. Tel: (Barry) 01302 364096. Very friendly venue formerly regularly visited by Trans-Yorks members. Two rooms… one for entertainment, the other more a chill-out room. The Vine is now the only gay venue in Doncaster following hate attacks. Admission on the door after 10.00pm Bar till 2.00am

TALKING HEADS 43 Silver Street, DN1 1JL. Tel: 01302 328720 Mob: 07968 319697. Specialists in wigs, hairpieces and hair extensions plus more. Contact Pam Chipisa

HUDDERSFIELD

CHADS 2 Brook Street Tel: 01484 469696. Open 9.00am till 11.00pm Mon-Sat and 10.00am till 10.30pm Sunday. Huddersfield's newest gay pub with Disco, Pool area, Chill-out bar and main bar. Food served from 9 – 5.30pm. Tried and established as a new Saturday, tranny friendly meeting place.

THE GREYHOUND 16 Manchester Road, Huddersfield Tel: 01484 420742. One of Yorkshire's oldest established gay bars, trans friendly with entertainment each weekend and karaoke on a Wednesday.

JENNIFER JUNIPERS (formerly Lily's Bar)Northumberland Street. Tel: 01484 533588. Gay cellar bar venue not far from main train station. Parking is rather restricted. Drag Queen hostess and occasional Drag show entertainment. Beer garden for those warm summer nights. Bar till 2.00am

HULL

ASYLUM @ The Shakers Club (Formerly Enigma) Holderness Road. A periodical 'Anything goes' night only recommended for the broad minded. Fetish dressing, Nudists, Bondage, Fem-Dom and anything else. The Trans contingent are considered as the least outrageous and best dressed people there. Details and tickets are available from Urbanite Clothing 24 Anlaby Road, Hull HU1 2PA. Tel: 01482 324946 Also See: http:/www.urbanite.karoo.net/asylum.htm

POLAR BEAR 299 Spring Bank, Tel: 01482 323959. A large Gay/Straight mix pub with live entertainment at weekends. Often used by local Trannies as a starting off point before going on to the Silhouette night club. The bar becomes very full.

Bridge

Blayds Bar

Churchills

Downtown

Birdcage

A Personal Report

SILHOUETTES CLUB Park Street. Tel: 08707 41491. A large converted house that provides a late night club for the straight community, though over the past few years it has become more of a gay / Tranny venue on Saturday evenings. Huge dance floor and a chill out room to avoid the crush of people. Door charge (£3.00) bar open till 3.00am

VAUXHALL TAVERN , THE 1 Hessle Road. Tel: 08707 41491. Regular venue for Hull's Trans population. The Vaux is bright and cheerful and very T* friendly. The local girls normally meet up in the back (pool) room on an evening.

MAYFAIR UNISEX SALON 398 Beverley Road H5. Tel: 01482 342981. Wig specialists. Free hair and scalp consultations, Qualified in all aspects of hairdressing. TV's Welcome. Open Tuesday to Saturday. Mail order service also available.

ROSIE MASON HAIR SALON 62 market Place. Tel: 01482 211311. Androgynous cuts, styling and discreet colouring for Trans people preferring their own hair, wig styling also available. Ask for the T* friendly Rosie.

SIMONE WIGS OF BEVERLEY HILLS UK handling centre, Sutton Fields, Hull HU7 0XD. Fantastic selection of top fashion wigs imported from America. Write to above address for free glossy brochure.

LEEDS

ADELPHI PUB 1-5 Hunslet Road, corner off Dock Street. Tel: 0113 2456377. Large pub with two floors and bars, just across the road from the Old Red Lion. Not often

visited when 'crawling' the city centre but Trans girls use the large upstairs bar for private functions.

ARCH 54 Heaton's Court off Lower Briggate, Website: www.arch54.com. Classy

Luxurious new venue. Sister bar to and adjoining the new Mission nightclub. Last Saturday of every month. Housed in a railway Arch, this venue is described as the perfect retreat away from the sister club. Lots of comfy leather sofa's, floor to ceiling drapes and subdued lighting makes arch 54 more a social affair venue. There is a connecting door back into Mission.

BAR FIBRE 168 Lower Briggate. Tel: 08701 200 888. web: www.barfibre.com info@barfibre.com. Opening Times: Mon – Wed 11am till Midnight, Thurs 11am till 1.00am Fri – Sat 11am till 2.00am Sunday 11am till 10.30pm. A smallish café bar which was created from the former Brigg-Shots Restaurant and has an entrance on Lower Briggate with a further entrance that comes out onto Queens Courtyard. Fiber is only open until midnight between Monday and Wednesday, 2.00am at weekends. There is a warm welcome any day of the week for our girls and the option of popping across the courtyard into Queen's Court. Coffee and light refreshments can be served. Not much dancing space, just somewhere to chill out and chat with friends. There is an upstairs balcony area that looks out onto Queen's courtyard. As well as being ideal for moving on to Queens Court, on a Saturday it is also a great

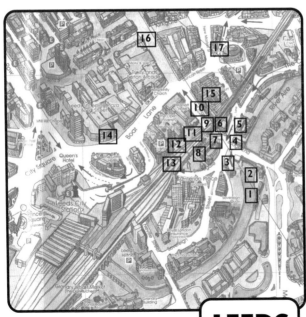

1. Old Red Lion
2. The Base
3. Malmaison Hotel
4. The Bridge
5. The New Penny
6. Elbow Room / Fruit Cupboard
7. Oslo
8. Blayds bar
9. Bar Fibre
10. Queen's Court
11. Mission Night club
12. Arch 54
13. Poptastic @ Cockpit
14. Birdcage
15. Revolution
16. City Centre Hotel (New Briggate)/Bar Phono (Merrion Centre)
17. Stinky's Peephouse / Speed Queen (York Street / Brick Street)

LEEDS

starting point / meet up place before moving on to Speed Queen nightclub.

BAR PHONO Merrion Centre, Leeds. Next to newsagents. Wade Lane entrance. Predominantly Goth but anything goes type venue with a good showing of Trans people for that 'different' kind of night. Usual night for trannies is on a Sunday but Saturday has also begun to become popular.

Birdcage

BASE, THE 24-32 Bridge End. Tel 0113 3684648. Mon to

Thurs 12pm to 12am Fri 12 till 2.00am Sat 4 till 2.00 Sunday 4 till Midnight. This large spacious public house, one of the latest venues on the Leeds Gay scene, is smart and nicely furnished yet it has never really taken off as a major venue, other than on the 3rd Friday of the month when it hosts a gay meeting. The bar is only open until 12.00 midnight and is therefore often passed by on a Tues evening by Trans people leaving the Old Red Lion and going onto bars such as The bridge and Queen's Court which remain open much later. The bar remains very welcoming and friendly towards the Trans-Community however and Trans people are always made very welcome. On Sunday evenings, commencing at 9.30pm there is Cabaret.

BIRDCAGE, THE 52-56 Boar Lane, Tel; (Marcus) 0113 246

7273. www.birdcagelive.com. 8.30pm till 2.00am. Ab-Fab new Leeds venue right in the city centre, a short walk from Leeds City railway station and many bus stops from areas right across the suburbs. Very popular already with the straight scene, especially Hen and Stag nights, The Birdcage tried out a brave new venture in promoting a Tuesday LGBT night, unfortunately this was not sufficiently supported to warrant it's continuation. Never the Less, promoter, Marcus, says that Trans people are always most welcome in the club at any time and will always be looked after, to prove it, trannies are waved past the long queues and enter free (normally entry fee £6.00). With a live cabaret show that includes the brilliant resident drag DJ Miss Orry plus glamourous drag hostesses, very friendly bar staff and all in a smart spacious, up-market club, there is little wonder that Birdcage became immediately popular with the Trans-Crowd. There is limited car parking on Mill Hill or at a multi story car park off Swinegate / Sovereign Street.

Girls Out Late

BLAYDS BAR Blayds Courtyard off Lower Briggate. Tel

0113 2445590. Blayd's bar, hidden away, was one of the first venues to be used by Trans -Yorks, for their TRANStastic meetings and later TG Leeds nights. The venue was also used by TY Management for various meetings. Although the Bar still welcomes Trans-Folk, latterly Blayd's tends to be more used by the Lesbian community. The upstairs room is

Les Femmes

A Personal **Report**

The 'portal' to everything tranny on the Internet

currently used for storage so only the small downstairs bar is open. At certain times cars can be parked (space provided) on Lower Briggate, otherwise parking is at the Meadow Lane car park and a walk up over Leeds Bridge.

BRIDGE PUB, THE Bridge End Jnc Call Lane Tel: (Deggsie)

0113 2444734. Tel: 0113 2444 734 or Deggsie on 07719098328. Opening times: Tues, Thurs, Fri, Sat 12 till late. Mon & Wed 1.00pm till Midnight Sunday 12 till 12.30am. The Bridge pub, a few doors away from the New Penny, has always welcomed Transvestites through it's doors and, of late, a succession of managers have done their best to 'encourage' T* girls to call into the bar. Several have wanted special 'Tranny Nights', though, with an already full events programme, no regular specific night has been arranged. The present manager went as far as laying on plates of food, specially for Trannies, when they turned up on Tuesday's after the Old Red Lion quiz night. The pub is predominantly gay / lesbian, but occasionally groups of straights wander in looking for late night drinking.., though there is never any trouble.

CITY CENTRE HOTEL 51a New Briggate, LS2 8JD Tel: 0113 242

9019 /1917 Very pleasant, friendly hotel over looking the Leeds Grand theatre. The only problem with this hotel is it is at the top side of the city centre, away from the quarter and there is limited parking area. Prices for Twin rooms are between £50 and £60 and singles between £27 and £32. There is TV in all rooms and a full English breakfast is served.

ELBOW ROOM, THE Call Lane. Next door to 'Break for the border' and opposite 'The New Penny'. This otherwise gay venue, because of it's bar dancers, now attracts a lot of the straighter crowd who may have an attitude towards Trans folk. There is weekend entertainment and a door charge

FRUIT CUPBOARD 52-54 Call Lane, Tel: 0113 2438666. Bar and Club venue newly refurbished. Bar hours 5pm till 11pm Club Hours 10.00pm till 3.00am Bar dancers

GLASSHOUSE @ HEAVEN & HELL 9 Grand Arcade off Vicar lane / Upper Briggate Tel: 0113 2439963. The night continues at Glasshouse, 4.00am till 8.00am

KAHUNA The After hours club that continues where Queen's Court finishes. Every Saturday Night. 2.30am until 5.30am The DJ's downstairs play a harder style of music on powerful sound systems. Tel: 078 99951603 or 07803 940582 for details.

THE LEEDS HILTON. Neville Street LS1 4BX Tel: 0113 244

2000 A more luxurious hotel accommodation for those able to afford it. The price for rooms range between £115 to £130 per

night. Sauna, Gym and heated swimming pool.

THE MALMAISON HOTEL Sovereigne Quay at the junction of

Bridge End. Tel: 0113 3981000.The Malmaison is a stone's throw away from all the more regular venues that the trannies in Leeds frequent. All rooms are priced at £78.00 en suite, the food and service is impeccable and the friendly staff cater for your every needs. The bar is kept open while ever you wish to use it.. Other visitors may be fascinated.There is a large car park across the road in Sovereign Street

MISSION NIGHT CLUB Heaton's Court off lower Briggate (Behind the Viaduct pub) Tel: 08701 220114. www.clubmission.com Newest, large trendy nightclub on the Leeds gay scene, opened September 2003. Three dance floors, Straight/gay mix clientele. State of the art sound system and a huge bar. Different promoters run evenings throughout the week such 'Heaven' from London and Manchester's queer club night 'Fussy Pussy' , see web site for details Mission is housed in five Victorian railway arches, two of which the main dance floor covers and another forms the chill-out room.

NEW PENNY PUB, THE 52 Call Lane.Tel 0113 243 8055.

Opening Times: Mon – Wed 12.00 till 11.00pm Thurs – Sat 12.00 till 2.00 am Sunday 2.00 pm till 12.30am. Pub manager Aidan always provides a big welcome for Transgender people to this public house in the heart of Leeds' Gay area. There is limited seating at present but big changes are planned in the near future which includes a chill out room upstairs where people can sit and chat. Downstairs Aidan is the DJ drumming out a music variety that should suit all tastes. There is adequate dancing space for the more energetic reveller's to 'strut their stuff'. Toilets are down the stairs. Good selections of drinks are available at the bar.

OLD RED LION PUB Meadow Lane Tel (David) 0113

2426779 Opening Times: Mon – Thurs 11.30 till 11.00 pm Fri & Sat 11.00 till 11.00pm Sun 12 till 3.00 7.00pm till 10.30. It is situated at the most Southerly end of Leeds' Gay area. It has, for a long time, been the home, on a Tues evening, to Trannies from far and wide. Many girls have taken their first 'public' steps here. Tues night is quiz night when as many as thirty plus girls can congregate in the side room to pit their wits with the regulars of this very friendly pub for a gallon of beer and chance of cash prizes on the 'Strike it Lucky' board. Unfortunately there is no changing facilities but, on the plus side, there is a spacious car park directly opposite the pub with additional parking along the side street. Tues is the regular tranny night but TV's are welcomed by landlady Paula and her customers at any time. Often after the quiz a handful of girl move on to nearby late bars.

OSLO 174 Lower Briggate Tel: 0113 245575. Cellar style bar. A little on the seedier side and is something of a drugs haven, occasionally used by local girls. Entry £2.00 before 11.oopm then £4.00

POPTASTIC @ THE COCKPIT NIGHTCLUB Swinegate, Leeds. Every Thursday 11pm till 2.30am Early bar at 10.30pm Entrance Fee: £3.50 www.poptastic.co.uk. There is three different music rooms rooms playing: Disco / Retro Pop, Indie and Alternative / Happy House and handbag so as to cater for all tastes. Poptastic was the recommended continuation, being on a Thursday Evening, when members of Trans-Yorks formerly held their TRANStastic evenings at Blayds Bar. A draw back was the entrance price, the walking distance and difficulty in parking, though Trans People are always well received. Poptastic takes place in the Cockpit Nightclub which is situated underneath the viaduct to Leeds City Railway station. A popular feature at Poptastic is the 'Shag Tags', everyone entering the venue being given a sticky numbered label to wear on arrival and, if someone fancies you, later in the night, your number will come up on screen along with the person who's eye you have caught. Dancers are also bombarded with giant plastic balls during the night, a fun venue and well worth a visit… but it does get very packed, very hot and very stuffy.

QUEENS COURT 167-168 Lower Briggate Tel: 0113 2450449. Leeds' largest gay bar. Open till 2.00am. Queens Court has always been a favourite with the Leeds Trans-Community, unfortunately the preferred upstairs bar and dance floor is now only open on a weekend and this has led to a drop in numbers, both gays and Trans, during mid-week. The ground floor is, however, more spacious with better tables and seating than the upstairs bar so, for those preferring to sit and chat rather than dancing, it is more ideal. www.kahuna.org.uk

REVOLUTION Off Call lane and at the end of Queen's

courtyard. Up from Queen's Court, The revolution sees more goths and alternatives than trannies but some of the Leeds T* Crowd used to use the venue regularly. Unsure of the new management views but maybe worth a visit.

SPEED QUEEN @ THE WAREHOUSE The Warehouse Night Club,

Somers Street Off St Paul's Street. Web: www.speedqueen.co.uk. A huge favourite with clubbers. Saturday from 10.00pm till 4.00am £8. Members £10 guests info@speedqueen.co.uk. Regarded

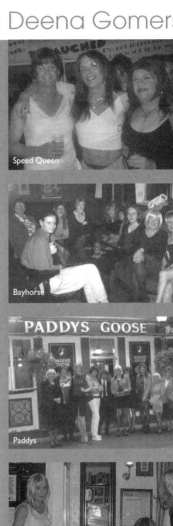

Speed Queen

Bayhorse

PADDYS GOOSE

Paddys

Paddys

Les Femmes

A Personal **Report**

UK ■ *A Personal* Report

by many to be the ultimate club experience, Speed Queen is now back at The Warehouse night club after a period of being held at Stinky's Peephouse, each Saturday night. There is two levels, the first floor level being the main dance floor where a host of top UK DJ's appear to boom out the reverb, the top room is the chill out room where more conventional music is played and where cocktails are obtainable. Speed Queen is at the West side of Leeds City centre and slightly away from the gay quarter but it is very much a mixed bag of straight, gay, Lesbian and Transgender club goers. A host of drag queens welcome you at the door and keep things moving. There is a £10.00 entrance fee into the club, which is waived for Trans-Folk and, if that isn't welcoming enough, T* girls walk straight in past the lengthy queues. Try it.

STINKY'S PEEPHOUSE 1 Brick Street, Leeds LS9 8AA Tel:

0113 247 0606   Kevin 07947 109117 Opening Times Sun to Thurs midday to midnight Fri and Sat Midday til 2.00am. The newest gay Bar in Leeds which is actually out of the gay area, though the management say that this makes the venue safer as more and more 'straights' are frequenting the gay area pubs and clubs. There's a large car park across the road. Thursday night was initially attempted to be a TV/CD night up in the loft bar which has a glass floor enabling people to see right down to the lower level (ie; Peephouse), Friday night was originally 'men only night' but it is now open to all. Check out the website at: **www.stinkyspeephouse.com.** There is an extensive beer (Queer) garden at the rear for those warm Summer evenings. A very smart and friendly venue. The club is members only (available to join on the night)

NORTHERN GIRLS @ THE WOODHOUSE DAY CENTRE The Woodhouse Day Centre, Pennington Street off Woodhouse Street, Leeds Contact :Stella Dee 01274 878033 Mob: 078556 74169 The Woodhouse Day centre is the meeting place of Northern Girls on the 2nd and 4th Mondays of the month. Initially a local section of the Beaumont Society, Northern Girl now runs entirely independent from any Trans Group. Particularly favoured by the Older Tv's and Ts's the Centre provides a clean relaxing place to chat with others over tea and biscuits (A chance to escape from alcohol for one evening). The centre is in it's own private grounds and has a secluded car park, which is ideal for the more closeted or nervous TV. There is no membership fee, just come along, as you are (dressed or in drab) or change at the centre in the clean toilet area and make a whole host of new, like minded friends.

VELVET BAR & RESTAURANT 11-14 Hirst's Yard off Lower Briggate, Tel: 0113 242 5079. Smart, pleasant restaurant with nicely prepared, mouth watering meals. Situated in the gay quarter nearby all the more popular venues.

The management had hopes of having a regular Tranny only night during mid week, but you know our girl…you just can't tie us down.
THE ITALIAN JOB No 9 Bridge End. (Between Bridge pub and river Aire). Small but pleasant eating place that serves excellent food. With friendly staff, Highly recommended. Pasta Meals, Filetto, Bisteeka, Lasagne, Tagliatelle, Cannelonni plus a variety of pizzas and deserts.
LUIGI'S 10 Lower Briggate. Tel: 0113 2424480. If you are feeling hungry at the end of an evening one of the best, fastest and cheapest venues to call at is Luigi's takeaway situated directly opposite Queen's Court and Bar Fibre, next door to Tappa's. You'll find anything you want here in the fast food department: A good variety of Pizzas, Burgers, Chips, Chicken meals and Donners, Lasagne, Taguatella all with side salads. The takeaway gets pretty busy at the end of the night so Trannies can have lots of fun educating all those curious types who have never seen us before, including students who believe Trannies only ever
THE RIZWAN BALTI Bridge End. Tel: 0113 2445151. Convenient take-away around the corner from both The Old Red Lion and The Base and next door to a taxi office. Serving Fried Chicken meals, Donner Kebabs, Balti Curry, Chicken & Chips etc.
RIVERESQUE CAFE Bridge End next to Leeds Bridge. Tel: 0113 244 5846. Nice little café serving Gourmet sandwiches and Coffee, Chicken meals with side salad
TRAVEL LODGE Blayds Court, Blayds Yard off Swinegate.

Tel: 0870 1911655. The Travel Lodge, conveniently situated to all the main venues in the gay quarter and close to both a multi story and a large open car park, is a favourite stay-over place for those girls stopping the night in Leeds. The price for rooms is £54.95 Bed & Breakfast at the time of writing.
BUTTERFLIES SUPPORT GROUP PO Box 417, Leeds LS1 5PN. Tel: 0845 3316106 Mobile: 07932 905120. Email: butterflies@mesmac.co.uk. A support group for Transsexuals, their partners and family. Information service. Meetings are held on the1st Monday of the month at the Yorkshire Mesmac building (see below) from 8.00pm until 11,00pm Props: Heather Beaumont and Val Deville
MESMAC PO box 317 LS1 5PN. Tel: 0113 2444209. Trans-Friendly sexual health promotion agency working particularly with Gay men, Bi-sexual men and men who have sex with men so includes Gay / bi Transgender people. Their premises on Basinghall Street is used to hold meetings of the Butterflies TS Support Group.
DARK SECRETS Granary Wharf. Excellent line of Gothic and Fetish clothing from sizes 8 to 20. Contact Karen & Max, Very Trans friendly
HAIR PLUS 10 County Arcade, Victorian Quarter. Tel:

0113 234 1046. Ask for appointment with Gale who is very pleasant and Trans-friendly for wig fittings from large range.

RICHARD'S WIGS AND HAIRPIECES Unit 82, Row D, Kirkgate Market, Leeds LS2 7HP Tel: 0113 2468304. Large supply of wigs plus Boas, nails, eyelashes etc. Large size shoes to order. Leave yourself in the hands of Collette who is very experienced in helping Trans Girls. Fittings done in private.

MEDISSA SHOES 115 Queen Street, Morley, Leeds LS27 8HE. Tel: 0113 25306369. Shoe factory that makes quality feminine footwear up to size 12. Quite pricey but the factory shop holds regular sales and open days. Free Catalogue upon request. Trans-friendly.

MADE TO LAST www.madetolast.org.uk. Shoe factory producing larger size ladies shoes up to fourteen. See web site for more details.

S.H. PUBLICATIONS 61 Lodge Lane, LS11. Tel: 0113 2708036. Large range of TV Mags and publications plus underwear, fun/party wear, wigs, make-up. Produces 'High Heels' TV contact magazine. Open every day. Evening opening can be arranged for extra discretion.

SHOUT MAGAZINE PO Box YR46 Leeds LS9 6XG. Monthly free magazine for the LGB & T community, Club/Pub reviews, reports and many other topics. Available at most gay venues throughout Yorkshire or £10 for a years subscription from the address above.

MIRFIELD NR WAKEFIELD

KAY'S COSMETICS PO Box 50. Mirfield, WF14 9XJ. Mail order only. Run by TG Kay Pullen. Cosmetics and feminising products. Kay is a Dermablend consultant. Details of the full range of cosmetics is available at: http:/ourworld.compuserve.com/homepages/kkay1/der mable.htm. Ordering by fax: 01924 503322

RIPON NR YORK

SAKS 23 High Skellgate. Tel: 01765 690125. Aculight hair removal carried out in a Trans-friendly salon. Ask for Ann.

SCARBOROUGH

THE ALBION 136 Castle Road, Tel: (Barry) 01723 379068. www.thealbionpub.co.uk. Scarborough's only full-time gay pub very close to the famous castle. Large and welcoming with live entertainment each Saturday and Karaoke on Thurs and Friday's. Local trannies have a meet here on the 1st Sat of the month. Many girls visit when up for the Harmony Weekend.

CLUB XS Aberdeen Walk. Tel: 07970 379068. Gay / Trans night on the First Tuesday of the month, following on from The Albion where privilege tickets can be obtained. open 11pm till 2.00am

THE KINGS Valley Road Gay / Trans friendly pub but not often used by T*girls. Open 7.00pm – 11.00pm

SOUTHLAND HOTEL West Street, Tel: 01723 361461. The Southlands Hotel is the twice yearly venue for The Harmony Weekend, run by Martine rose of Rose's TV

Less Femmes Beer Garden

Queens Courtyard Leeds

Ma Bakers Sheffield

Via Fossa

A Personal **Report**

UK ■ A Personal Report

Repartee magazine. Each November and mid-year trannies from all over the country congregate in Scarborough for this 2-3 day weekend event which has stalls, entertainment and the Miss Rose and Miss Fantasy competitions plus full breakfast and evening meals. Details from: Martine Rose, 208 Holmley Lane, Dronfield. S18 3DB. Tele: 01246 291333

FEM-MEN 122 Osgodby Lane. Tel: (Martin) 01723 581697. Large range of cosmetics and accessories plus jewellery, nails, eyelashes, silicone boobs and hosiery by mail order or at various venues. Martin will travel to venues by arrangement.

SHEFFIELD

COSSAK, THE 45 Howard Street S4. Tel: 0114 2812654 / 07765 578058. The oldest gay venue in Sheffield. Open till 11pm Monday to Saturday, Sunday till 10.30 with DJ's from Friday to Sunday, Karaoke on Thursdays and Beauty Salon from 8.30pm on Wednesdays

LES FEMMES @ CLUB XES, THE NORFOLK ARMS 195 Carlisle Street, Tel: (Garry) 0114 2750828. www.les-femmes.da.ru. 2nd, 3rd and 4th Friday's are Tranny night at The Norfolk Arms. Very popular Gay bar, the Tranny numbers fluctuate from between just a handful to dozens, wearing... whatever! There's a Pool Room and stage with occasional entertainment. Disco and Fair sized dance floor, parking outside the pub.

MA BAKER'S 5 Carlisle Street East S4. Tel: 0114 2789547. www.mabakers.co.uk. Recently re-opened with a change of proprietor. Ma Baker's is popular as a break-away from Les Femmes on a Friday evening as there is more seating space and more chance to chat before returning across the road to finish the night.

DEMPSEY'S Hereford Road, Moorfoot. Tel: 0114 2552761. Bar and Club open from 11.00am serving a selection of food and bar meal Tuesday is quiz and games night while Wednesday and Sunday is Karaoke. Disco with popular DJ's is on Friday and Saturday nights

FAIRY LIKUID City Hall Ballroom, Baker's Pool. Tel: 07977 110362. Special LGBT night held at Sheffield's City Hall on the 1st Friday of the month. Two rooms of camp and dance from 10.30pm till 3.00am. £5.00 admission. Some of the local Trannies attend.

SWAN HOTEL Attercliffe Road, Tel: 0114 2447978. Popular bar / Hotel for those girls travelling from a distance going to Les Femmes and stopping over. The bar stays open, serving alcohol and hot drinks while ever anybody requires them

PRIORY LODGE HOTEL 40 Wolstenholm Road S7, Tel: 0114 2584670, Very friendly hotel used by some of the girls staying over after a Les Femmes night. The proprietor looked into the possibility of holding a regular tranny night on the premises.

BUTTERFLY LINGERIE 281 Eccleshall Road S11, Tel: 0114 2681444. Recommended by the local girls. Trans-Friendly staff.

DESIGNER WIG SALON 87, Castle Market. Lower Ground Floor. Tel: 0114 2755885. Stella Bridges; consultant. Used to helping and dealing with Trans-people. Private

fitting booth provided.

TRENDS 337 Glossop Road S10. Tel: 0114 276 8676. Supplier of Quality wigs including Monofilament and Dermalite as well as budget and fun-time wigs. Plus false nails and eyelashes along with a range of cosmetics.

PAT'S PLACE Tel: 0114 2491379. Cross Dressing service.

DESSUS B&B Nr junction 30 of the M1. Tel: (Chris) 0779 920160. Bed & Breakfast and dressing service / Make-Over's provided by genetic female with TS partner.

WAKEFIELD

DOWNTOWN 46 Upper Kirkgate off Lower Warrengate. Tel: (David) 01924 299662. http:/takeoff.to/downtown. Smart, pleasant night club with DJ, regular entertainment and strippers. Each 1st Friday of the month good numbers of Trans girls and partners assemble in the back room (Jackie's Bar) between 9.00pm – 2.00am. There is ample parking at the back of the venue and discreet entry, Hot food available and changing facilities if required. For more Info contact Deena on 07903 524193.

BAR ZEUS 6 Lower Warrengate, Tel; 01924 201705. Gay pub close to Downtown, very friendly with Drag Queen DJ Connie Lingus spinning the discs. Bar open till 12.00 Mon – Wed, 1.00am Thurs – Fri, 2.30am Saturday and 6 till 12.30am Sunday. Car park near the Rainbow pub close by.

YORK

YORK ARMS High Petersgate off Bootham RoW. Tel: (Mark) 01904 624508. Transfusion night @ the York Arms, a gathering of the local transgender on the 3rd Wednesday of the month at this small but friendly gay venue. Landlord Mark.

IDOLS @ TOFF'S NIGHTCLUB 3-5 Toft Green Tel: 01904 620203. Email idolsyork@aol.com. Idols takes place at Toffs nightclub on alternative Sundays. T* friendly and often frequented by local Trans girls and those from surrounding areas. Opening times 9.00pm till 1.00am Admission £2.50. (For more details/up-dates, concerning York meetings/venue dates, Email: amy_gadd@yahoo.co.uk.

HAIRWORKS 3a Main Street, Wheldrake, Tel: 01904 448900. Trans-friendly hair salon that do 'Raccoon' European hair extensions.

Most venues given in this report have been tried and tested by myself and friends or by local Trannies in their specific areas. Shops. Beauty salons etc are those that are particularly friendly towards TG's but, as anyone in Yorkshire will tell you, almost all shops will be friendly and helpful towards T*Girls.

The large shopping Centres in Hull *PRINCESS QUAY*,
Leeds *WHITE ROSE CENTRE* **and**
Sheffield *MEADOWHALL*
are particularly recommended.

Bar Fibre

Old Red Lion Quiz Winners Leeds

Old Red Lion Girls Leeds

A Personal **Report**

discreet appointment services. Any fantasy can be made, tutus, party dresses and ballgowns all at moderate prices. Dye shoes to match dresses. Jill also sells make-up & wigs.

BIRDCAGE (DRESSING SERVICE)
Preston Lancashire J28 off M6 Tel: 07887 654434; Email: birdcage@bryany.demon.co.uk; Website: www.bryany.demon.co.uk Ask for Pauline . . . . 04 - Dressing service within a private detached residence, surrounded by half an acre of secluded gardens. Full make-over, advice and training, wigs & clothes for every occasion or fantasy. Weddings a specialty. Accommodation available. Escorted outings. Bring your own camera or video.

CASANDRA
Between Grantham and Peterbourgh Tel: 01476 550167 or 07866 341849; Ask for: Casandra . . . . 04 - Dressing Service close to A1. Maids, brides, schoolgirls etc. 1 to 1. Help with shopping. Wigs, make-up, full wardrobe. Storage & laundry available. Restraint equipment and domination equipment.

CATHOUSE FETISH CLOTHNG & ACCESSORIES
1st Floor, Bennett & Thornes Building, Bennett Street, Millbridge, Liversedge, West Yorks, WF15 7ES Tel/Fax: 01924 412662 info@cathouseclothing.co.uk; www.cathouseclothing.co.uk; Ask for: Caroline; . . . 04 - Made-to-measure clothing by Cathouse in rubber, pvc, lycra and mesh. Stockist of Daxine, Honour, Phaze, Skin two etc. Credit and debit cards accepted.

CHIC BEAUTY
Joseph Wright Building, 1st Floor Suite, 34 Iron Gate, Derby, DE1 3GA Tel: 01332 207712; . . . . 04 - Waxing, Intense pulsed light hair removal (Depilite), laser hair removal (ND:Yag), electrolysis, facials, manicures, pedicures, make-up lessons, body-wraps, pamper days, slimming treatment, reiki and indian head massage, aromatherapy, reflexology and crystal clera treatments.

CHIL-TEX LTD INCORP (COOPERS OF ASHBOURNE)
Moorfarm Road West, Airfield Industrial Estate, Ashbourne, Derbyshire DE6 1HD Tel: 01335 343277 / 01335 343384; Email: sales@chil-tex.com; Website: www.chil-tex.com.. . . 04 - Makers of traditional corsetry, bras, suspender belts and corselettes. Send for free catalogue.

CLOTHO LTD
Shereston House, Holly Hill Road, Shenstone, Nr Lichfield, Staffordshire, WS14 0JF Tel: 01543 483336; . . . . 04 - Small & friendly dress making company. Making handmade individual clothes designed for you, copy your designs or existing garments. Pleasant surroundings and complete confidentiality. Sensible prices.

COLETTE
Nottingham Tel: 07732 360309; Email: colette.tv-england@virgin.net; Website: www.transvestite-colette.co.uk . . . . 04 - Enjoy a complete make-over in pleasant discreet surroundings. Over 200 outfits, including ball gowns sizes 10-30. Colettes phoneline - Colettes Diary Explicit Extracts 0909 988 9517 (calls charged at £1 per minute).

CROSS+ROADS GID SUPPORT & TRANSWATCH UK
Tel: 01388 607925 / 01207 582167; Email: andrea:andlou.co.uk; Website: www.crossroads-gid-support.org.uk Ask for Paula or Andrea; . . . . 04 - Specialising in helping people who feel gender dysphoric and those transitioning on medical GID programmes, primarily Northern England with an outreach membership throughout UK.

DESIRE (SHEFFIELD)
619 Atterclife Road, Sheffield, S9 3RD. Tel: 0114 2442626; . . . . 04 - Retail shop for wigs, lingerie, corsets, shoes, videos & much much more. Open Mon-Fri 9.30-8pm, Saturday 9.30-6pm, Sunday 11pm-4pm.

EQUINOX
39 Brook Avenue, Arnold, Nottingham Tel: 0115 956 1976; . . . . 04 - Intense Pulse light system for hair removal and vascular applications.

FACE & BODY THERAPY
8 Howard Street, Edinburgh, EH3 5JP Tel: 0131 624 7123; . . . . 04 - A full range of treatments including waxing, electrolysis, with many TG customers.

FLAMINGO'S
170/176 Talbot Road, Blackpool, FY1 3AZ Tel: 01253 624901; Email: Flamingo@itp.uk.com; Website: www.itp-leisure.co.uk. . . . 04 - This is Blackpool's major gay night-club.Open Mon-Thurs 10.30-2am. Fri 10- 3am,Sat 10-4am, Sun 10-12.30am (charity nights 2am) The clientele is extremely diverse, coming from all over the country, with many females in the crowd. The club splits into four levels providing quiet bars & large dance floors. The Flamingo has drag acts plus top named acts regularly. The staff often drag up for 'themed' nights. Cross-dressers are always very welcome in fact the management often recruit for 'Funny Girls' here.

FUNNY GIRLS
1-9 Queen Street, Blackpool, FY1 1NL. Tel: 01253 291144; Email: Funnygirls@itp.uk.com; Website: www.itp-leisure.co.uk . . . . 04 - Open Mon-Sat Doors open 7pm, Bar closes 11pm Show finishes 11.30. Sunday Doors open 7pm, Bar closes 10.30, Show finishes 11pm.Promoted widely as a 'Transvestite Bar' by Blackpool's mainstream publicity machine. The main bar is reminiscent of the program 'The Good Old Days'. The bar staff are also attractive TVs. But this is NOT the best place to go 'dressed', as if you are not working there, the straight punters will be most confused, if not a little hostile. For 'girls' wanting to work Funny girls regularly advertises for energetic attractive TVs to serve behind the bars.

GWENAP
3 Princes Avenue, Kingston upon Hull, Yorkshire, HU5 3RX Tel: 01482 493227; . . . . 04 - Visit or contact for mail order. A stock of books, magazines, lingerie, ring doorbell for access.

HAIR PLUS
10 County Arcade, Victoria Quarter, Briggate, Leeds, LS1 6BN Tel: 0113 234 1046; . . . . 04 - A good selection of wigs at reasonable prices is sold at this wig shop. Private fittings are available. Ask for Michelle, Alison or Sue to make an appointment.

HOTEL MARDI GRAS
41-43 Lord Street, Blackpool, FY1 2BD Tel: 01253 751087 / 751088; . . . . 04 - A friendly place to stay with 20 rooms, all the regular facilities with a smile. Highly recommended. Although a mainly gay hotel, they do welcome TV's and TS's in their establishment.

JAYJAY DRESSING SERVICE
Lincoln Tel: 07940 407470; Email: jayjaytv@hotmail.com; . . . . 04 - Dressing Service.

ALTERNATIVE FOOTWEAR
53 Bolton Street, Ramsbottom, Bury, Lancs BL0 9HU Tel: 01706 823283 11am-9pm 7days; Website: www.alternative-footwear.co.uk Email: sales@alternative-footwear.co.uk; Ask for: Mark & Donna; . . . . 04 - Supply a range of thigh high boots & sexy shoes mailorder.

KASTLEY
P.O. Box 24, Blackburn, Lancs, BB2 7QD Tel/Fax: 01254 873247; Website: www.kastley.co.uk Email: rubber@kastley.freeserve.co.uk Ask for: June; . . . 04 - Made to measure dresses and undergarments. A catalogue is available at £6 (refundable with order).

LA FEMME @ SELLABRATION
82 High Street, Marske by the Sea, Redcar, Cleveland, TS11 7B A Tel: 0781 6544465; . .04 - Make-Up lesson, wigs, dress making, photo shoots & escorted trips. Dressing service just 15 m iles from Middlesborough. Fully stocked fancy dress shop catering for the feminine side. A friendly & discreet service.

LES FEMMES (SHEFFIELD)

Club Xes, 195 Carlisle Street, Sheffield, S4 7JL. Tel: 01142 750828 or 07932 51042; Website: www.clubxes.co.uk . . . . 04 - Les Femmes is held on the 2nd, 3rd & 4th Friday of each month. A friendly mixed crowd. Limited changing facilities. 8.00 - 4am. Nights not exclusive to T-girls

LINCOLNSHIRE DRESSING SERVICE

Coningsby Lincs Tel: 01526 342003 Contact: Jean; . . . . 04 - This husband (TV) & wife team provide a full dressing service with top to toe wardrobe & make-up. A wide range of products & clothes are available to buy. Counselling & will accompany a convincing customer shopping or to a local pub.

LYNMAR HOTEL

74 High Street, Blackpool, FY1 2BP. Tel: 01253 290046; Email: mikestanley@blueyonder.co.uk; Website: www.lynmar.net Ask for Mike or Steve; . . . . 04 - Very friendly run hotel, 5 minute walk from Blackpool North Station. Very clean & a fabulously cooked breakfast. Prices start at £14, max £21.50 per person. The hotel is frequented by most visiting Drag Queens and is within easy reach of Funny Girls & Flamingo etc.

NEWS FROM NOWHERE

96 Bold Street, Liverpool, L1 4HY Tel: 0151 708 7270; . . . . 04 - Radical & community bookshop committed to social change. Stockist of many TV/TS and transgender books & magazines.

NICE N NAUGHTY

129 Brook St, Chester, CH1 3DU Tel: 0870 742 7261; Website: www.nicennaughty.co.uk Ask for: Trish; . . . . - Lingerie, hosiery, clubwear and leather are just some of the stock at this tranny friendly shop, Open 9am-8pm Mon- Sat. If you are in the area it is worth a visit to check out their other items of stock.

NORTH EAST SUPPORT GROUP

Darlington, Co. Durham. Tel: 01325 361018; Email: christinatvdom@yahoo.co.uk; Website: www.christinatv.co.uk Ask for Christina; . . . . 04 - Christina offers long term cross-dressers free support & advice plus a safe address for mail order & a large collection of catalogues to order from. The group holds occasional social evenings another website address www.uktvmistress.com.

PRETTY CHIC BEAUTY CLINIC

39a Leicester Road, Wigston Magna, Leicester, LE18 1NR Tel: 0116 288 7433; Website: www.prettychic.co.uk Ask for: Ask for Sian or Lisa; . . . . 04 - Waxing, Intense pulsed light hair removal (Depilite), laser hair removal (ND:Yag), electrolysis, facials, manicures, pedicures, make-up lessons, body-wraps, pamper days, slimming treatment, and nail extensions. Also other salons in Burbidge, 01455 619147, Lutworth 01455 559440 and Derby 01332 207712.

PRETTY THINGS

Market Hall, Brooks Street & at 7A The Springs, Wakefield Tel: 01924 374700; Web site: www.prettythings.co.uk . . . . 04 - Foundation Garments, all styles of lingerie and nightwear including stockings.

RENAISSANCE (GROUP)

Blackpool Tel: 01253 400160; Email: petra@renaissanceblackpool.org; Website: www.renaissanceblackpool.org Ask for: Lynda Collins; . . . . 04 - Renaissance is a very popular social club for TV's, TS's and TG's. They hold meetings on 2nd & 4th Tuesday of every month.

RIVA HOLIDAY FLATS

216 North Promenade Blackpool FY1 1RU tel: 01253 626601 Website: www.rivablackpool.co.uk Email: holidays@rivablakpool.co.uk . . . . 04 - Transexual run B&B on the seafront with some flats that have magnificent seaviews. Easy stroll to the Tower & North Pier. Flats are self contained sleeping 2-7. Reserve flats by phone, post or email.

ROCKIES BAR

78 Scotswood Road, Newcastle on Tyne, Tel: 0191 232 6536; . . . . 04 - Tranny friendly gay bar DJ dancefloor Wed and Sun cabaret.

THE WIGGINS

119 Penny Lane, Liverpool L18 1DF, Tel: 0151 475 0328;Website: www.thewiggins.co.uk . . . . 04 - This is a wig shop which is friendly & sympathetic to cross-dressers. A catalogue is available & orders can be dealt with through the post as well as at the shop.

SERENITY BEAUTY

Sketchley Grange Hotel, Sketchley Lane, Hinckley, Leicestershire, LE10 3HU Tel: 01455 619147; Website: www.serenitybeauty.co.uk. . . . . 04 - Waxing, Intense pulsed light hair removal (Depilite), laser hair removal (ND:Yag), electrolysis, facials, manicures, pedicures, make-up lessons, body-wraps, pamper days, slimming treatment, and nail extensions.

S-MART

45 Talbot Road,Blackpool . . . . 04 - Sell thigh length boots £30-£40. Showgirls shoes under £20. Day & evening styles large sizes.Private changing area. We are told "they look after you" & supply shoes to the girls from Funny Girls.

THE LASER HAIR CLINIC

38 Billing Road, Northampton, NN1 5DQ Tel: 01604 634999; Email: enquiry@laser-clinic.co.uk; Website: www.laser-clinic.co.uk; Ask for: Helena-Marie; . . . . 04 - This clinic offers hair removal treatment using the Alexandrite laser and also the Plasmalite Intense Pulsed Light device (aimed at treating Asian Skin types). Also laser treatment for thread veins. A good understanding of the transgender need for removal of facial and body hair. Free pick up service by a member of staff at Northampton Train Station.

TRANSGENDER-UK

136 Bedford Street South, Liverpool L7 7DB Tel: 0151 709 1432; Email: rebecca@tranger.freeserve.co.uk; Website: www.transgender-uk.info . . . . 04 - A organisation for transgendered individuals in the United Kingdom, currently building a resource website with links to useful websites.

TRANSISTER GROUP
Wirral Tel: 0151 649 8128 Email: transitions_1@yahoo.co.uk . . . .
04 - Held on Tuesday nights.

TV HAVEN
West Yorkshire 07971 364027; . 04 - Sympathetic & experienced lady offers a full dressing service. Escort service for shopping, dining out & social events. Jacuzzi & body massage. Photography. Open 7 days a week, overnight accommodation available.

WIGS AND PIECES
Unit 44, Top Deck, Princes Quay Shopping Centre, Hull, HU1 2TD. Tel: 01482 221160; Ask for Karen; . . . . 04 - Wigs & much more. They can accommodate early or late appointments.

YVONNE BARLOW ALTERNATIVE HAIR
171a Church Street, Blackpool, FY1 3NX Tel: 01253 624977; Email: additionalhair@aol.com Website: www.alternativelook.co.uk; Ask for: Yvonne; . . . . 04 - This shop has wigs, hairpieces both ready made & custom made. Your own hair can also be cut & styled. Private fitting rooms.

UK SOUTH

AMAZING FANTASY
105 Fisherton St, Salisbury, Wiltshire Tel: 01722 417085; . . . .04 - A large TV friendly adult/sex shop, with a fab range of clothes upto size 32 and boots & shoes upto size 13, and lots of toys!

A Personal **Report**

With sea, hills, good food and a large gay community, Brighton is the UK's answer to San Francisco - only without the weather! For it's size, it's a remarkably tolerant and cosmopolitan place. There's a huge Pride festival in August, a thriving arts scene, and a year-round readiness to party, making it a great place to live and perfect for a weekend break. All the same, it has its share of idiots too, so do be on your guard.

The City's legendary nightlife caters to every possible taste, and many clubs are 'LGBT-friendly'. In practice this means lots of LGB and rather less of the T, but even if you're the only 'T' in the house you'd be unlucky to get hassled (the exceptions being the barn-like venues clustered around the Clocktower).

NIGHT LIFE

Best of all is the '*GAY VILLAGE' OF KEMP TOWN,* just to the East of the Pavilion, and where there's quite enough going on to wear out most dancing shoes.
Top billing goes to '*REVENGE*' on Old Steine, which is the South's largest gay club. Open 7 days a week it's one non-stop party, with huge rooms on two floors and a wildly varied, super-friendly crowd. I've been there countless times and always had a ball. Just around the corner is '*ENVY*', formerly known as '*POOL*', and right above the co-owned '*CHARLES ST' BAR* which is a good spot to warm up with a few aperitifs. Envy is home to the twice-monthly '*WET PUSSY PARTY*', a girls-only lesbian night with excellent tunes from DJ Kate Wildblood and a full-on party atmosphere. Part-time girls are equally welcome and the event is highly recommended. Here too, on alternate Fridays, is '*PERFUMED GARDEN*', a storming hard trance night billed as a 'polysexual' affair (i.e. anything goes).
Elsewhere in Kemp Town there's a wealth of fine bars and pubs. First up is the '*CANDY BAR*' on St James's Street, satellite of the well-known London lesbian bar of the same name, and organiser of the Pussy Parties. Gay men are allowed in as guests and TG customers are welcome any time. It's a very special place to have around, and the best news of all is that rumours of impending closure have proved happily untrue. The bar will indeed leave its current site but reopen soon after as a larger venue in the same street. Nearby in Broad Street is the tiny '*MARINE TAVERN*', sister bar to 'The Harlequin' (of which more later). This is a quiet, intimate, home-from-home sort of place where you might even find one or two other girls wetting their whistles. For superior cocktails

pop in to '*BRIGHTON ROCK*' in Rock Place, which has a young, trendy, mixed clientele and very friendly staff. Still in Kemp Town there's also '*THE MARLBOROUGH*' in Prince's St, long term lesbian favourite with a theatre upstairs and a relaxed atmosphere. And if that's still not enough for one area then a good time can always be guaranteed at some of the better-known gay bars such as *THE QUEENS HEAD* (Steine St) or *THE QUEENS ARMS* (George St), where you can usually expect karaoke, cabaret, excess and the kind of behaviour you might have thought only happened on New Year's Eve.
Hop in a cab and in no time at all you can be at *THE HARLEQUIN* (if you're driving you can park right outside). Tucked away in Providence Place, just off the London Road, this is the only club in town where the non-gents loo is designated 'Ladies + TV/TS'. It's also one of the friendliest places you'll ever visit. Here on Thursday nights you might bump into a party of girls from the monthly Lacies dinners (see below), or else from the Sussex-based Mayflower Group, who also come here every month (1st Thurs). Fridays and Saturdays are busiest of course, and the tiny dance floor soon packs out, whilst on any night the grand staircase is perfect for showing off that new evening gown. If you ask nicely, and arrive early, there's even a secret room where you can get changed. There should be a 'Harlequin' in every town – lobby your MP now!
For eating out 'en femme', as for shopping, there are no rules as such, so I can only talk from my own experience. In Kemp Town, '*MUANG THAI*' on St James St is good value and well-placed for going on to all the bars and clubs. So too is '*THE SAINT*' on the same road, which offers really excellent modern British food and is deservedly popular so it's best to book. Over near The Lanes (East Street) is the nationally famous vegetarian restaurant, '*TERRE A TERRE*'. The food is great, staff are welcoming, and booking is a must. And finally, after all that eating, drinking and dancing you'll be needing somewhere to crash out, in which case I can recommend '*THE COURT CRAVEN HOTEL*' in Atlingworth Street (01273 607710). As far as I know this is the only hotel to display 'TV/TS News' on its lobby info table, along with all the usual stuff from the tourist board. Single rooms start at £30 per night and all the amenities of Kemp Town are walkable.

SHOPPING

Brighton is also famed for its excellent shops, particularly the many small and often quirky stores found in North Laine and The Lanes (yes it is confusing – just remember the former is due north of the latter). As readers of this guide will know, any shop can turn out to be 'TG-friendly' just as long as you ask nicely and don't create a scene. Among the big name stores, most of which are in or around Churchill Square, I've always found **DEBENHAMS** and **M&S** to be very relaxed and helpful, though I don't shop dressed (yes - I'm a streaker!). Among the independent stores, '**WALK IN WARDROBE**' in Western Road (not far from Trendco) is great for glamourous evening wear and has an understanding owner. Also '**GET CUTIE**' in Kensington Gardens is great for funky, modern designs. For jewellery there's a really huge choice, including '**AVATAR JEWELS**' and '**THE LAVENDER ROOM**' in Bond Street, '**SOMA**' in The Lanes and, on Saturdays, the lady who sells vintage pieces from a garage at the southern end of Upper Gardner St (brooches for under £5 – wow!). For contemporary shoe designs in sizes above 8 there's '**BOX 2**' in Duke St, or '**BRANTANO**' on the outskirts of town (near Asda). And if there are any girls out there who like to make their own clothes, or modify the ones they've bought, then '**VELVET**' in Gardner St is a must – full to the brim with gorgeous ribbons, buttons and fabrics in a super girly setting.

IN DEPTH

Last but not least, are the Brighton shops and services I've talked to in depth, some of which you'd be unlikely just to chance across as a visitor (or even as a resident!). Interviewing them has been fun, and in some cases an education! Full details follow - hope you like them - and don't forget, if you're out and about in Brighton and you see a 50s-fashion fan knocking back the G&Ts, then that's probably me – so do come and say hello.

MAC 6 Dukes Lane, Brighton BN1 1BG Tel 01273 720026 (open 7 days)
Many readers will know Mac not only for the high quality of their beauty products and accessories but also for the famously open-minded attitude encapsulated in their motto: "all colours, all sexes, all ages". True to form, a new shade of lipstick and lip-gloss was recently designed for them by Eddie Izzard, and a big in-store promotion coincided with his sell-out 'Sexie' tour. You'll find the Brighton branch of Mac in The Lanes, where TG customers are guaranteed a warm welcome and the kind of expert advice which you could otherwise pay serious money for. Best of all are the make-overs, which typically last around one hour and cost £20, fully refundable against any purchase (and if that's not a bargain I don't know what is!). Most girls arrive dressed, but the choice is entirely up to you. There are no private rooms, so you'll have to be comfortable with sitting in the open store, but the ambience is so benign it's no surprise that many local girls are regulars. The sessions can be fully tailored to suit your needs, perhaps concentrating on the eyes or

A Personal Report

The 'portal' to everything tranny on the Internet

on foundation, or else – as many girls have done – you could bring along a photograph and ask them to recreate a favourite look. If you'd rather leave all the decisions up to Mac then that's fine too, and it's worth remembering that the staff are all qualified make-up artists, not mere salespeople. Their main aim is to make you look good, rather than fill your handbag with surplus creams and lotions. At the end you also get to take away a face chart which is annotated to record all the things discussed in the make-over. It's advisable to book, especially for Fridays and Saturdays, and the latest appointment is at 4.30. The range of products is enormous, and yet the subtle colour-coding system makes it easy to maintain a consistent palette. Apart from the dozens of lipsticks, powders and so on there are also less familiar items such as colour correctors, and even a range of false eyelashes which the staff will happily fix in place for you if you fancy just popping in for that finishing touch. Professional and courteous to a tee I'd say 'three cheers for Mac!' only three doesn't seem enough.

AXFORDS 82 Centurion Road, Brighton BN1 3LN. Tel 01273 327 944. www.axfords.com
Axfords have been making corsets since they were everyday wear back in 1880 to be precise. A family-run business to this day, there's nothing they don't know about busts, busks and the benefits of tight lacing. Based in a quiet residential street, there's no shop as such (more a small factory) but they are very happy to receive personal callers from Monday to Thursday between 10 and 5. The lack of a fitting room isn't a problem, just as long as you turn up with some honest measurements of your chest and waist (i.e. the size they actually are, not the size you'd like them to be!). With over 3000 corsets in stock at any one time, Mr Hammond and his staff are confident of having just the thing you're looking for. Unlike the 1880s, today's corsets are made of modern materials which are light and comfortable to wear. They are boned with stainless steel and each garment is individually made from start to finish by a single corsetiere. Prices start at £65 and rise to £140 for a top of the range satin number (though leather items can go for more). There are 'over bust' and 'under bust' styles in dozens of varieties, and something for every conceivable size and shape. Whatever you have in mind, these guys are the experts so you're in safe hands. There are a few non-corset items such as undies and petticoats but the emphasis here is firmly on taming that waistline. If you prefer to buy from the elegant catalogue, or via the website, the company policy is always to offer an exchange or refund if a customer is not fully satisfied. Most of all, Axfords is extremely approachable, and they welcome calls or emails asking for advice. One of the nicest companies you'll ever deal with, they are as much a local institution as the Pavilion or the Pier.

TRENDCO 112/116 Sheridan House, Western Road, Hove BN3 1DD. Tel 01273 774 977. www.trendco.co.uk. With outlets in London and Birmingham, as well as a huge mail-order business, Trendco must rank as one of the best known sources of high quality wigs. But the company's HQ for nigh on 40 years has been down here on the South Coast. The building is on a busy shopping street and looks like an office at first, but ring the buzzer and you'll be ushered in to the discreet yet lovely and bright display area with dozens of gorgeous wigs ready for you to try on. The service couldn't be friendlier, and as you'd expect the staff are hugely experienced. Trendco has long had close ties with the TG community and this makes for a truly relaxed and unpressurised environment. By the time you leave, you can be sure you'll have the hair which is absolutely the best for you. If you want to do things in style then book in advance for an appointment with one of the hairdressers, when you'll also get to use one of the superbly appointed private rooms. The wigs themselves are very fairly priced, with the budget 't'co' range selling for as little as £52, and most other styles selling for between £90 and £140. You'll only have to dig deep if you want something in 100% human hair (those cost several hundreds). Needless to say, the variety is enormous. The 'Noriko' collection alone has over 30 different designs and comes in as many colour choices. There are bobs and wispy fringes, tousled locks, tapered ends and textured layers in every imaginable length, all boasting beautiful lifelike movement. The 'Amore' range extends the choice yet further, and includes 6 styles in human hair. All wigs are sized by three key measurements – crown, fringe and nape – and if you want something custom designed then there's a hand made service which promises delivery within 7 weeks. Another delightful local company, Trendco is highly recommended.

TABOO 2 Surrey Street, Brighton BN1 3PA. Tel 01273 263 565. As Brighton's "only licensed fetish shop" Taboo brings something new to the local retail scene. The stylish interior is divided into three parts, with clothes at the front, and smaller rooms at the back for videos/DVDs and toys or S&M gear. If your tastes extend to the shiny end of the spectrum then Taboo is the place for you, with a stunning selection of curve-enhancing outfits in latex, rubber and PVC. Owner, Jules is passionate about the clothes she stocks and there's nothing in the shop which she or her staff wouldn't wear themselves. With long experience of serving TG customers, she also knows which clothes are best for a particular physique. She singles out for attention the tailor-made and beautifully constructed garments by Krystina Kitsis at Ectomorph. These make allowances for extra width or length in the back, or for larger chests, and so are ideal for those whose starting point is not the typical female body shape. A fantastic 'long corset dress' in striking red PVC (£190) has a rear zipper for most of its length but laces up for the final few inches, enabling a really snug fit where it matters most. Taboo is also a superb source of shoes, all up to size 12. These include the 'Vicky Lee Range' (honest!) with PVC courts at £27, knee boots at £45 and thigh boots at £50 for zip ups, or £60 for the fully laced variety. There are also 'Showgirl' shoes with 6" heel and 2" platforms in red, black or clear plastic, at around £40 a pair. Elsewhere on the rails are bikinis, hot pants and mini skirts by hard-to-find label, 'Space Cowgirl'. With their ruffles and retro designs these add a real splash of colour, whilst a small selection of Vollers corsets in silk completes the perfect wardrobe for a kinky night out (or in!). If you're looking for something in particular then let Jules know the details and she'll enjoy tracking it down. Naughty but nice!

LACIES 164 Portland Road, Hove.
Tel 01273 710 656. www.fantasygirl.co.uk.

Lacies opened in Brighton in late 2002 and is the area's only dedicated 'TG shop'. Owner Sue has had many years experience running her sister shop in Folkestone, and together with helpers Lisa and Dezzie she'll make you feel as welcome as can be. Behind an attractive window display the shop's first room boasts a huge range of make-up, stockings and lingerie, with a particularly nice line in matching sets of bras and nix. Move on to the middle room and you'll find wigs from brands such as Trendco, Harry Margu, Mermaids and Beauty Dreams, all ranging in price from around £50 to £135. Here too are gaffs and a great many breast forms, including both the US variety and the deluxe ultra-realistic French-made versions. This room also has a stock of books and mags ranging from the helpful (Repartee, Miss Vera etc) to the steamy (i.e. Sabre publications). The rear part of the shop is given over to shoes and boots (up to size 12) and a sizeable selection of clothing. There are corsets, uniforms (maid and nurse), fashion items for the girl about town, and even a number of beautiful wedding dresses, bridesmaid's gowns and southern-belle numbers selling for as little as £50. But Lacies is more than just a shop. It sets out to be a real home from home for local girls or visitors alike, providing a full make-over service and hosting regular girls' nights out. The make-overs cost £20 and last about an hour, though it's best to bring your own make-up to save on buying new stuff for the session.

... Continued page 244

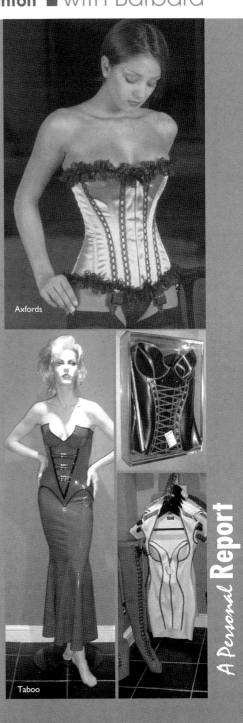

Axfords

Taboo

A Personal **Report**

BEESLEY & GOODMAN HAIR AND WIG CENTRE

100 High St, Sandhurst, Berks, GU47 8EE. (2 miles M&S superstore Junction 4, M3) Tel: 01252 871764; Website: www.wigswigswigs.co.uk Ask for: Tricia & Sally; . . . . 04 - Offer a personal service in a private wig consulting room which is stocked with over 600 wigs from 5 suppliers with the latest up-to-date styles. Advice is readily available on style, colour & suitability by 3 highly qualified & experienced hair & wig consultants. Clients are welcome to come by appointment (please ring) dressed & made up. Est over 30 years. Mail order available.

BOGNOR/CHICHESTER HELP GROUP

Near A259 south of Drayton roundabout, to the rear of Abelands House Tel: 0124 382 5536 . . . . 04 - First Friday of month.New group that is very popular. Disco, buffet & bar. Admission £5. Held in secure and nice surroundings.

CAMELEON (SOUTHAMPTON)

20 Bellevue Road, Southampton, SO15 2AY Tel: 023 8022 1771; . . . . 04 - Laser hair removal from a company that advertises to trannies. Open 6 days.

CAMEO

Tel: 07768196990/ 0120 276 8298; Email: cameoeditor@aol.com; Website: www.members.aol.com/cameoeditor/ Ask for Sophie; . . . . 04 - This is a friendly support group for the transgender community, based in the Bournemouth and Poole area that meet on 3rd Wednesay of month at Courtyard Centre, Lytchett Minster. Have a bi-monthly magazine. We welcome all TV's, TS's and their partners.

CENTRE STAGE

Nr Uckfield, East Sussex Tel: 01825 890080; Ask for: Judy Neame; . . . . 04 - BBC Make-up artist with a wealth of experience trained in the art of stage, film & photographic make-up & hair design enjoys helping trannies find their feminine image. Learn the skills from Judy. Make-up & wigs can be purchased.

CHICHESTER HELP GROUP

at Bush Inn, 16 The Hornet, Chichester Tel: 0124 382 5536 Ask for: Maureen Website: www.bushinn.com . . . . 04 - Held on 2nd Saturday of the month, it is Free.

CLASSIC CLOTHES DRESS AGENCY

8 Wesley Lane, Bicester, Oxon Tel: 01869 327727; Ask for: Gina Ross; . . . . 04 - Run by tranny friendly Gina this is mainly an agency catering for women. The shop is well stocked with a range of nearly new clothes in all styles. TV's should phone in the first instance to ensure Gina will be present. Open Tue-Sat.

CONFIDENTIAL COUNSELLING

Southampton Tel: 02380 485 769; Email: romenycentre@hotmail.com; Website: www.romenycentre.co.uk; Ask for: Bob & Gloria Hammett; . . . . 04 - Bob is a counsellor and a life coach who offers help to TGs with relationships, partners, families, friends & primary gender confusion issues. Bobs partner Gloria is a qualified clinical hypnotherapist who can help with problems like confidence, weight & anxiety.

ELECTROLYSIS STUDIO

Chichester Tel: 01243 539700; . . . . 04 - Electrolysis Specialist & beauty therapy. TV/TS welcome. Clients dealt with total confidentiality.

FOCUS ON FANTASY @ CHEVY

Bournemouth Tel: 01202 426233 Mobile 07778 800 132; Email: mishca@chevy.co.uk; Website: www.chevy.co.uk; Ask for Michelle; . . . .04 - A comprehensive range of services by a beautician including dressing service, photography, trips out & a full range of beauty treatments & image consultancy. Nail studio available.

... Continued from page 243

Once a month Lacies also organise a dinner at a local restaurant (just a short walk away) which attracts 10- 15 people at a time, including several wives and female friends. This is followed by a trip to tranny-friendly nightclub, The Harlequin (see above). All this costs a mere £25, and the shop is available for getting changed beforehand (at a small additional cost). These evenings are a great way to meet other girls and especially good for newcomers taking their first steps into the big wide world. In short, Lacies has something for everybody and makes the best case yet for a trip out to genteel Hove.

KENTUCKY WOMAN 29 Fernwood Rise, Brighton B1 5ER. Tel 0771 364 8998. www.kentuckywoman.co.uk and **THE COMFORT ZONE**, National House, 50 Brunswick St West, Brighton BN3 1TL. 01273 728312. Kentucky Woman has been a feature on the Brighton scene for many years, and even though the shop in George Street is no more, owner Sandy has never been busier. She now offers a whole line-up of products and services under a variety of company names and from two separate addresses. The range covers everything from the sweet and innocent to the hardcore 'forced-fem': you have been warned!

First of all there's Kentucky Woman itself, which now operates from a nice house in the suburbs with lots of space for parking. Here you can enjoy Sandy's dressing service, which benefits not only from her great experience but also from an enormous wardrobe catering to your every whim. Cost is £120 for a minimum two-hour stay, which can be extended to as long as 6 hours if you wish. To get a better idea of the clothes on offer take a look at the KW web-site, which is the main retail outlet for Sandy's exquisite range of garments. The emphasis is firmly on the feminine, with multi-layered petticoats offerings lashings of lace and 40-yard sweeps of pure chiffon. Glamourous gowns and cocktail dresses – all made to measure –

start from around £200, and there is also a wide range of traditional 'maids' uniforms (from £175). For prospective buyers, anything can be adapted to suit specific tastes, however unusual (rest assured, Sandy has seen it all!). The site also links to 'Classic Corsets' which is KW's sister company specialising in delightful - and again very feminine - corsetry.

Which brings me to Sandy's second Brighton address, at National House. This is the place for wholesale enquiries for the corsets, but the real interest for most readers will be the other services on offer. To begin with there's 'The Comfort Zone', which is a brand new members club offering permanent storage space for your clothes (in lockable wardrobes), along with make-up tables and a lounge where you can "flounce, pose or relax as you please". For £46 per week members have unlimited use of the facilities between 9 and 6pm, whilst additional services such as make-overs and photography can be arranged at an extra cost. The lounge has a TV and PC, shower and kitchen, and there's even a mail collection service (so you can let yourself go on mail order!). The only rules are: "no guests; no smoking" – and all you need to join is to pay a minimum of one month's fees plus a deposit. Downstairs from the Comfort Zone, and separate from it, the mood changes dramatically. Here, behind a solid looking door, is Sandy's piece de resistance - a fully equipped dungeon just like you've seen in all those Channel 5 documentaries! This won't be to every reader's taste, but the room is intended for the exclusive use of TVs/CDs of the submissive variety. You might want to take advantage of Sandy's 'Hellish Photos' service, where you can be photographed here at the mercy of "glaring beauties" acting out your every fetish fantasy. Or else you might come here as a member of 'The Etiquette Society' which is run by the demanding Lady Scarlett Derriere. Applicants must learn "correct behaviour, deportment and dress code" – which means that all those feminine items mentioned earlier will be brought into play, only this time for those of a more 'reluctant' persuasion. The room itself has everything you can imagine, and probably more besides (I was lucky to emerge unscathed!). The cost is £120 for a minimum 2 hours session, and all make-up, wigs and uniforms are provided. As if all this wasn't enough, Sandy is planning yet more ventures, such as a possible TG hotel in Northern France. Watch this space!!

Kentucky Woman

Kentucky Woman

A Personal **Report**

HASTINGS HAVEN

Hastings Tel: 01424 426264; Website:
http://freespace.virgin.net/hastings.haven/ Email:
hastings.haven@virgin.net; Ask for: Dorothy; . . . . 04 -
Well respected and active group running for over 10
years. Meets on first Sat of each month. Call for details.

JENNIFERS

23 West Street, Ringwood, Hants, BH24 1DY Tel:
01425 471312;; Email:
jenny@jennifers99.freeserve.co.uk Website:
www.jennifers99.freeserve.co.uk; . . . . 04 - Still the
South Coasts best stocked friendly fetish store with
discretion and service offering wigs, boots and shoes to
size 12, corsets, dresses, uniforms, lace, PVC, latex,
clubwear, bondage, toys, AB wear & beautiful exclusive
satin made dresses. Wed to Sat 10am to 6pm. Mail
order catalogue available £5.

JOULES HOUSE - IMAGE ZONE

Romsey, Hampshire Tel: 01794 521001 Mob: 07778
931468; Email: joules_house@yahoo.co.uk; Ask for:
Joules; . . . . 04 - Joules offers private & confidential help
with image consultation, hair & wigs, make-up nails,
waxing & all those girlie extras. All Joules's customers
are very happy with the service.

LETS GO GIRLS

Bournemouth Tel: 07092 314330 Website: letsgogirls.tv
04 - Wigs, jeweller, hair, outgoings, dinners.

PRO-ACTIVE WORLD CLASS BREASTS

107 Oaks Drive, St Leonards, Ringwood, Hants BH24
2QS Email: proactivepros@hotmail.com . . . . 04 - 3
Breast ranges, real skin colour and feel (not plastic
wrapped). Send 5 1st class stamps for a breast photo
pack or £5 for amateur video (refundable against any
breast order). Please indicate which product info
required.

READING TV CLUB

Berkshire Tel: 01489 893451; Email:
robyn@tel07768165734.fsnet.co.uk; Ask for: Danielle; .
. . . 04 -Monthly meeting for TVs £6 inc hot buffet and
wine, 4th Weds, and gourmet evenings / pub dinner
parties.

SEAHORSE SOCIETY OF GREAT BRITAIN

BM Seahorse, London WC1N 3XX Email:
Seahorse.Society@btinternet.com; Website:
www.btinternet.com/~seahorse.society Ask for:
Catherine Townsend (president); . . . . 04 - A society
that is actively holding meetings, dinners and other
events. They offering a monthly magazine called
'Seahorse Scene' for members and partners in Southern
England.

SHOUT LGBT SOCIAL GROUP

PO Box 57, Ilfracombe, EX34 0LF Tel: 08710 971069;
Email: info@shoutlgbt.org.uk; Web site:
www.shoutlgbt.org.uk . . . . 04 - North Devon's social
group for the lesbian, gay, bisexual & TG community
and friends. Been running for over 10 years and hold
regular social event in central Barnstaple. Contact for
more details.

TALLGIRLS.CO.UK

P O Box 29,Alton,Hants,GU34 5EP Tel: 01420 587400;
Email: sales@tallgirls.co.uk; Website:
www.tallgirls.co.uk . . . . 04 - Collection of fashion
footwear and clothing. Ring for a free brochure.

THE CLARE PROJECT

Brighton & Hove Tel: 01273 777 177
Email; parsons@portslade.fsnet.co.uk. . . .
04 - Support group in the Brighton & Hove area 1st
Friday of each month between 7.30 & 10, 1-2-1's,
social events, changing facilities, guidance on clothes &
style including shopping trips. Advice on feminisation
techniques.

THE MAYFLOWER CLUB

Southampton Tel: 02380 771798 Mobile: 07005
337157; Email: michelle@mayflower-club.org.uk; Web
site: www.mayflower-club.org.uk Ask for: Michelle; . . .
04 - Large, well organised active & outgoing club.
Meetings held along South Coast from Brighton to
Bournemouth. Holds balls, dancing & meals out.
Monthly magazine. Newcomers welcomed. 7 meetings
every month.

TINA LIVINGSTONE COUNSELLING

Tel: 02380 226050 . . . . 04 - The Premier Partnership.
Over a decade of support experience with TV, TG and
TS's. Working within the the BACP code of ethics.
Tina has B.Ed Hons, Dip.Couns. Person centred
counselling.

TUDOR COUNSELLING & ADVISE SERVICE

Essex Tel: 01268 556334; Email: s.seward@virgin.net; .
04 - Specialising in Gender related problems, anxiety,
depression, pet bereavement & redundancy issues,
phone for an appointment. Flexible rates for clients in
receipt of state benefits.

VA-VA-VOOM

49 Springfield Road, Elburton, Plymstock, Nr Plymouth
PL9 8EP Tel: 01752 402777 Email:
ovavavooom@aol.com Ask for: Olivia Stacey . . . .
04 - Understanding lady who can help you become the
beautiful bride or bridesmaid of your dreams,

BRIGHTON

AQUARIUM

6 Steine Street, Brighton, Sussex, BN2 1TE Tel: 01273
605 525; . . . . 04 - Friendly gay bar.

AXFORDS

82 Centurion Road, Brighton, Sussex, BN1 3LN Tel:
01273 327 944 Fax:01273 220 680; Email:
michael@axfords.com; Website: www.axfords.com
Ask for: Michael; . . . . 04 - Makes back lacing, boned
corsets to give you the hour glass figure you want.
Available in a wide range of styles, materials and
colours, by mail order or online by secure server.

CLASSIC CORSETS

29 Fernwood Rise, Brighton BN1 5ER Tel: 0771-364-
8998 Email: enquiries@classiccorsets.co.uk Website:
www.classiccorsets.com . . . . 04 - Glorious fashions of
the past can be the luxury garments in your immediate
future. Beautiful designs, antique & modern, made in
top quality materials & to your exact requirements.

Visit the Classic Corsets web site to choose the Corset or Petticoat of your dreams or write or telephone for a £5 catalogue.

CLUB REVENGE
32-34 Old Steine, Brighton, BN1 1EL Tel: 01273 606064 Fax: 621063; Email: info@revenge.co.uk; Web site: www.revenge.co.uk; Ask for: Collin Day . . . . 04 - This is Brighton's largest gay night-club. It attracts a young, often mixed crowd. Where trannies are very welcome. The club stages regular drag cabaret in the comfortable cabaret bar which has a magnificent view of the pier. Open 7 nights.

DANCIA (BRIGHTON)
8 Western street, Brighton BN1 2PG Tel: 01273 719001; Email: dancia@lineone.net; Website: www.dancia.co.uk. . . . 04 - We are a dancewear shop specialising in all types of dance apparel, we stock capezio hold and stretch tights in Suntan which are useful for drag

DRESS TO FRILL
Brighton Tel: 07968 099536; Ask for: Tinkerbell; . . . . 04 - Miss Tink is a Tranny trapped in a woman's body who enjoys providing a discreet luxury dressing service with glam wardrobe.

FETISH WAREHOUSE
National House, 50 Brunswick Street West, Brighton BN3 1EL Tel: 0771 364 8998; Email: enquiries@fetishwarehouse.co.uk; Website: www.fetishwarehouse.com . . . . 04 - Designer clothes, shoes, toys, perfume etc. Guaranteed fast delivery and excellent service all at great prices.

GLITZY TARTZ
26 Sydney Street, Brighton BN1 4EP Tel: 01273 674477; Email: info@glitzytartz.co.uk; Website: www.glitzytartz.co.uk . . . . 04 - Prohibition UV clubwear. New in-house collection - many items can be made to measure, this includes corsets. We cater for larger sizes!!

HAIRDRESSER TO THE STARS
Brighton Tel/Fax: 01273 693823 . . . . 04 - Wigs supplied, cleaned & re-dressed. All types of hairdressing undertaken. Very reasonable prices.

HARLEQUIN
43 Providence Place, Brighton (Behind Woolworths in the London Road) Website: www.harlequin-brighton.co.uk Tel: 01273 620630 . . . . 04 - Still recommended as a great night out. A mix of entertainment and a healthy love of tranny customers this is a must visit spot. Also added information and photos at www.realbrighton.com

KAIS BAR
Underneath The Star of Brunswick, Brunswick Street, West Hove, Brighton, Sussex Tel: 01273 771355 . . . . 04 - Brighton's Tranny friendly bar. Sunday lunches. Available for hire.

KENTUCKY WOMAN
29 Fernwood Rise, Brighton, BN1 5ER Tel: 0771 364 8998 Email: enquiries@kentuckywoman.co.uk; Website: www.kentuckywoman.co.uk . . . . 04 - Indulge yourself in ideal surroundings, design studio, for made

to measure clothes, exclusive designs with specialist experience in period costumes, lingerie, corsets, petticoats, haute couture, maid, school and nurse uniforms. Alterations to existing clothes. Customers by appointment only. Telephone for catalogue.

LACIES FGL (FANTASY GIRL) - BRIGHTON
164 Portland Road, Hove, Sussex Tel: 01273 710656 or 0870 203 0402 Email: sue@fantasygirl.co.uk; Website: www.fantasygirl.co.uk . . 04 - Stocks breastforms, shoes, boots, corsets, beardcover, lingerie, wigs and Victorian corsets. Mon-Sat 10.30-5.30pm. Hold Dinner parties in Hove, ring for details.

NEW EUROPE HOTEL
31-32 Marine Parade, Brighton, BN2 1TR www.legendsbar.co.uk Tel: 0127 3624462 . . . . 04 - A gay hotel on the sea front in Brighton. Prices are from £20-30 for a single. The hotel bar, 'Legends' is very popular, hosting regular drag cabaret and karaoke. Very camp. Entertainment most nights of the week. Friendly staff with a lively atmosphere.

SASHA
Brighton Tel: 01273 818307; Ask for: Sasha; . . . . 04 - She-male Sasha offers an exclusive dressing service. Choose how you want to enact your femininity. Select your outfits from exclusive wardrobe. It is now open 7 days a week.

CAFE 22
129 St James Street, Brighton, Sussex Tel: 01273 626682; . . . . 04 - You'll find a genuine warm welcome here, even though it's listed as Brighton's only gay coffee bar.

THE COMFORT ZONE
National House, 50 Brunswick Street West, Brighton BN3 1EL Tel: 0771 364 8998 ..... 04 - Storage Space offering secure wardrobes, drawers and chests, only you will have the key.

THE MARLBOROUGH
4 Princes Street, Brighton Tel: 01273 570028; . . . . 04 - A camp little pub with some drag events. The pub has a tiny theatre upstairs with interesting playlets.

THE QUEENS HEAD
3-10 Stein Street, Brighton. Tel: 01273 602939; . . . . 04 - Freddy Mercury's face swings on the pub sign & a lesbian & gay clientele are served by a lovely couple. This is a fun place to visit. Occasional cabaret.

TRENDCO (RETAIL BRIGHTON)
Sheridan House, 116 Western Road, Hove, Sussex, BN3 1DD Tel: 01273 - 774977 Fax: 01723 720116; Email: trendco@fsbdial.co.uk; Website: www.wigsattrendco.co.uk . . . . 04 - Mon - Sat 9am - 5.30pm. Trendco's head office also has a retail outlet. Offering their range of wigs and hairpieces for those that can visit. They also offer semi permanent make-up. Write for a free catalogue you will not be disappointed. (See also London Hair and Beauty).

UK EAST

ABATE BEAUTY CLINIC
Several Clinics/Salons located throughout Essex Tel: 01268 763912 Mob: 07940 436372; Ask for: Susan Lennie Website: www.abatebeautyclinic.co.uk; . . . . 04 - Botox, Lip enhancement, Chemical facial peels and Electrolysis laser and waxing hair removal, by appointment with Susan Lennie, I.F.H.B. who works alongside medical doctors. She also offers a wide range of other health & beauty treatments and is fully supportive to TSs & TVs.

This club welcomes transvestites, transsexuals, spouses and partners. The club is socially orientated and we meet regularly for company and friendship. The Mayflower has a good reputation and we keep our standards high.

LONDON PUB Some of us every Sunday

HAYLING ISLAND - YEW TREE . (Mixed with Public) 1st Saturday each month we have a meal and drinks there. This is intermingling with the general public, so you need to have a reasonable amount of confidence, and dress convincingly. It has an excellent atmosphere and very comfortable. The owner and staff are very tranny friendly. Food is a speciality and at very reasonable prices. In summer, it is frequented by holiday makers so we major on this pub in winter.

KINGSCLERE - THAMES VALLEY 1st Wed each month we meet at a Hall between Basingstoke and Newbury. Good for the less experienced TV's. Held in a village hall, which is maintained to a very high standard and has efficient heating in winter, so no need to wear a fur coat, unless you want to. It is basically a stand or sit and chat evening. Samantha runs it and provides light snacks and other refreshments. £3 entry.Changing facilities.

THE HARLEQUIN 1st Thursday of every month in Brighton. This is a New Meeting and we meet in a very pleasant venue in the heart of the city. There is disco and cabaret and it is open until the early hours. £2.

WILLOW BARN 1st Friday of every month at the Function Suite, Drayton, Nr Chichester on A259 (Bognor Regis) - a New Venue - first meeting 6th February with big opening night cost £5, disco and buffet & free draw. Don't miss this one.

LYNDHURST HOTEL 2nd Thursday each month. This is a cellar bar at a good hotel, and we have it to ourselves, Just drinks and a chat, no smoking. It is in the centre of the New Forest with easy access to the M27. Being a hotel, food is available in the restaurant. Although not with the public, you do get invited upstairs occasionally to mix with group happenings and make their evening. Changing facilities.

CHICHESTER - THE BUSH 2nd Saturday each month for a social evening and chat. The Bush is a particularly friendly gay pub in the centre of town. There's a dance floor and the music is excellent. Free apart from drinks at pub prices.

TOTTON DISCO 3rd Thursday each month near Southampton . Our monthly disco is held in a large hall. This event has become very popular and is to be recommended for those who want to dance and not talk! Changing facilities.

LANGSTONE CONSERVATIVE CLUB 3rd Friday every month at this New Venue from 16th January. This is a first class venue for drinks and chat. No smoking. £2.

KINGSCLERE - (SEAHORSES) 3rd Saturday each month between Newbury and Basingstoke. This includes a buffet and a couple of drinks freedom bar

FREEDOM BAR 4th Thursday. A transgendered bar in Southampton

SOUTHAMPTON Last Friday of every month we meet at a venue not far from the centre of town. This is what we call the nursery class, for those very new to dressing, who might want advice from more experienced members. Then some members move to the London (pub) and /or the magnum (nightclub) to finish off the evening.

THE GEORGE & DRAGON - SKITTLES NIGHT At Wolverton. Saturday 28th February 2004. Cost £12 includes hot buffet

BOURNEMOUTH WEEKEND
We also run a weekend in Bournemouth in December. a Halloween Ball each year at the end of October, and also an event on Transvestite Day on the 6th August at Totton Disco

SOUTHAMPTON AREA Other TV Friendly Pubs, Clubs & Hotels -
THE EDGE (Club),
THE HONEST LAWYER (Pub),
BAR FUSION (Club),
BOTLEY GRANGE MANOR HOTEL

Further details of The Mayflower & The South - Contact Michelle
Tel: 023 8077 1798
Mobile: 07867 555798
Email: annkin@tiscali.co.uk
Mayflower web site
www.mayflower-club-org.uk
Transgender helpline
Tel 023 8077 1798

A Personal Report

The 'portal' to everything tranny on the Internet

ARABESQUE
50 Queens Road, Buckhurst Hill, Essex Tel: 020 8505 3711 . . . .04 - Dance wear specialists for children and adults. Also stage make-up, hats, masks etc. Costumes made to order. Fancy dress hire. Opening times Mon - Fri 9.30am - 5.30pm. Sat closes at 5.00pm.

BELLEGROVE CLINIC
80a Ruskin Avenue, Welling, Kent DA16 3QR Tel: 020 8298 0155; Website: www.bellegroveclinic.com Ask for Roz. . . . 04 - DepiLite intense pulse light hair removal. A step beyond lasers. Suitable for all areas of the body. Digital Blend electrolysis and full body waxing. 25% TG clientelle. Discreet location close to station.

CAMBRIDGE TV/TS GROUP
"Bird in Hand" Public House, Newmarket Road, Cambridge (Pub Landlords - Contact: David or Roger Tel: 01223 353791) . . . . 04 - Local group that meet weekly in this pub. Usually 1-2 dozen girls turn up each week. (With thanks to Hannah)

CAMBRIDGE TV/TS HELPLINE
Cambridge Tel: 01223 861167 helpline; . . . . 04 - A TV/TS helpline offering support and advice which covers all areas south of Kings Lynn. The helpline is 'manned' after 6pm and at weekends. WOBS support too on Tel: 01223 441246. Social gatherings every Wed at 'The Bird in Hand' pub, Newmarket, Cambridge.

CHRISTINE JENNIFER
P.O.Box 456, Lincoln, LN7 8NL Tel: 07979 49 48 47; Website: www.christinejennifer.co.uk . . . . 04 - Extremely friendly & confidential dressing service with an exceptional range of dressing and fantasy role-play services for first time and long term cross-dressers. For grown ups only also www.discipline-uk.com.

CLIFF HOTEL
48 Hamlet Road, Southend, Essex Tel: 01702 344 466; . 04 - Open: Mon-Sat 12 noon-11pm, Sundays: pub hours. This establishment has regular drag entertainment and music from a resident DJ. Trannies are accepted here.

DEVIANT
P O Box 5516, Southend On Sea, Essex SS0 9UZ Tel: 07833 104159; Email: info@deviant-clothing.co.uk; Website: www.deviantclothing.co.uk Ask for: Haley or Bill; . . . . 04 - We specialise in unusual, unique designs including made to measure service and custom made items including Jo LaVey Corsets, for all your specific needs and desires offering a friendly and prompt service.

ELLA'S DRESSING SERVICE
Grays, Essex Tel: 0795 150 4594 / 01375 394014; . . . . 04 - Dressing facility without time restriction.

EROTIC FANTASY
14 Broomfield Road, Chelmsford, CM1 1SN Tel: 01245 346131; Ask for: Diane or Steve . . . . 04 - Welcomes Trannies to choose from a variety of magazines, videos, shoes and lingerie. Open Mon - Fri 9.00am - 5.30pm & Sat 10.00am - 5.00pm.

FOX AND HOUNDS
Bently Road, Little Bromley, Colchester, Essex CO11 2PL (Off The A120 Harwich Road) Tel: 01206 397415; Contact: John, Website: www.gay-fox.co.uk . . . . 04 - This pub plays host to the major weekly event for East Anglia trans-people and friends on Wed nights. It has grown from strength to strength. People travel from afar to come to this predominantly gay country style pub with a lovely enclosed garden. At weekends they have a disco bar. Changing facilities available but ring Charlie first. Great food especially Sunday roasts. Internet group at http://groups.yahoo.com/group/foxyfriendsuk/

FUDGE
Redbourn Road, (On The Old A5) St Albans, Herts www.fudgeclub.com Email: 01582 794053 . . . . 04 - This friendly gay pub, has a dance floor where they spins the turntables playing great music. Trannies welcome.

WIGS 4 U
4 Stermyn Street, Wisbech, Cambridge, PE13 1EQ Tel: 01945 587584 Fax: 01945 4644444; Email: orders@wigs4u.co.uk; Website: www.wigs4u.co.uk . . . 04 - With well over 25 years of experience, discretion, privacy, & individual care this is a great service. Synthetic & real hair wigs plus reconditioning service for any wigs.

JENNIFER'S DRESS AGENCY
Kent Tel: 07752 161575 Email: jennifer131@btopenworld.com . . . . 04 - Dress in the comfort of a private home with some clothes available to hire/buy. Shopping trips, Escorted Evening trips & Storage facility.

JULIE BABETTE
Herts Junction8 / M11 Tel: 07866 830716; Email: juliebabette2@hotmail.com; Website: communities.msn.co.uk/juliebabettesexualtherapist/welcome . . . . 04 - For individuals, couples or groups seeking to expand their horizons, Julie offers a full range of cross-dressing services, wardrobe, make-overs, wigs. A free counselling service is also available for couples going through transitional changes resulting from gender or fetish issues. Therapies taught include Tantric Massage to Tarot Reading Julies goal is to bring to others a better understanding of sexuality & spirituality.

JULIETS LINGERIE
571 Lincoln Road, New England, Peterborough PE1 2PB Tel: 01733 342234; Email: sales@julietsonline.com; Website: www.julietsonline.com Ask for: Steve Gant; . . 04 - Adult Shop for Fetish,TV wear, restraints, mags, marital aid etc. Open Tue-Sat 10-6pm, Thu 10-7pm.

KENT CROSS-DRESSING SERVICE
Kent Tel: 01303 253194 Mobile: 07944 306113; Email: barbara.tarris@btopenworld.com; Ask for: Barbara; . . . . 04 - Make-up and dressing service, health & beauty diploma. Full make over by qualified beautician. Clothing & wigs. Professional photographs, Wig cleaning.

LACIES FGL (FANTASY GIRL) FOLKESTONE
At Lacies, 127 Dover Road, Folkestone, Kent CT20 1NL Tel: 0870 2030402; Email: sue@fantasygirl.co.uk; Website: www.fantasygirl.co.uk Ask for: Sue; . . . . 04 - Transgender specialist shop & mail order company specialises in breast forms, wigs, footwear & lingerie. Also offers make-up & consultation Complete discretion assured, changing facilities & make overs available.

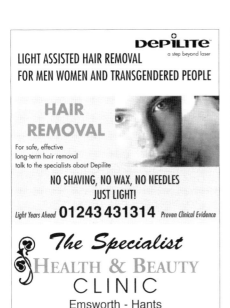

A *Personal* Report

The year began with our (now annual) escape to a winter sun and where better than Maspalomas and Playa del Ingles in Gran Canaria, famous for its friendly nudist beach, and *YUMBO CENTRE*, with lively gay bars, restaurants, drag shows respectively. With temperatures in the high 80's it was perfect to go and top up that all important all over suntan.

February Saw Valentine's *DECADENCE* at our home 'Tranny Grange' in Northampton. Attended by many of our old and very dear friends, we were also pleased to see a few new faces too, and, of course all were given the full Tranny Grange welcome.

March Was the *MISS TRANNY GRANGE CONTEST* at *HOUSE OF DRAG* in Mayfair (where else ?) where Jo was most put out that she was pipped to the post by a pair of shoes (Stella Cottee's)!

May Time for a Tranny expedition to *LAS VEGAS - MARDI GRAS*. Six of us met up with Steph and Jane Grey from Detroit. The Americans LOVED us and a huge cheer went up, as our Mardi Gras vehicle, covered in stickers and union flags, drove past the judges. The local gay newspaper, The Las Vegas Bugle, reported with a colour photo of our own Lynn Daniels with Sasha Scarlett on the front page. The shopping there was wonderful, and everyone was so friendly. Mention must be made here of a fetish shop called *BARE ESSENTIALS*, where the two gay owners gave us plenty of time to make our selections and also provided us with a lot of information about the local scene. Just a couple of doors down the street we came across *RED SHOES* – just the place for those spectacular heels.

From Vegas we went to Palm Springs. Where in addition to clubbing, we went to *PARADISE NAILS*, a nail clinic run by a Vietnamese family who were just lovely. We had manicures, pedicures, eyebrow waxing, In the evening we went to fabulous clubs such as Toucan's and Blame it on Midnight. I even entertained the natives at *CACTUS JACK* with a karaoke spot. We also visited the local hardware store, *TRUE VALUE*, where we made friends with Evan and Jay. The result was an illuminated pink flamingo and palm tree on which we had to pay excess baggage to get them home !

We spent a couple of days in Hollywood shopping, more wigs, more shoes, more lingerie from Fredericks. (see our last report in the 11th Tranny Guide for details of these shops). Everywhere we went we were greeted by warm friendly people and we really didn't want to come home,

June Fresh from Mardi Gras in Las Vegas we were ready for Gay Pride in London. Our t-girl driver, Jennifer, provided us with a float vehicle, Tranny Grange girl, Stella Read made the signs, and Miss Debbie Di Amante designed our sparkly dresses which were adorned with feather boas. With the Palm Springs flamingos, palm tree, and of course, WayOut girls including Vicky Lee with life partner Leslie, Steffan and Sarah Lloyd, along

with Lynn Daniels, we were ready to go. All that remained was to start up the generator and open the champagne. What a wonderful day we had. Starting in Whitehall Place just off Northumberland Avenue, the parade went along the Embankment, right past the palace of Westminster, Downing Street, up into Trafalgar Square, Piccadilly Circus and finishing in Park Lane. The sun shone, the music was loud, the whistles blew, the crowds cheered and waved. It was CARNIVAL and we were a part of it. A Magical day.

August As the summer drew to a close it was time for a holiday at **TRANNY COVE**. This has become a popular annual event and several of our friends made the journey down to our seaside retreat near Padstow. As well as relaxing in the sunshine, guests helped out with our latest project - transforming an old summer house into a delightfully camp (and very pink !) bar.

By day they relaxed by the patio log fire, and as Miss Debbie prepared a banquet under a parasol bedecked with pink sweetheart lights, Nicki hostessed one of her famous barbecues. Friends old and new, including a visitor all the way from Copenhagen, Miss Katarina Collins, of whom more later, all joined together for four days of relaxation in warm and friendly like minded company.

September

Heralded Richard O'Brien's **TRANSFANDANGO BALL** in Manchester. This event was extraordinarily well organised, and presented us with opportunities to meet many famous celebrities from stage & screen. The theme was Fairy Fantasy and Richard truly was Prince (or was it Princess?) Charming. We were entertained while we dined in the truly

I would like to take this opportunity to thank Nicki & Debs for their support and friendship again this year. Thanks you for twisting our WayOut arm to help get the London Mardi Gras float off the ground (and I mean "off the ground" at least I felt like I was flying that day). I very much look forward to your company at SCC in Atlanta.

Vicky Lee

I asked Vicky Lee, how long an article did I need to write. She said to my astonishment that she had put aside four pages in the 12th Tranny Guide. The prospect of filling those pages filled me with trepidation, and then I started looking at our diary and remembered just what a SPECTACULAR year it has been and what FABULOUS things we have done, and I began to wonder, how am I going to get it all in ?

Gran Canaria in January,
Valentine's Decadence in February,
Miss Tranny Grange at Silicone Dolls in March,
Vegas and Palm Springs in May,
Repartee Thames Boat Trip in July,
London Mardi Gras also in July,
Tranny Cove Bank Holiday in August,
Transfandango in September as well as,
Rocky Horror at the Queens Theatre
Schoolgirls of St. Trannians in October,
Copenhagen in November,
and, of course,
Festive December with Christmas Decadence,
The WayOut Christmas Party
and finally New Year at Las Moggas
(where ? Well it's actually Carn Moggas
Caravan Park near St. Austell- Not what you'd
expect, trust me, it was FABULOUS)
and of course every spare weekend we
alternated between WayOut in London and
our seaside retreat, Tranny Cove in Cornwall.

A Personal Report

glamourous setting. The 'ladies' and gentlemen were dazzling in sparkles, glamour and tuxedos.

This was such a worthwhile event not to be missed. Not only for the quality of the night and the opportunity to mix but also because the night was held to raise money for the Manchester Children's Hospital via Wallness Children's Charity. We are looking forward to the event moving to London where many more will be able to attend. However the Manchester venue did give us the added opportunity to explore MANCHESTER'S GAY VILLAGE around Canal Street and try out a couple of fabulous restaurants I am sure we will be back here too.

November As the nights drew in it was time for another Decadence party at Tranny Grange. Called SCHOOLGIRLS OF ST. TRANNIANS this was a huge success, not only with those that attended, but also with a lot of people who would have LOVED to have been there. Miss Debbie donned a cap and gown to become a severe School Mistress whilst Nicki did was she does best – misbehaved ! I think this might be one we shall repeat before too long.

'Schoolgirls' was hot on the heels of our first visit to the Queens Theatre (in drag of course!) to see the ROCKY HORROR STAGE SHOW. The evening started with a meal at the fabulous RANDALL & AUBIN'S FISH RESTAURANT in Brewer Street, Soho, where we were made VERY welcome by manager, Daniel, a real cute Aussie guy, and attended to by equally lovely waiters. This lent itself to a wonderful photo opportunity outside the restaurant and in PIRATE the sex shop across the street – firm favourite of ours.

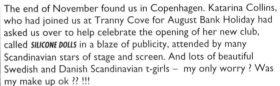

The end of November found us in Copenhagen. Katarina Collins, who had joined us at Tranny Cove for August Bank Holiday had asked us over to help celebrate the opening of her new club, called SILICONE DOLLS in a blaze of publicity, attended by many Scandinavian stars of stage and screen. And lots of beautiful Swedish and Danish Scandinavian t-girls – my only worry ? Was my make up ok ?? !!!

December Soon arrived, and with festive lights festooning the front of our home 'Tranny Grange '
(am I the first tranny National Lampoon I ask myself ?), in readiness for the first of the season's parties, CHRISTMAS DECADENCE. This was another spectacular party, featuring Lady Debbie Di Amante's Delectable Sumptuous Grande Buffet, as usual = smoked salmon and prawns, vol-au-vents with a choice of fillings, cold meats, chipolatas and cheese-and-pineapple-on-a-stick ! To help it on its way, there was bubbly in abundance. There were of course the usual regulars, and we were pleased to welcome a couple of new girls too. By the end of the night the new girls had made lots of new friends. Tranny Grange is discreetly located so girls can arrive dressed or in civilian mode – which ever way they feel most comfortable. Once inside, visitors are introduced to other guests, who invariably help to make them to feel at home. Help with make up, hair styling, and choosing outfits, is always available.

Christmas came and Christmas went – on December 27th we packed our best frocks, vanity cases, shoes and my wigs, to travel down to TRANNY COVE once more. A couple of days later we were partying to celebrate the Grand Opening of The Pink Flamingo, our bar conversion, upon which our dear friends, Amanda and Natasha, had worked especially hard. With tinsel, twinkly pink and white lights, animated and illuminated pink flamingos in the corner, and a roaring log fire on the patio outside, the stage was set for yet another FABULOUS party.

January

Of course, New Year's Eve was fast approaching and we were making our way across to CARN MOGGAS, near St. Austell, for what is now an annual party, where all our old friends from PINKIES at the Sandridge Hotel in Newquay, all get together, after its closure in the Spring of 2002. We slept in caravans, it was freezing cold, and raining – but in the clubhouse the atmosphere, the welcome, the joy of seeing our friends again made it all worthwhile. There were only three trannies there that night, of which I was one. But it really didn't matter. What fun! What joy! And we celebrated the chiming of Big Ben at midnight, which we watched on a huge screen on the wall, along with countless millions across the country.

Yes 2003 was a busy year at Tranny Grange – one in which we made so many friends in several different countries. In 2004 we have already returned to Gran Canaria, and to Copenhagen, back to Kat's club, Silicone Dolls, There will be more visits there, as well as many, many, visits to our favourite London venue, THE WAYOUT CLUB, and the usual Tranny holidays at Tranny Cove. There will be Decadence parties, with schoolgirls and a welcome (I'm sure) return of BRIDAL DECADENCE in the summer. We are also making plans for our contribution to Mardi Gras parades in London and Copenhagen, and looking forward to this year's Transfandango Ball.

"The tranny lifestyle is truly FABULOUS and we consider ourselves to be extremely fortunate to be able to meet and count many wonderful people as our friends".

We are also planning a return to Las Vegas and Palm Springs in the Autumn, taking in on the way the legendary SOUTHERN COMFORT t-girl conference in Atlanta USA, where there will be around 600 t-girls and numerous girlie make up courses, trade stalls where we can buy anything from shoes, to make up and the most fabulous hairstyles, not forgetting, jewellery. Of course not forgetting the Grand Ball……..The stage is set for yet another FABULOUS party.

More information about our adventures, friends and the chance to join us can be found , either on our website **www.trannygrange.com**, where, incidentally there are lots more photographs of the events described here, or by e-mail to
nicki-and-debs@trannygrange.com

Nicki & Debs In association with a t-friendly holiday accommodation provider in Padstow, North Cornwall are pleased to offer delightful, self-catering holiday accommodation in a discreet location and yet not far from the local town with all its shops, restaurants and amenities.

The property itself is a detached bungalow with conservatory in a quiet lane about 3/4 mile from Padstow town centre. Entrance is largely un-overlooked.

The cottage is particularly suitable for 'shoulder' and low season holidays when the area is particularly quiet and tranquil.

In order to book, or make enquiries, please use the link on the web page, and be sure to mention the Internet 'T' Discount Rate. This will automatically qualify you for 10% off our published tariff. **www.trannygrange.com**

A Personal Report

UK ■ East

LAKESIDE & BLUEWATER
Dartford / Greenhithe Tel: 08456 021021; . . . .
04 -Two enormous shopping malls. Heaven for clothes shopping and a beautiful place to visit. Try afternoons of the early days in the week up to 9pm for an un-hurried experience. Larger sizes in the latest trends from House of Frazer, John Lewis, M&S, Team, Evans and many of the smaller shops. Nearby Lakeside has a slightly cheaper range of shops plus Debenhams, Bentalls and Suzy Wigs

LINDABRIGGS.CO.UK
Phoenix House, Main Street, Welney, Norfolk, PE14 9RB Tel: (01354) 610368 fax610393 or 07702037925; Email: info@lindabriggs.co.uk; www.LindaBriggs.co.uk 04 - Independent cosmetic surgery advice in UK & Overseas. Permanent hair removal with Plasamlite. Cosmeceuticals for problem skin. Cosmetic Surgery Insurance. New on-line shop with new products being added. Anything not in the shop already Linda will try to stock it for you.

MICHAEL ROBERT WIG CENTRE
9 Queens Road, Southend on Sea, Essex SS1 1LT Tel: 01702 341791; Email: michaelwigs@yahoo.co.uk; Website: www.wigsbymichaelrobert.co.uk . . .
04 - We supply ladies wigs and offer for our T.V/ T.S clients if required evenings or Sundays and Monday appointments when the salon is closed.

MICHELLES FASHIONS
105 Epping New Road, Buckhurst Hill, Essex, IG9 5TQ Tel: 020 8504 0418 fax 020 8559 0999; Email: sales@michellefashions.com; Website: www.michellefashions.com. . . . 04 - Offering a very comprehensive range of sexy clothes for any occasion. clubbing, fetish party, boudoir or just your mirror. If it is rubber or uniforms that turns you on they have those too. Boots & shoes from sizes 4-13,clothes sizes from 8-24. Free list of catalogues on request.

MISS-BY-ELAINE
Lifestyle, Lifestyle, PO Box 438, Epsom, Surrey, KT19 9YQ Tel: 01474 324238; Email: elaine@miss-by-elaine.com; Website: www.miss-by-elaine.com . . . .
04 - We sell made to order and measure fantasy clothing

NATALIE - DRESSMAKER
Maidstone, Kent Tel: 01622 744 530; . . . . 04 - Natalie is a real lady who offers dressmaking services to cross-dressers at inexpensive prices. She can make anything from cocktail dresses and evening wear to hip shapers tailored to your own measurements. Some ready-to-wear items of clothing are available, as well as her very special Can-Can skirts.

OASIS GROUP
Tel: 0150 849 2551 . . . . 04 - Held on 1st Friday and 3rd Saturday of month. At Loft, 80 Rose Lane, Norwich and Castle, 1 Spitalfields, Norwich

ROSE & CROWN
77 Norwich Road, Ipswich Tel: 01473 211117; Ask for: Sarah; . . . . 04 - Friendly pub with a warm welcome gay / straight mixed clientele. TVs are welcome & they have occasional tranny nights with drag entertainment.

SELF HELP ESSEX
Essex Tel: 01255 861432; . . . . 04 - Between 6pm-9pm. Upon ringing this line you'll speak to Penny who will tell you that this helpline has been running for over 11 years, by full time transsexuals, for TVs and TSs. Their aim is to help prevent others from being 'ripped off' and to give common-sense practical advice.

SHEILA GRACE, HAUTE-COUTURE DRESSMAKER
Essex Tel: 01702 200067; . . . . 04 - Made to measure quality clothes from a lady who knows how important it is to express femininity. Day, evening & bridal wear.

SUZI WIGS
506 Brompton Walk, Lakeside Shopping Centre, West Thurrock, Grays, Essex, RM20 2ZL Tel: 01708 865515; Email: sales@suziwigs.co.uk; Website: www.suziwigs.co.uk Ask for: June and Jean; . . . . 04 - Fashion wigs from many suppliers. Established since 1976. Now with better private cubicles in their shop. This very friendly wig shop have over 200 styles to choose from, starting from £35 & if they haven't got your exact colour they will get it for you. They will maintain & re-style a wig bought from them. The staff are fully familiar with the needs of trannies.

T & T EPILATION & BEAUTY
South East Tel: 01376 322209 / 07887 723239; Web site: www.ttepilation.com Ask for: Tina and Tracy; . . . . 04 - Offering Plasmalite hair removal for the transgendered community by fully qualified TV.

THE LODGE (UPMINSTER)
West Lodge, 67 Corbets Tey Road, Upminster, Essex, RM14 2AJ Tel: 01708 220730 or 01708 224724; . . . . 04 On the 1st Wed of every month The Lodge runs this night for glamour, with a disco cabaret & events. Parking & changing facilities. TV/TS admirers welcome. Entrance between Prefect Pizza & a nail parlour.

THE BIRD IN HAND
73 Newmarket Road, Cambridge CB4 8EG Tel: 0122 335 3791; . . . . 04 - Club held every Wednesday but welcomed anytime. Basic changing facilities.

TRANNYGRANGE
Northampton Email: nicki-and-debs@trannygrange.com Website: www.trannygrange.com. . . . 04 - Debbie and tranny partner Nicki hold their decadence parties at their home. These parties are well attended & often move on to a local resturant which stays open till late. Limited accommodation is available. Plenty of pictures on their website. Limo trips to events inc

TRANSCARE
PO Box 3, Basildon, Essex. SS13 3WA Tel: 01268 583761; Email: stacy@transliving.co.uk; Website: www.transliving.co.uk; Ask for: Stacy (quote tg03); . . . . 04 - Offering all beauty salon services, make-up lessons hairdressing wig care, wig sales, dermablend beard cover, Avon eyelash building fibres, heated eye lash curling wand, underwear & corset items along with fun clothing, Breast forms, boob boosters, all tranny beauty needs catered for including waxing.

TRANSLIVING GROUP

P.O. Box 3, Basildon, Essex, SS13 3WA Tel: 01268 583761; Email: stacy@transliving.co.uk; Website: www.transliving.co.uk Ask for: Stacy; . . . . 04 -This is a TV/ TS support group based in Essex, with one of the best group magazines. Established as a non-profit company serving the interests of transgendered people everywhere providing support not only for them but also for those with whom they interface. The Help line is manned Wed & Sun 7pm to 10pm, ansaphone other times. Membership benefits include four copies of their magazine 'Trans Life', periodic newsletters, discounted admission to parties, confidential contacts, special discount benefits on products. They hold monthly parties with themes and competitions.

TRANSLIVING (NIGHTCLUB)

PO Box 3, Basildon, Essex SS13 3WA Tel: 01268 583761; Email: stacy@transliving.co.uk; Website: www.transliving.co.uk Ask for Stacy Novak; . . . .
04 - Nightclub run by TransLiving on 4th Friday of every month. Members £5.00 Non-Members £7.00. Open 7.30pm to Late. Easy going disco with competitions including their annual 'Supergirl' pageant.

WENDY JANE

168a Station Road, March, Cambridgeshire, PE15 8NG Tel: 01354 661467; Email: sales@wendyjane.com; Web site: www.wendyjane.com . . . .04 - The UK's Best Stocked Fetish & Adult Shop. Manufacturers and Supplies of Tinkerbell's AB & Sissywear, Trade Enquires Welcome.Tue-Sat 10-6, Thu 10-7.

UK WEST

ANDREA MCGILL WIGS

Near Manchester Tel: 01746 768833; . . . . 04 - Day, evenings & weekend appointments. Andrea offers a large selection of quality wigs from the USA, Europe & Asia, which she can cut & style to suit you. She has many years of experience serving the TV & TS's community. Tuition given in how to wear the wig with confidence. Highly recommended. Convenient for M25, M6, M40, M42, M54.

APPEARANCES

Gloucester Tel: 01452 610389; Email: laura@appearances.freeserve.co.uk; Website: www.appearances-by-laura.co.uk Ask for Laura; . . . .04 - Help and advise on selecting feminising hairstyles, the care of and products for maintenance, by mutual appointment in a calm and supportive atmosphere.

What is your name and what is your background?

My name is Karen Clark T-Girl, I am divorced and now single and live and work in Suffolk as a professional artist.

Are you happy to be called a Tranny and what does this name mean to you?

Yes I am ok with being called a Tranny, although I do prefer T-Girl, but definitely not happy with being called a Transvestite or even worse a Cross-dresser. I look upon Tranny being the collective term for all who are transgendered.

How old are you and how young can you remember thinking about or actually cross-dressing?

Well you shouldn't ask a girls age but as you have, I am 40 something. First memories go back to about nine years old and since then I have followed the same Tranny journey as so many others.

Where do you buy clothes?

Mostly in the High Street, seldom mail order, unless it is fetish fashion, then I order from outlets like Honour or Westward Bound. My fav shop though is in my home town, a small boutique that sells one off designer clothes from Paris.

What leads you to choose the styles you wear?

Well I follow the fashion trends of the moment, I am lucky to be only 5'8", size 12, and shoe size 7 so buying clothes to fit is not a problem. Although I love short skirts, I am just as happy wearing jeans or long evening dresses. Shoes though must have a heel of 4" or higher.

Do you have one look or many images?

I have played around with looks and images over the years, that is just the learning curve, if you don't experiment then you will never find the look you want. Last year I settled with the look I have now.

Is make-up and hair important to you and if so how do you achieve your look?

Absolutely important, I learnt a lot about make-up techniques at Image Works and would advise any girl who has not had a make-over to visit Pandora and her team at Image Works or Jodie Lynn at the Boudoir. As for achieving my look, well I use Kryolan paintstick and powder for my foundation and Kryolan eye shadows. Liquid eyeliner is a must, as is lip liner. My hair, well I have now settled with one style of wig and colour, all my wigs are made by Noriko, expensive but worth every penny. I also have my own hair cut in a short female style.

To what degree do you practice hair removal and other body feminisation?

Body hair is not to much of a problem, so shaving sees to that, by the time this is read I will have had my first sessions of laser treatment on my face. As for other feminisation, I pluck and shape my eyebrows and have both ears and my belly button pierced.

Who knows you dress?

Just about everyone I know, I came out fully last year. Made the decision to tell, as I could not live a lie any longer. The response was amazing and fully supportive from everyone.

How often do you dress and if you go out where to?

I do not have much in the way of a male wardrobe now, so you could say I dress every day. On Wednesday nights I can always be found at the Fox and Hounds in Essex, now the number one venue in the East of England for tranny's. At weekends if in London, I can be found at The WayOut Club, Stormes, Transmission or Angelic. But not only tranny venues, myself and my three closest girlfriends will also do normal clubs, restaurants and bars, also shopping.

How much of a sexual turn on is trannying for you?

Not at all, ok if I'm honest it was in my early teens, but not now!, although I am bisexual, so will leave that to your imagination.

What is your definition of feminine?

To not only have the image of being female, but to have an inner feeling of femininity and being able to use that in your body language. I see so many girls let themselves down by the way they walk, sit and failing to use female mannerisms.

To what degree do you feel gender dysphoric?

Feelings have been confused over the years, but now I am happy with who I am and Karen is the real me.

To what degree would you consider permanent hair removal, hormones, or surgery?

I am having permanent hair removal and I am on hormones, as for surgery! well if I was a lot younger then that would be a serious option, but at the age I am I will stop at GRS. Just a personal decision.

What one piece of advice would you give to someone that has just found they are not the only tranny in the world?

Well they are really lucky!, in this day and age the transgender world has opened up so much, that the only advice I can give is, be proud of who you are and get out there and have fun.

259

CENTRAL FINANCIAL PLANNING LTD
2nd Floor, Rigby Hall, Rigby Lane, Bromsgrove B60 2EW Tel: 01527 879555 Mob:07811 945045; Email: Fax: 01527 879575; Website: www.centralfinancialplanning.co.uk Ask for Ian Smith; . . 04 - Tranny friendly financial planning company that is authorised and regulated by the Financial Services Authority. They were also the sponsors of the 2002 Alternative Miss London Contest.

DANA'S INFERNO
Cardiff City Tel: 07799 032010/07949 327369 £1.50 min Email: mistress@danasinferno.com Website: www.danasinferno.com Ask for Mistress Dana; . . . . 04 - This is an excellent dressing service based in a private premises. Large selection of clothes, wigs, shoes, boots, etc. Photographs available on digital camera & video. Make-up lessons. Monthly TV parties.

DAUPHINES OF BRISTOL
34 Clouds Hill Road, St George, Bristol, BS5 7LA Tel: 0117 9551700; Website: www.dauphines.co.uk Ask for Madeleine or Allen; . . . . 04 - Excellent wig service with private studio, prices from £50. Make-up advice too, qualified member of the British Association of Skin Camouflage. Large selection of eyeshadows, blushers, lipsticks & nail polishes. Est 39 years. Postal service available.

ERICA POOLE I.P.T.I.   A.R.M.T. (WALES)
Wales Tel/Fax 01932 867502; . . . . 04 - Ring for appointment. With over 24 years of experience treating TVs and TSs through electrolysis including state of the art computer controlled electrolysis (almost painless). She also offers qualified counselling.

FEELING FOXY
2-4 Skinner Street, Newport, South Wales NP20 1GY Tel: 01633 252536; Email: feelingfoxyuk@hotmail.com; Website: www.feelingfoxy.co.uk; . . . . 04 - Also another shop at: 26 Castle Arcade, Cardiff, South Wales CF10 1BW Tel: 02920 342020 Sells Basques up to 42" back, bra's up to 46" back. Outsize full briefs, stockings.

HEYWOOD LODGE COUNTRY HOUSE HOTEL
Heywood Lodge Country House Hotel, Heywood Lane, Tenby, Pembrokeshire,Dyfed, SA7O 8BN Tel: 01834 842684 fax 01834 843796; Email: kt@lodge95.freeserve.co.uk Website: www.heywoodlodge.com; Ask for Marion Stone; . . . 04 - TV friendly four star luxury hotel set in an acre of well groomed relaxing garden. Marion has luxury features in her various rooms, so you can choose from jacuzzi bath four-poster bed. Food here is a speciality. If a relaxing girly weekend away is on your list of TV treats, this may be the location all year. Send now for the latest brochure. Essential to telephone first to book your tranny visit and be sure to ask for Marion Stone.

KRYSTYNA
North Wales Tel: 0161 928 2344; Email: krystyna.bradley@lineone.net; Website: http://website.lineone.net/~krystyna.bradley . . . . 04 - Krystyna & her female staff offer a very professional & comprehensive service including B&B, & a vast wardrobe. Escorts are available for trips out. A range of beauty treatments, clothing, wigs & specialist tranny products are available such as hip & bum pads £18.50 + p&p £2.50, silicone breast forms £125 + p&p £8.50. Krystyna's is highly recommended.

LLANBERIS COTTAGES
Tan-y-Coed, North Wales Tel: 01286 674481 Mobile: 07887 790714 Ask for Anne Marie; . . . . 04 - Northern Concord member and OTV Anne Marie, offers a welcome and a choice of 3 cottages with all mod cons, amongst the lakes, beaches of North Wales at the foot of Snowdon Mountains.

MANHATTANS
49 Oxford Street, Weston Super Mare . . . . 04 - Saturday nights til 2.30am

SPANK
Email: spankreservations@hotmail.com www.spankpromotions.co.uk and www.theinnercircleclub.org.uk . . . . 04 - Club events arranged see websites for details.

THE QUEEN'S SHILLING
9 Frogmore Street, Bristol Tel: 0117 926 4342; . . . . 04 - The Queen's Shilling is a mixed gay bar with disco Thursday to Sunday (Cabaret alternate Sundays). The lively locals are friendly to cross-dressers.

THE WORKZ
10 Bastion Road, Prestatyn, North Wales, L19 7ES Tel: 01745 856816; Ask for: Jayne; . . . . 04 - Beauty and tanning shop. Very tranny friendly.

TRANSFORMATION (BRISTOL)
273 Southmead Road, Southmead, Bristol Tel: 0870 741 5544; Email: orders@transformation.co.uk; Website: www.transformation.co.uk. . . . 04 - Open: 9am-8pm Mon-Sat. We have heard very good reports about the help and service at this branch of this well known UK chain of TV/TS shops which offers a broad range of goods and services to cross-dressers.

UNIQUE TS/TV GROUP
North Wales Tel: 01244 548973 Email: uniquegender@yahoo.co.uk . . . . 04 - Helpline on Tues/Thurs 6.30-10.30. Meetings 2nd Thursday every month. Changing facilities.

WEST COUNTRY WIG MAKERS
Freepost, Callington, Cornwall, PL17 7BR Tel: Freephone: 0800 592 179 Fax: 01579 384685; Email: jackie.gawman@btconnect.com . . . . 04 - Tranny friendly Wigmakers, they also have imported wigs. Offering a great nationwide Home Visiting Service.

261

WASHINGTON NIGHT CLUB

Llandudno, North Wales Tel: 078814 78675 Email: ken4ian@aol.com Ask For: Ken & Ian . . . . 04 - Popular Club Every Thursday night, doors open at 9pm, club busy by 11 so doors close approx 12. Bar open til 1.30am. Fun, safe environment with small side shows weekly and big entertainment once a month.

UK SOUTH WEST

BODMIN 'OURWAY'

Tel: 01209 215887 . . . . 04 - Group that meets the 3rd Friday of the month.

LATEX BALL

Plymouth Devon Tel: 01752 221416 Fax: 01752 221417; Email: info@westwardbound.com; Website: www.westwardbound.com . . . . 04 - A decadent night in association with Westward Bound. These parties have set the south-west alight with fetish fever and sell out so book ahead. Friendly light hearted with outfits to die for but with a strict dress code. Next event on 26th June 2004 and 30th October 2004 - tickets sell out quickly so get your tickets in advance. See website for latest dates and further details

PENZANCE 'OURWAY'

Tel: 01209 215887 . . . .
04 - Group that meets the 4th Friday of the month.

REDRUTH 'OURWAY'

Tel: 01209 215887 . . . .
04 - Group that meets the 1st Friday of the month.

SOPHIE'S (DRESSING SERVICE)

Bath Tel: 07754 780034; Email: sophies@btinternet.com Website: www.sophies.co.uk Ask for Juliette; . . . . 04 - "Five Star" say our correspondents. Ask for Juliette for details of this dressing service, where you can stay for a few hours or an extensive holiday. Clothes and wigs can be provided, but take your own undies. You may well be sharing the lounge and self-catering facilities with a number of like-minded visitors. Juliette is a qualified make-up artist, so you can have a facial or make-over.

SPECIAL SAUCE

180c Cheltham Road, Bristol, BS6 5RB. Tel: 0117 9247177; Email: emma@specialsauce.co.uk; Website: www.specialsauce.co.uk . . . . 04 - Corsetry.

SWG

Trinity Rd Library, Opposite Police Stn, Bristol Tel: 0117 951 4481; Email: leonard@vowles.fsworld.co.uk; Ask for Rita; . . . . 04 - SWG meet on the 4th Saturday of every month followed by a night at Roosters night club or a meal. Twice a year in May and October they run the Kentisbury Revival Group which is a weeks holiday at St Audries Bay Holiday Club, that has Caravans and Chalets available and is made exclusive for the transgender community. Contact Mary or Jo on 01984 632515 for more info.

THE CLIFFHOUSE HOTEL

St Marks Rd, Torquay, Devon, TQ1 3EH Tel: 01803 294656; Website: www.cliffhousehotel.co.uk Ask for A.

Wilson or Rob Smith; . . . . 04 - A gay hotel within 5 minutes walk of Torquay Harbour. Very tranny friendly. Bar & lovely gardens, an ideal place to go & unwind. The management are very welcoming & supporting. Thanks to Vicky Valentine.

THE UNDERCROFT

Torquay Tel: 01803 212483 or 07971 791975; Email: warwickw@tinyonline.co.uk; Ask for Rev'd P Whelan . . . . 04 - Highly qualified counselling, psychotherapy, pychosexual therapy for the trangendered.

TRANNYGRANGE HOLIDAYS

Cornwall Email: nicki-and-debs@trannygrange.com; Website: www.trannygrange.com . . . . 04 - Debbie & tranny partner Nicki offer friendly accommodation near Padstow close to "Rick Steins" restaurants. Deb's & Nicki host Decadence Holidays ask for dates.

WESTWARD BOUND (SHOP)

44 Drake Circus, Plymouth, Devon PL4 8AB Tel: 01752 221416 Fax: 01752 221417; Email: info@westwardbound.com; Website: www.westwardbound.com Ask for Steve; . . . . 04 - Wigs, heels, corsets plus own brand PVC, latex and fetish clothing. Free catalogue full mail order service. Open Tues-Sat 10.30-5pm.

WICKED WARDROBE

Aldershot Tel: 01252 640417; Email: wickedwardrobe@ntlworld.com; . . . . 04 - Wide range of costumes, lingerie, daywear, evening gowns, wigs, shoes, boots and jewellery. They offer make-overs, escorted trips and maid training and scenarios. A mailbox and storage facility is available and occasionally hold a TV dinner party.

ZERO'S NIGHT CLUB

24 Lockyer Street, Plymouth Tel: 01752 662 346; Ask for: Robby; . . . . 04 - Predominantly mixed gay but tranny friendly nightclub, recently refurbished, occasionally hosting special tranny nights.

SCOTLAND

3G (GRAMPIAN GENDER GROUP)

Contact Info Line: 07050 562175 (7-9pm), Email: ggg_aberdeen@yahoo.co.uk; . . . . 04 - A group that meet once a month supporting the transgendered community in Aberdeen and Aberdeenshire, Scotland.

A AND A STUDIOS

8 - 10 Tanfield, Inverleith, Edinburgh, EH3 5HF, Scotland Tel: 0131 5567057 Fax 0131 5563223; Ask for Gordon; . . . .04 - Wigs & Hair extensions by the recognised specialists. Complete privacy and individual attention, consultations & advice on styling and make-up. Grimas make-up products & brochures available.

AROMATHERAPY & REFLEXOLOGY

11 Attow Road, Glasgow, Scotland, G43 1BZ Tel: 0141 632 1440 Ask For: Linda Alexander . . . . 04 - Linda has been to Crosslynx group giving talks on aromatherapy and reflexology. (listing with thanks to Ruth)

BELMONT BRIDAL STUDIOS
Aberdeen Tel: 01224 641 741; Email: jane@belmontbridal.com Website: www.belmontbridal.com; Ask for Jane; . . . . 04 - A range of gowns and accessories is available. Our service to the crossdressing community is strictly mail order or by prior private appointment with myself Jane so phoning or e-mail essential.

BENNETS
80-90 Glassford Street, Glasgow, Scotland Tel: 0141 552 5761 fax: 0141 552 5761; Email: BennetsWeb@aol.com; Website: www.bennets.co.uk. . . . 04 - This very popular gay night-club attracts a friendly gay crowd, who welcome trendy trannies. The club has regular drag cabaret acts from around the country, as well as great music.

CONNIE FAIRBAIRN M.DES
Scotland Tel/Fax: 0131 557 6554 or 0797 9000701; . . . . 04 - Designer Connie makes possibly the 'best fantasy corsetry in the country'. Including special wild theatrical costumes, & she can make one off made to measure corsets for you.

COUPLE COUNSELLING (SCOTLAND)
18 York Place, Edinburgh,EH1 3CEP Tel: 0131 558 9669 of fax 0131 556 6596 Email: enquiries@couplecounselling.org; Website: www.couplecounselling.org . . . . 04 - Trained sexual and relationship counselling and sexual therapist. All relationships, gender and sexualities. 14 agencies throughout Scotland.

CROSSLYNX TV/TS SUPPORT GROUP
Glasgow & West Scotland c/o SGLS, P.O. Box 38, Glasgow, G2 2QF Tel: 0141 847 0787 - Mon 7.30 - 9.30pm; Email: caroltaylorg@tesco.net; Website: www.geocities.com/crosslynx. . . . 04 - Helpline Mondays 7.30-9.30pm. A TV/TS support group wives & partners most welcome. "An A-Z Guide to Crossdressing" compiled by Carol Taylor, is available from the group or Crosslynx, c/o GGLC, 11 Dixon St, Glasgow, G1 4AL

DENNIS (DENISE) AND SHEILA
Inverness Tel: 01667 462073; Email: dennis.mccrudden@tesco.net Ask for: Dennis (Denise) & Sheila; . . . . 04 - Dennis (Denise) and Sheila invite you to their small, friendly guest house in the Highlands, 5 minutes from Inverness Airport. 10 minutes from Inverness. Fort George and the beach are just a few minutes away. Plenty of walks and places to visit. TV's or TS's are welcomed. Stop for a few hours or longer if you wish. Need to talk they are there to listen.

DIVINE BEAUTY
Unit 4, Forfar Avenue, Cardonald, Glasgow, Scotland Tel: 0141 883 8281 Ask for Roseann . . . . 04 - Make-up beauty treatments and lesson, waxing, advice and help for cross-dressers.Also has a sundome tanning lounge.

EQUALITY NETWORK
22 Forth Street, Edinburgh, EH1 3LH Tel: 07020 933952 Fax 07020 933 954; Email: en@equality-network.org Website: www.equality-network.org . . . 04 - The Equality Network campaigns for human rights for LGBT people in Scotland. They aim to bring about changes in the laws and institutions of Scotland to remove the inequalities facing LGBT people. For more information see their website.

EXTRA HAIR SALON
118 Sauchiehall Street (2nd Floor), Glasgow G2 3DH Tel: 0141 332 5130 Website: www.wigs-hair.co.uk . . . . 04 - This company supplies a variety of ladies and gents wigs, hairpieces and hair extensions. Their services include, all aspects of hair replacement including permanent hair systems, personal attention, professional advice, repair work and aftercare service.

GAY & LESBIAN CENTRE CAFÉ BAR
11 Dixon Street, Glasgow, Scotland Tel: 0141 221 7203 Website: www.glgbt.org.uk. . . . 04 - Plays host to Crosslynx TV/TS support group on second Wednesday of the month so well used to TVs. Probably a good place if you are just starting out on the scene.

GLASGOW GUEST HOUSE
56 Dynbreck Road, Glasgow, Scotland Tel: 0141 427 0129 . . . . 04 - Near junction 23 on the M8 motorway. Tranny friendly many girls who go to Crosslynx TV/TS group have stayed there. (listing with thanks to Ruth)

HAIR STYLE
Unit 6, Bridge Market, St Enoch Centre, Glasgow, G1 4BW Tel: 0141 248 8050 . . . . 04 - hairpieces, wigs, extensions and accessories. 3 Branches also at Trafford Centre Manchester 0870 755 8520 and Bluewater Kent 01322 423 921 - Hair Style, West Mall Arcade, The Village, Bluewater, Greenhithe, Kent DA9 9SE

HELLFIRE ALTERNATIVE CLOTHING
101-105 West Nile Street, Glasgow, Scotland Tel: 0141 332 4200; Website: www.hellfire-clothing.co.uk . . . . 04 - Very tranny friendly shop with some wicked designs. Well worth a visit.

HIDE & SLEEK
14 St. Leonards Place, Kinghorn, Fife, Scotland, KY3 9UL Tel: 01592 891344 Fax 01592 891376 Also in Glasgow hide.sleek@dial.pipex.com www.hideandsleek.co.uk. . . . 04 - A full dressing service available called Studio Lounge plus a shop stocked with everything you may need. Friendly advice is freely given. Clothes can be made to suit you. Leather clothing is a speciality. A super free catalogue is available.

ILOTHIAN GAY & LESBIAN SWITCHBOARD
P. O. Box 169, Edinburgh, EH1 3UU Tel: 0131 556 4049 Ask for Jean Reid Events director . . . . 04 -Available every evening between 7.30-10pm. Details of their social events are available on request.

MS DEMEANOUR
Tel: 07831 372154; Email: msdemeanouruk@aol.com Website: www.msdemeanour.co.uk Ask for Tabby . . . .04 - TV/TS Night Club - Check dates and more information at email address: msdemeanouruk@aol.com

NAILS UNLIMITED
10 Lauriston Street, Edinburgh, EH3 9DJ Tel: 0131 477 2633 Ask for Myra . . . . 04 - Nail salon & beauty room. Myra offers a full range of treatments, nails, waxing, make-up etc.

A Personal Report

Our biggest news is our new activities in Glasgow which you might think would swallow up our year but no in 2003 we enjoyed more events than ever that I am happy to say were enjoyed not only by our local regulars but 'girls' from all over the UK and beyond

the Show" with their cast of actors delivering the storyline during dinner. They mingled with our guests – all the time remaining in character and when the unfortunate lady met her demise, we all acted as detectives trying to solve the murder, with much fun chatting, drinking and laughter into the wee small hours.

The Elgin is a small family run hotel, who pride themselves on providing top quality food in a warm and friendly environment, we all enjoyed a wonderful dinner. All rooms have wonderful views either over the River Forth of the picturesque village of Charlestown.

AN EVENING OF MURDER & MYSTERY

After the excesses of the Festive Season – the tranny calendar falls quiet in January, so an evening of "Murder and Mystery" at a small country hotel was a wonderful idea!

Juliette was arriving from Switzerland, attending the opera in London then coming north to Scotland for fittings of her latest designs, giving Hide and Sleek an opportunity to organise something a little different.

Around 20 guests arrived at the hotel during a wonderfully crisp, sunny Saturday afternoon. Everyone settled in for a leisurely afternoon, ready for pre-dinner drinks at 7pm. We booked Heritage Events to perform "After

We all enjoyed an entertaining and humourous evening, this was definitely a popular mini event and we certainly host future "Evenings of Murder and Mystery"

TRANSFANDANGO BALL

Charity fundraising events don't come any better than The Transfandango Ball – Richard O'Brien hosted a wonderful celebration to raise funds for the Manchester Children's Hospital. I had no trouble selling places on the Hide and Sleek tables, as everyone loves the chance to dress up in fabby frocks and give lots of money away to a very good cause.

After a champagne reception, dinner was served at beautifully decorated tables in the elegant Ballroom.

As much money as possible was raised for the charity through tombolas, auctions, raffles etc. There's was a wealth of entertainment provided too, with cabaret, dancers, Rocky Horror tribute performance, live band, disco etc. It was a packed evening, with so much going on. It is impossible not to have a fabulous time.

SUMMER BOAT TRIP

If you're going to be 40 and you're going to have a party you may as well do it in style! Lorraine and Bella Jay decided to invite a bunch of friends to sail up and down the Thames on a party boat to celebrate this auspicious occasion.

A group of us came down from Scotland to enjoy a weekend in London. It proved to be one of the hottest of the year so we spent it shopping in Oxford Street. It was quite an experience to arrive at the location and join everyone waiting to board the boat – all the sexy skimpily clad girls attracting whistles and cheers from passers-by. We look forward to doing it all again in 2004 and look forward to seeing you there.

HIDE AND SLEEK IN GLASGOW

Hide and Sleek has been providing a service for trannies for over 8 years. From our base at Kinghorn on the east coast of Scotland we have steadily grown and now offer a very comprehensive range of services. There is such a large population mass in the Glasgow area, it became clear this was the best place to base our second shop when we were ready to expand. The location is in a very quiet little street with no other shops around yet still central and easy to get to.

Now, when you step inside, you will find yourself in Tranny Heaven! – a shop that is relaxing to be in, that stocks a full range of wigs, shoes, make-up, lingerie, tights and stockings, jewellery, body shaping, boobs, magazines and clothes.and you don't have to worry about what the assistants are thinking. They KNOW you're a tranny – so no need to pretend those tights are for your wife! What a relief! In fact the manager of my Glasgow shop is my daughter Marisha, she and her staff will make you feel completely at ease. You are welcome to pop in for a chat about hairstyles, get advice on the latest fashion trends, or pick up a leaflet for our next events. With Magdaleine – our make-up consultant – we offer full makeover appointments or a make-up lesson if you just want some help mastering eye shadow and mascara or spiders – oops sorry – false eyelashes!

Although our main workrooms are still at Kinghorn, you can order designs at Glasgow and have your fittings there.

Hide and Sleek, 9 St Margarets Place, Glasgow. Tel:0141 552 6999

A Personal Report

MISS TV SCOTLAND WEEKEND

Miss TV Scotland is the only weekend to be hosted north of the border and 2004 will be our 6th successful year. Read on to see how 2003 went.

On a Friday afternoon in late October, Ann and I have a hectic morning packing up all the stock for the - trade day. It's wonderful to arrive at the hotel after a busy year of planning – to finally relax a little and enjoy meeting old friends again and try to reassure nervous first timers they'll have a fabby time. Guests come from all over the UK – some from overseas – and this year Jodi Lynn from the Boudoir brought a party from London. We arranged for them to be picked up in style, with a stretch limo and Rolls Royce from the airport, champagne served en route!

Guests checked in and were soon picking stillies from suitcases and cement from sacks to prepare themselves for the evening. The highlight of the evening was to be a fabulous Fashion Show and the ladies at Hide and Sleek had been busy for months sewing the latest designs for our new collection. Soon guests were gathering for the "Ice Breaker Party", to be followed by a hot buffet, by this time our models were nervously changing into their first outfits – almost wishing they hadn't volunteered to wear umpteen designs, change clothes in speed record time and have an entire roomful of dressers and see them in all their corset, hip-pad and silicone glory!

Our Fashion Show was a great success, it gives ladies a chance to see what suits who and that an outfit made-to-measure can be a very wise option.

Saturday is a very busy Trade Day, with lots of exhibitors, including Hide and Sleek, Cyber with Corsetry, Saks Fifth Avenue – beauty, Colour Analysis, Nails Unlimited, P.R.T. Photography – Paula covers our entire weekend and also offers personal portraits on the day. Some guests enjoyed a trip into Edinburgh.

Our afternoon Demonstration showed three models transformed before their very eyes. Gary and Ann worked miracles at high speed and changed the ladies usual style, make-up and hairstyles, showing even if you have a great look, inspirational changes can give a whole new image.

Appointments for make-overs were in great demand and our five make-up consultants worked non-stop from mid afternoon so everyone looked amazing for the "Evening Ball". Advance bookings this year are an absolute must.

Saturday evening is the culmination of a year's hard work and the reason everyone has come – the "Miss TV Scotland Competition". This year for the first time we presented "Ms Hide and Sleek", for our over 50's contestants.

After a wonderful Gala Dinner, girls rush away to change into their daywear outfits and very soon mistress of ceremony Louise was introducing our nervous contestants to a delighted audience.

The Ms Hide and Sleek contestants were wonderfully elegant in their evening wear. This new contest was quickly followed by the final parade of Miss TV Scotland contestants in evening wear. Our trio of judges announced the results, Second Runner Up – Jennifer White, First Runner Up – Zazoo, and Miss TV Scotland 2003 is Sarah Grey.

Scotland ■ with Hide & Sleek

The winner of Ms Hide and Sleek 2003 was Diane. The room went wild and it looked like Miss World as hundreds of cameras flashed.

Both winners received an original outfit, designed to the winners specification just them to the value of £200.

If you have been to this weekend before, we look forward to seeing you again this year, if you are now considering joining us for the first time, we can assure you of a very warm welcome.

For further details and forthcoming dates of all our events see our website or give us a call:

www.hideandsleek.co.uk
Tel: 01592 891344

LADIES NIGHT IN GLASGOW

Since the opening of our new shop mid September 2003, we have been continually asked about places to go for trannies in Glasgow. There is a very good support group in Crosslynx and some established tranny friendly bars and clubs, but we felt the need for something a little more special. The manageress of my Glasgow shop is my daughter Marisha. We are very pleased to have found the perfect place, "The Trophy Room" in The Polo Lounge,

"Ladies Night At The Trophy Room" will provide a warm & friendly, safe environment where new girls can mix socially for the first time. We know some girls are nervous about dressing in company for the first time, but you are welcome to come along as you are, to see how you'll feel. We offer make-up appointments on the night to help you look your best, please book these in advance. The atmosphere we aim to create will make sure wives and girlfriends feel comfortable there too. Our approach is always about having a great time and a laugh and we hope it will be just as popular with more confident girls who can be sure of meeting friends old and new and having a good night out.

"Ladies Night At The Trophy Room" in the Polo Lounge, Wilson Street off Glassford Street, Glasgow - Loraine Tel: 01592 891344 or Marisha Tel: 0141 552 6999

Open 7.30- 10.30pm. Easy Parking in surrounding streets. Changing facilities from 6.30pm with mirrors and make-up lighting.

March 22 2004- Opening Night, April 26, May 24, June 21, July 26, August 23, September 20, October 25, November 22, December 20

A Personal Report

A Personal Report

Natalie & Sara (TV) Owners of the Gemini Club

The Gemini Club our very friendly dressing service and club is run by myself, (RG) Natalie and (TV) Sara. The club is located in North Dublin City centre.

The dressing service part of our club includes full make-up, wigs, lingerie, clothes and shoes. There is no time limit to your stay and you can have as many changes as you like during a visit. We also sell wigs and make-up. There is also a private bar. Our opening hours are Monday, Tuesday and Friday from 12 – 5.30pm.

We regularly escort girls on local shopping trips, restaurant visits, theatre outings and nights out. We also have enjoyed this year's trips to London for visits to the WayOut Club and also our regular August party at the Royal Dublin Horse Show.

In March we went again to Gran Canaria for the Carneval and in September to Manchester for Richard O'Brien's Transfandango Charity Ball. This event is a real annual treat and we are looking forward to returning to Transfandango for the event in London in 2004.

At Gemini we continue to hold social nights on Thursdays with the last Thursday of every month being a theme night which is announced a few weeks in advance. Thursday social nights are for TVs and TSs from 9pm to very, very late.

Our Saturday night events are run by TV Amanda and it is called 'Trannie Haven' www.tranniehaven.com. It is a very welcome night for TVs, admirers and friends from 9pm – 2.30am. Contact Amanda 00 353 86154 8936 for more information.

Tel: 00 353 1 8720171 Mobile: 00 353 87 629 3878 Email: geminiclub@hotmail.com Contact: Natalie or Sara

Jane, Natalie, Sheila, Marianne, Phyllis & Camille at the Four Seasons Hotel

Richard O'Brien & Natalie at Transfandango Ball

Stephanie, Amber, Natalie & Lola at Transfandango Ball

Triple

BAR
↓

Gemini Girls at the Horse Show

Natalie with Fidel Owner of 'Chez Funny Boy' in Puerto Rico, Gran Caneria

A Personal **Report**

POSTAL TAROT READINGS

Seoras c/o Tartan Skirt, 34 Waterloo Place, Inverness IV1 1NB, Scotland Email: tarot@macthearlaich.fsnet.co.uk Ask for S. MacThearlaich . . . . 04 - Tarot Readings on gender related issues and sexuality. It is inclusive of the spiritual tradition.

SUSAN BROOKES BEAUTY & LASER CLINIC

Kincardine, Scotland Tel: 01259 730100 Email: susanbrookes@btopenworld.com . . . . 04 - Laser Hair Removal. Conveniently situated between Glasgow & Edinburgh. Appointments necessary.

THE HIGHLAND T-GROUP

c/o Reach Out Highland,34 Waterloo Place, Inverness, IV1 1NB Scotland Tel: 01463 711585 Website: www.reachouthighland.org.uk Email: Tgroup@reachouthighland.org.uk . . . . 04 - This is a self-help and support group that meets in Inverness. Wives and partners are welcome. Ring for details.

THE POLO LOUNGE

84 Wilson Street, Glasgow, Scotland, G1 Tel: 0141 553 1221 . . . . 04 - Recommended as the most popular pub for Glasgow trannys. Bar upstairs with a club downstairs. The staff and "punters" are friendly!!

THE SUGARING CENTRE

7c Nicol street, Kirkcaldy Tel: 01592 640009 Ask for: Doreen; . . . . 04 - Heather recommends Doreens services for hair removal using the sugaring technique. Ring for an appointment and do respect other customers who may be less familiar with the concept of well groomed trannys.

WEST LOTHIAN TRANSGENDER SUPPORT GROUP

Livingston Tel: 0780 8564626 Mon to Thur 6-10pm; Email: kira@westlothiantsg.co.uk; Website: www.westlothiantsg.co.uk Ask for Kira . . . . 04 - Last Saturday of every month 5pm onwards. A small support group for TV/TS's, partner, family & friends. An initial meeting is required for new people wishing to become members of this small friendly group.

IRELAND

AD HOC (IRELAND)

14-14a Crown Alley, Temple Bar, Dublin 2, Ireland. Tel: 01 616 9919 www.adhoclondon.com Email: enquiries@adhoclondon.com . . . . 04 - A great collection for disco dollys from necklaces to shoes. There is no need to be shy about being a tranny in this shop. One stop shop for theme parties.

ASPENS BEAUTY CLINIC

83 Lower Camden Street, Dublin 2, Ireland Tel: 00 353 1 475 1940/1079 Email: neelaminfo@aspenireland.com; Website: www.aspensireland.com Ask for Neelam . . . . 04 - TV friendly salon offering full beauty service including waxing and make-overs. Open 9am to 8pm Monday to Friday, 9am to 6pm on Saturdays. And appointments only on Sundays from10am 3pm.

BASIC INSTINCTS

56 South William Street, Dublin 2, Ireland Tel: 00 353 1 671 2223 Email: basicins@iol.ie Website: www.basicinstincts.com Ask for Mike Ryan . . . . 04 - Adult fetish store, rubberwear, leatherwear, intimate lingerie, boots, shoes & c/p equipment. Stocks "The Tranny Guide" & other magazines, Very friendly shop ask for Damien, Steven, Mike or Mary.

BELFAST BUTTERFLY CLUB

P.O. Box 210, Belfast, BT1 1BG Tel Helpline Wed 8-10pm 028 926 3720 Email: kellie@belfastbutterfly.org.uk Website: www.belfastbutterflyclub.org.uk . . . . 04 - Helpline Wednesday only 8pm-10pm. The club's network of help could be the support you, your family or friends need. Meetings are held 1st & 3rd Tuesday from 7.30-11.30pm & their programme includes guest speakers, group discussions, demonstrations

CINDERELLA SHOES

Tullamore, Co Offaly Tel: 0035 350 626696 Website: www.cinderellashoes.ie . . . . 04 - Based in Tullamore Co Offaly in Ireland. Focusing on 'real' womens shoes, smart work styles and pretty evening wear (not drag queen/lap dancers) from £40.

FRANKIE'S GUEST HOUSE

8 Camden Place, Dublin 2, Ireland Tel: +353 1 478 3087; Website: www.frankiesguesthouse.com Email: frankiesguesthouse@ireland.com Ask for Frankie or Jo . . . . 04 - Situated on a quite street off Camden Street, on the edge of the city centre. This guest house has been established for a long time and comes highly recommended for a visit.

GEMINI CLUB

Dublin Tel: 00 353 1 872 0171 Ask for Nathalie or Sara-Jane. . . . 04 - This is a very friendly dressing service run by a real girl Nathalie and TV Sarah-Jane. Located in north Dublin city centre, the girls will escort you to The George or arrange shopping trips. They also arrange trips to London a few times a year and Gran Canaria for Mardi Gras in March and October. Gemini also hold a social night on the last Thursday of every month. Full make-up and a wide choice of clothes and wigs available. Private bar.

INN ON THE LIFFEY

Upper Ormond Quay, Dublin 7, Ireland Tel: +353 1 677 0828 . . . . 04 - 100% gay run inn which welcomes the transgendered community with accommodation rooms that overlook the river Liffey. It is very centrally located. Based in the city centre close to all amenities.

THE GEORGE (DUBLIN)

89 South Gt. George's Street, Dublin 2, Ireland. Tel: +353 1 4782983 . . . . 04 - The longest established gay bar in Dublin. The transgendered community is welcome. Open from 5pm till 2.30am Wednesday to Sunday, then 5pm-11.30pm on Mondays and Tuesdays. Public bar open at 12.30 everyday.

VIKING LODGE HOTEL

34-36 Francis Street, Dublin 8, Ireland Tel: +353 1 473 2111 Email: vikinglodge1@eircom.net . . . . 04 - Gay friendly hotel.

LONDON REPORTS

LONDON PROFILES

LISTINGS

Photo by ullirichter.com (URP London) Tel: +44 (0) 7980 920580
Makeup & Styling by Lorraine@annodom.com
Model Jo@annodom.com

Thank you very much to the
following people that
helped in the compilation
of this section of the guide:
Jodie Lynn (photos)
Sarah Lloyd (report)

Adam & Eve Party

Boudettes at the Thai Princess

House of Drag

House of Drag

A is for 'Adam and Eve This new service have celebrated their first tricky year building a loyal clientele. Based in East London offering a drop in service, day and evening, with a full range of services and products. RGs, Josie, Teresa and Liza, have the advantage that with a good size, central London location, and three people to hand, they can respond to the short amount of time you may have available to call in dress and chat. A&E clients tend to be "shy" girls, but regular parties at their salon and group trips out, is seeing those with growing confidence taking the opportunity to spread their wings.

B is for the 'Boudoir' who's strength is their escorted trips for individuals and groups to get the best from London's attractions. Jodie Lynn and her team of RGs provide wardrobe, make-overs, products and styling help in their north london shop shop and photo studio. Some clients progress to escorted shopping trips, or tea at the Ritz. Proving rule one – one tranny might "pass" - two trannies together wont "pass" – a tranny and a female have a great chance of "passing". Often clients go on to join a group trip to the tranny clubs or main stream restaurants, theatre, opera, night clubs and more extreme events like riding the London Eye, Royal Ascot or even trips to New York. A great camaraderie has built up among regulars who call themselves "Boudettes" and keep a web site to record their adventures.

C is for 'Club Rub' a favourite place to push the boundaries. Many more trannies have discovered the fetish scene this year where, like every sexuality and gender the extreme boundaries of style, dress and behaviour can be explored in comparative safety. Club Rub is their favourite.

H is for House of Drag where, Steffan provides a mid week night every Wednesday. The strength of this night is the welcome Steffan offers. Often misunderstood to be just an awesome Diva (which he is), Steffan also has a the most loving heart and really connects with every type of person given the time to do so. House of Drag provides that time and intimacy. Now in the forth year and new venue each week Steffan and a co-hosts provides cabaret and a theme so that each week there is a time and place for all including: male admirers, sexy gay boys, she-males, fetish fashion sissy-maids, karaoke-kweens and YOU.

I is for 'Image Works' who's great strength is proprietor Pandora DePledge herself, whose skills at female to male transformations have to be seen to be believed. Of course they can be seen, on her extensive website and many publications. There is nothing like a Pandora make-over and photo shoot to turn your fantasies into reality. Pan works with a growing team of experts from her home, which has been specially designed to make your stay a quality experience. Her skill with hair and wigs can take your image

uudettes on thames boat trip

London is a great city. If you are a local or a visitor you are lucky to be part of such a great city. But if you are Transgendered you are VERY lucky to be part of this great city.

Most London attractions, restaurants, and hotels, are coolly happy, to provide, (appropriately dressed), T-girls with the same degree of service as any other customer. Of course quality of service varies from place to place who ever you are, (and WHAT ever you are).

Londoners though coolly polite, still struggle with Sir, Miss, Madam etc - I guess they are just too honest ... What they see - is what you get.

London's enormous and amazingly diverse population provides anonymity. A kind of a "blessing" to be who you want to be. However, (if you know where to find them), there are always "like minded" people within a short distance.

In these post 9/11 years, terror, (we are told), is ever more a threat. In this fear it is all too easy to allow yourself to be scared of those that are different to ourselves. But if we allow ourselves to be scared, logically we can then only expect others to be scared of of us. It is there-by that diversity can be divisive and dangerous.

This brings me to request that you find tolerance and indeed love for those that are different to your self. If you can find this love in you, London can be enjoyed at it's best and your difference becomes your strength.

The number of consistent, quality, TG opportunities in London has grown over this last year. To a degree this has fostered divisions in our community. Those that prefer this service and *Those that prefer another*. Those that prefer to be all trannies together and *those that like to be in mixed company*. Those that prefer to be out and loud and *those that prefer to be secretive and "naughty" etc*.

Chitter chatter along these lines can turn a few peoples opinion and silly gossip, into divisive gossip creating "gated communities - virtual ghettos", - cutting your opportunities and choices, for no real reason.

If we allow ourselves to think badly of others or to speak badly of others we regress to the point of being scared of what others think of us. That is the route back to the closet and unhappiness.

So here I am going to describe in detail some of the best from my London A to Z of what I want you to understand are "choices" and I urge you all, to try them. It is only then that you will truly feel a part of the full London experience and know for yourself what suits you.

A Personal Report

ouudettes on thames boat trip

mmy Vicky & Jade at Thai Princess

Trans-mission

Trans-mission

to new heights and she now offers an exclusive and customised range of wigs and make-up products. Just when your feeling your best a safe escorted trip to any of London's tranny hot spots can be arranged along with accommodation at her home if needed.

L **is for 'Lips'** You could be forgiven for thinking that Monday would be a quite night on the scene but no – 'Lips' is a tranny promotion at the Philbeach Hotel attracting year after year a growing crowd. This is a particularly nice experience on a mid summer night with the added pleasure of the patio and fragrant garden.

P **is for the 'Philbeach'** a gay hotel that is busy midweek with a through flow of cute guys from around the world. The relaxed pleasure of The Thai Princess restaurant (with lady boys Sammy and Jade) and Jimmy's bar is available to trannies every night and Friday is almost as popular as Lips on Monday. Anne's dressing service is located in the hotel and of course accommodation is always available along with a comfortable lounge and pay as you go internet terminal. The Philbeach Hotel remains a haven for trannies.

R **is for 'Ron'**. Miss Hillaire's hijacking of the name Stormes now appears to have fizzled out. Meanwhile Peter White's love of (the Late) Ron Storme is as unswerving as many of Ron's other friends. Many fondly remember those nights in Bow and at Stepneys. Peter is arranging "A Ron Storme Tribute Fall Ball" an event that he hopes will be the first true reunion of "Ron's Regulars" and that the tribute will become an annual event. The venue is The Pink Punters Club in Milton Keynes on 2nd October 04.

S **is for 'Stunners'**. Some trannies shun sexual advances - but for those that seek it - London has 'Stunners' a nightclub run by TGs for all that swing. Stunners has moved around quite a bit but has endured 2 years with an increasing clientele of every sexuality. Just play safe that's all I say and if you don't know what is safe – find out (see HIV & TRANSGENDER in the book listings).

T **is for at 'Trans-mission'** on the first Saturday of the month is where those that prefer not to be bothered with sexual advances could not feel safer. DJ's Jasmine and Vicky Valentine put this club together 2 years ago. Trans-mission is now very busy, attracting transgendered girls ranging from first night out to evangelical. The atmosphere is friendly (and very white). Most regulars knew each other through the internet before they visit the club. Chat features high on the menu. and the ground floor provides for plenty of that. Trans-mission also attracts dancers to bob to a flock of tranny DJs. What the club does not attract is she-males and men looking to meet them, therefore there is little, (if any), sexual tension and what there is, could be described as T-girl-lesbian.

Pride float in Piccadilly

Pride float approaching Trafalgar square

Pamela from Belgium meets the girls from the Philipines at the WayOut CLUB

Kim Angel (Angels UK), Jasmin Clarke (Transmission) Vicky Lee (WayOut) and Vicky Valentine (Transmission) hope we can ALL come together in what could be the ultimate TG experience of the year at The Marriot hotel in London on October 30th at The Transfandango "Halloween Ball" with Richard O'Brien.
An opportunity to show what we can do (for needy others) by being together.

I for one will have many friends and family join me on that night in my 50th birthday week. I don't want any presents I just want them, and YOU, there with me.

I hope to meet you soon and please when we meet - don't say **"what are you doing here"** as how on earth do you think I have written this book for 12 years if I had not **"been there seen it done it"** I am there for you to have the best info and and choices because when I first found the scene in London I had so little.

I would like to take this opportunity to thank Nikki and Debbie for twisting our WayOut arm to join them in organising a Mardi Gras (Pride) float. I hope YOU will join us on the float this year Sat 3rd July.

Nikki, Debbie & Vicky Lee Pride float passing The Ritz

A Personal **Report**

275

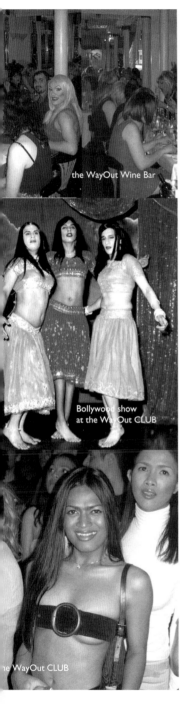

the WayOut Wine Bar

Bollywood show at the WayOut CLUB

he WayOut CLUB

W **is for WayOut** Friday night is a prime night to go out or to stop over after work. Many including myself, (in a past life), like to make it a long weekend but up to now have very little reason with very little on a Friday.

'The 'WayOut Wine Bar' aims to fill this gap. We also recognised that there has been no weekly opportunity to mix and mingle without unwanted male attention. The WayOut Wine bar aims to fill this requirement too. Single males are not encouraged at the wine bar - but male or female as guests of T-Girls are very welcome. The venue has a small basement bar and dance floor plus a great chef with a varied menu of snacks and full a la carte menu in the "comfort zone" on the ground floor. The original WayOut Wine Bar started 11 years ago in Goodge Street a year after the first Tranny Guide book and two years later became The WayOut CLUB when we moved to Knightsbridge. The WayOut Wine bar was the first weekly purely transgender club. At this time everyone at WayOut would be familiar with 'The Tranny Guide' at a time when everyone on the tranny scene was finding their feet and "admirers" (we called them tranny fcukers) were still in their own closet and no worry to us. People then were looking for safety with "like minded others". I hope that a new generation of 21st century T –girls will enjoy and support this weekly opportunity to be with like minded others any week they want to.

'The WayOut CLUB' every Saturday remains the most consistent, unique night out on the transgender scene Steffan and myself have run this club now for 11 years. We recognise that WayOut CLUB has evolved. Now many people at WayOut would not know the Tranny Guide book, and can't remember a time without the internet and the confidence it has inspired. Now WayOut is as much a diversity club as a transgender club. Every week see's an amazing mix of people of every background, culture, age, race, sexuality and gender. The cream of London's beautiful transsexuals are regulars along side groups of white heeled Essex gay boy/girls, sari clad Indian 'girls' and silk clad oriental 'girls'. With over 200 people every week there are always those that are better dressed, (and worse dressed). There are always "like minded others" and extraordinary others. Every Saturday I "step back" amazed at the mix. It is good to be with so many that are "not normal", when you know that you are also "not normal". However I know that this heady mix which can make the club feel euphoric and spiritually uplifting can also feel intimidating and awesome to some. (I used to feel the same way about the late Kinky Gerlinky nights, which were fantastic).

The men that are attracted to the WayOut CLUB are often misunderstood and are themselves a diverse mix. Some are trannies who don't feel able to dress outside their home but want to meet others that do. Some are looking for their very own "Mirium" a chick with a dick. All are expected to be polite and take a polite 'no thanks' for an answer or they will be expelled. Some of the guys are real "gentlemen" who know how to make a feminine person feel happy, comfortable and safe. Somehow the men make the club feel less surreal, more like a straight club, as they watch you dance and admire even desire you.

Cabaret is a feature of the club because Steffan and I believe that an evening without a focus, (a reason to remember the night), can leave you hollow on the way home. The discovery of new talent on the last Saturday of the month who then progress into bigger shows with boys girls and inbetweenies performing with costumes and scenery is a major part of the magic that keeps Steffan and myself so committed.

More details in the following listings

Bottom row Lesley (Vicky's partner), Bonny (Steffan's mum), Vicky Lee, Jane (Steffan's sister) at the WayOut CLUB

Miss Ambre (france) Miss Sasha (Malaysia) International performers at The WayOut Club

Vicky Lee and Steffan at the WayOut CLUB

WayOut CLUB

Vicky Lee and DJ Titch on stage at the WayOut CLUB

A Personal Report

London ■ *A Personal* Report

Jean, Mary & Dave

Alternative Dance DJ Jo Purvis

GLOBAL VILLAGE DANCE

My dances are held occasionally in East London. They are aimed at all sorts of people who enjoy, in the main, partner dancing.

Young and old, (from teenagers, twenties, thirties, forties, fifties, up to eighty years old) straight, gay, transexual, transvestite, rich, poor, whatever! All are welcome.

At my Global Village Dances we play a very wide range including Ballroom, Argentine Tango, Swing dance, Lindy-Hop, Jive and Salsa as well as a few line dances and a bit of individualistic disco and party music.

All sorts of dancers go from those who are very good to complete beginners. But no-one knows how to do all of the dances. The aim is to mix in and have a go and enjoy oneself. With the range of dances there is something for everyone to enjoy. For example even if you have never danced a progressive barn dance before, by the time you have gone round a few times you know what to do. It's great for confidence building, socialising and fun. On the other hand there are also opportunities for good dancers to strut their stuff.

> *"dancing together with another person in the tradition of 'Come Dancing', adds a new and bigger dimension"*

The philosophy of the Global Village Dance is in the name. They are saying there is One "Global Village" with all its wonderous diversity to enjoy. The dance is like a "Village Dance" where people enjoy each other in a festive but gentle way. It is not a fetish or overtly sexual event. By having old people, children, straight, gay and transgendered they find that people respect themselves and each other well, and behave accordingly. It is a very good opportunity for trannies who want to try mixing with broad spectrum of society in a safe environment.

Other Alternative Dance Places
For a similar mix of partner dancing try

JACKIES JUKE BOX at The Rivoli Ballroom opposite Crofton Park railway station, Brockley Road, SE4 London 7.30pm – 12. First Saturday of each month. It is principally a ballroom dance for gay men and women but some straight people and a few trannies go. A truly fabulous venue.

THE TEA DANCE at The White Swan, corner of Butcher row and Commercial Road E1 / E14 London every Sunday 5.30 – 11pm. Mainly gay men, a few women and trannies.

JO'S TEA DANCE AT THE BLACK CAP (First Sunday of the month 4.30-10pm) Camden High Street, Camden Town, NW1 London. A gay pub with drag, tranny friendly.

DANCE DIARY If you live in South East England and want to find dances and teachers near you, phone 01438 840066 www.dancediary.co.uk

Photo's by Tony Lane at the River Cultures Festival

RIVER CULTURES FESTIVAL
AT WEST INDIA QUAY

In August 2003 the annual "River Cultures Festival", was held on the Isle of Dogs. They invited me to organise a "Tea Dance", as the theme for the event was 'Tea' it was held on West India Quay, and there was a definite oriental flavour to the whole festival. This gave me the opportunity to wear my lovely pink silk "Cheong Sam" dress.

The dancing was even more varied than at the usual Global Village Dances and included performances by Indian and Chinese groups, marching girls, children in Mad Hatters Tea Party costumes and local youth group dancers.

My objective was that the dance area should be the energy centre of the festival. In fact in two afternoons and Saturday evening there was 17 hours of non stop dancing of every description. During that time thousands of people passed through the area, and hundreds joined in the dancing.

Several other trannies came along to enjoy the opportunity for a gentle, easy going, friendly, open air, public dance. A far cry from the heavy, pounding, violent, homophobic atmosphere of Notting Hill Carnival!

Security was excellent and the weather on both days was fine. Several outdoor restaurants catered for the hungry, whilst the budget conscious brought picnics.

THE PLEASURE OF PARTNER DANCING

I love to dance, to move with the music, but to dance with another person in the tradition of "Come Dancing", (returning to the television in 2004), together adds a new and bigger dimension. It's fun, it's communication, and by doing it together the pleasure is multiplied.

As a follower I love it when a confident dancer takes me in their arms and guides me round the floor. As my dancing has progressed I am now better able to lead. As a leader it is also wonderful to take a nice person in your arms and give them pleasure too."

ONE TO ONE TUITION

I can help you get started in simple social ballroom and latin dancing. If you want to learn Argentinian Tango or Swing Dance / Lindy-Hop I offer one-to-one tuition for trannies who would like a basic introduction to either following or leading.

Toni Vain & Jean Le Clerc   Photo by Jean L. Winchester

For details of coming

GLOBAL VILLAGE DANCES

or

FREE OUTDOOR DANCING
in the summer at the River Cultures Festival on 29th August 2004 or

ONE-TO-ONE TUITION
phone Toni 020 7538 3852
www.globalvillagedance.com

What is your name and what is your background?
Kate (although I'm considering a different name). I'm single and live in East London. I've spent most of my life in macho denial and so now work ineffectively in computer support. I have no idea what I could have done better.

Are you happy to be called a tranny and what does this name mean to you?
It's as accurate as any other. The fact that I have one view of what I am whilst the world assumes another from the word is not something I can do very much about. Fact is it doesn't matter which word we use the world will come to their own (unflattering) conclusion anyway.

How old are you and how young can you remember thinking about or actually cross-dressing?
I'm 44 now. My first awareness that there was an issue with my gender identity was when I was about 18 months old. My denial then set the pattern for my life where I avoided doing anything that might have been mistaken as effeminate, irrespective of how much I wanted to do them. Although I first dressed when I was 13, I've only occasionally participated as I've really tried hard to pretend nothing was wrong. But there came a point a few years back when I realised that all I was doing was making myself unhappy. I wish I'd realised that years ago; decades even.

Where do you buy clothes?
Anywhere that has what I want. I no longer feel self-conscious about it. That said, I rarely try things on in the shop but that's more because I'm not spending enough at any one time to warrant the hassle.

What leads you to choose the styles you wear?
For casual I'm an old hippy chick. It also happens to suit me (other people's opinions). I avoid wearing straight skirts or dresses as you need a good hip/waist ratio to make that work and I just don't have that. Shame really as I got some lovely clothes before I realised why it didn't work for me.

Do you have one look or many images?
My main interest is belly dance so I love playing with those styles, from the raqs orientale style (think Ginger Rogers) to the saucier styles you'll see in restaurants.

Is make-up and hair important to you and if so how do you achieve your look?
Very much so, I have a heavy beard so I need dermablend for my own peace of mind. Beyond that everything is play.

To what degree do you practice hair removal, and other body feminisation?
I shave, everywhere that matters. However I find that the skin on my body dislikes being shaved every day so I tend to do it only when it might matter. I also have prosthetic breasts to complete the look.

Who knows that you dress?
Most of my friends, mainly because I told them.

How often do you dress and if you go out where to?
I dress 2/3 times a week. At least one of those times I will be going out. I regularly attend an Egyptian dance class where I'm dressed but as I go to this from work I change when I'm there. I'll also go to gay discos if other friends are going.

How much of a sexual turn on is trannying for you?
It can be, but frankly it's not why I do this and consider such a reaction is distracting. I'd rather it didn't happen at all. I specifically reject the dictionary definition that the turn-on is the reason why I do this.

What is your definition of feminine?
Can anybody define masculine either? The dictionary helpfully says "suitable to or characteristic of a woman". There are about 3 billion women on this planet. This means that there are already 3 billion and one different and contradictory answers to this question. All of which are right. Whilst I'm reluctant to add to this

confusion, here's my tuppence anyway tho' it isn't really an answer to that question. My gender identity is rooted so deep in my brain that it's below thought, below feeling and emotion. It's buried right in the foundation of my being and there are not words for how this is impressed upon my personality. My sense of "femininity" arises from that place and cannot be described; it just is. That said it's worth noting that our ability to describe our situation improves each year. That doesn't mean we're even close yet but each new idea enable yet more concepts to be realised.

To what degree do you feel gender dysphoric?
In parts; very. In others; not much. I wish in all honesty I could say that I felt very feminine in all things, but so much of my day to day persona is habitually bloke-ish that I cannot in all honesty now say what is rooted in my nature and what was acquired by self-nurture. What I mean there is that I did a lot of copying when I was a kid and a teenager because I didn't have the 'right' reactions and wanted to fit in. So I taught myself how to behave invisibly male. Nowadays I can't separate the truth from the artifice. I'm beginning the untangling process, but I doubt I'll ever feel confident answering the question.

To what degree would you consider permanent hair removal, hormones, surgery?
I've got very strong beard growth and so permanent hair removal is something I will be starting on soon. However I feel that hair removal without hormones is not permanent; it grows back eventually. So I'm also going to start on hormones as well. This will give me a certain bodily feminisation as well, or at least a move towards androgyny, is a serious plus. Whether this would then lead to surgery I don't know. I'm still not convinced I could be invisibly female. Without that I couldn't have the social acceptance of being a woman that would be the pre-requisite for me having the op. But to refer back to the previous question it's the thing between my ears, not between my legs that makes me what I am.

What one piece of advice would you give to someone that has just found they are not the only tranny in the world?
Keep your tongue flat. It promotes a feminine smile and gives a feminine lilt to the voice. And one other thing, most of the time, nobody cares.

What is your name and what is your background?

I'm Miss Michaela Marbella and that's Michaela

with a soft 'sh' and not a hard 'k' in the middle

thank you very much!!!

Advanced Question – **How did you choose your 'T' name?**

It's a piss-take on Michelle M'belle by the Beatles !!!

Are you happy to be called a tranny and what does this name mean to you?

I much prefer Sissy Princess because I am one !!!

How old are you and how young can you remember thinking about or actually cross-dressing?

I'm 47 and have been frocking-up all my life !!!

Advanced Question – **Do you feel you have any choice in your TG thoughts and actions?**

None at all thank God!!!

Where do you buy clothes?

All my gorgeous outfits are made specially just for me!!!

What leads you to choose the styles you wear?

Sissy Princesses wear sissy princess dresses!!!

Do you have one look or many images?

Sissy Princess is always my look!!!

Is make-up and hair important to you and if so how do you achieve your look?

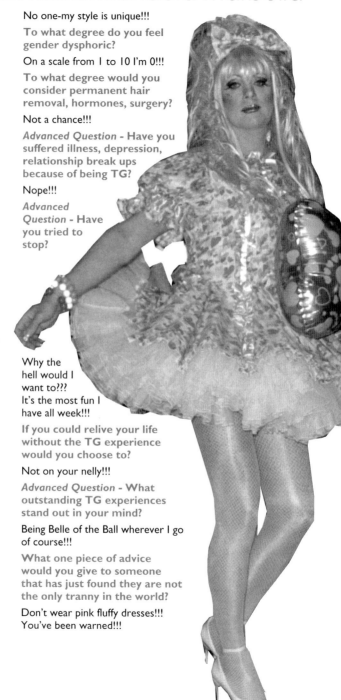

Fabulous over the top make-up and beautifully styled little girly hair is the icing on this Sissy Princess' cake!!!

To what degree do you practice hair removal, and other body feminisation?

Bollocks to that!!! I just shave my arms!!!

Who knows that you dress?

My fabulous slim blonde attractive girlfriend and two horrified ex-school friends !!! We speak no more!!!

How often do you dress and if you go out where to?

With so many outfits, my accessory bill alone could feed a family of four for a month !!! So once a week is enough!!! I particularly enjoy showing-off to the ordinary public who all seem to love me to bits!!!

How much of a sexual turn on is trannying for you?

It gives me a hard on like you would not believe!!!

Advanced Question - **Are your sexual preferences changed by your TG experiences?**

No way!!! I love women and they love me!!!

What is your definition of feminine?

Pink and fluffy and more pink and fluffy and even more pink and fluffy!!!

Advanced Question - **What individual has inspired you most in relation to your TG inclinations?**

No one-my style is unique!!!

To what degree do you feel gender dysphoric?

On a scale from 1 to 10 I'm 0!!!

To what degree would you consider permanent hair removal, hormones, surgery?

Not a chance!!!

Advanced Question - **Have you suffered illness, depression, relationship break ups because of being TG?**

Nope!!!

Advanced Question - **Have you tried to stop?**

Why the hell would I want to??? It's the most fun I have all week!!!

If you could relive your life without the TG experience would you choose to?

Not on your nelly!!!

Advanced Question - **What outstanding TG experiences stand out in your mind?**

Being Belle of the Ball wherever I go of course!!!

What one piece of advice would you give to someone that has just found they are not the only tranny in the world?

Don't wear pink fluffy dresses!!! You've been warned!!!

How old are you and how young can you remember thinking about or actually cross-dressing?

I have now joined the "life begins at " age group and started dressing at about eight years old so that's thirty two years I have been riding this roller coaster, ...

Where do you buy clothes?

I buy my outfits from the high street and the internet ... mainly the internet as I like the more fetish type outfits (pvc and latex).

What leads you to choose the styles you wear?

Having spent many years trying out different styles I have now settled for the glam style fetish outfits as they give me the ultra glam femme look and feeling that I want when I am enfemme.

Do you have one look or many images?

I have many different looks ranging from "normal" girl to ultra glam drag-queen. I am always playing around with different looks too see what works and what doesn't. It's fun to spent a rainy day.

Is make-up and hair important to you and if so how do you achieve your look?

Makeup and hair are very important in how I achieve my looks. I am now onto my fourth cement mixer and have over forty wigs living in various parts of my house! I have always loved playing around with makeup from a very early age (best part of being a girl) but its only since I have had the pleasure of the truly magical touch of Pandora De'Pledges artistic wand and that of her very creative assistant miss Debonair that I have started too refine the style I am looking for.

To what degree do you practice hair removal, and other body feminisation?

I keep my body totally hair free which means shaving my entire body at least twice a week, I also have facials at a salon at least twice a month which is a really fab way too de-stress yourself too girls

Who knows that you dress?

None of my family and girlfriends know that I have another lifestyle. If they do none has said anything. The clinic where I had collagen injections know because they asked why I

What is your name and what is your background?

My name is Alexis Divine, I come from the n/east of England but came south at the age of seventeen. I am single and have in my time been a semi-pro footballer, student, soldier, world traveller, now working for a well known German car company.

Are you happy to be called a tranny and what does this name mean to you?

I am more than happy to be known as a tranny, in my view the word tranny is simply someone who dresses in the clothes of their opposite sex, genetic women have been trannies since forever !!! Genetic males will be one fine day ??....

wanted it done - so I told them and showed them some pictures which they thought was a genetic girl who I wanted too look like !!! So no problems there.

How often do you dress and if you go out where to?

I dress alone maybe once a fortnight to do picture updates for my website and I spoil myself about once a month visiting Pandora's where I gorge myself in the sheer high class of her home and where I meet other girls who I have the pleasure to call my friends. My normal haunt on my London trips is the WayOut Club, a super place too see friends and make new ones.

How much of a sexual turn on is trannying for you?

I used to find dressing a big turn on but I passed that stage a long time ago. I decided just to accept my being a tranny and to embrace it and enjoy it rather than feel guilty.

What is your definition of feminine?

"Feminine" wow that's a hard one! Its an emotion, its a look, its a smell, its a style, What is " feminine" who really knows but its what I am - like it or not! I took a test once for a survey in connection with my workplace and the computer came up with the result that this person is 87 % female so who am I too argue ?

To what degree would you consider permanent hair removal, hormones, surgery?

I have tried hormones but I started putting on weight and stopped because of that reason but for some strange reason I kept my budding cleavage !!! I have also had collagen put into my top lip I would consider permanent hair removal, breast implants and some facial surgery but that is never likely too happen so I am happy in being who and what I am without those things really.

What one piece of advice would you give to someone that has just found they are not the only tranny in the world?

Don't feel guilty or ashamed of who you are. You are a special person in a world of special people. Also being a tranny is like having a dog its for life not a day so embrace it and enjoy!

Alexis sharing some gossip with Miss Sarah Lloyd at The WayOut Club

Help & Support

ANOTHER NAME
United Reformed Church, Buck Street, Camden Town, London NW1 Tel: 020 8533 3262 Ceilia Francis 020 8802 0962 Pressley; Web site: www.MCCNorthLondon.com . . . . 04 - A befriending and support group on 1st and 3rd Thurs of month 7.30 - 9.30 sponsored by the Metropolitan Community Church for all within the TG community, irrespective of their spiritual beliefs.

BEAUMONT SOCIETY
Nationwide 27 Old Gloucester St, London WC1N 3XCX Tel 01582 412220 24hr info line; Email: enquiries@beaumontsociety.org.uk; Website: www.beaumontsociety.org.uk . . . . 04 - National UK self support group established in 1966 for TV's/CD's/TS's and their partners and friends. For your regional representative & details of meetings throughout the country please phone our 24 hour info line or visit our website.

BEAUMONT- LONDON MEETINGS
Tel: 0794 1696609 Email: sandrafirebird@hotmail.com Ask For: Sandra . . . . 04 - 4th Sunday at The George Twickenham Road, Isleworth 2nd Saturday of month at Bird in Hand 291 Sydenham Road, Croydon. 2nd Sunday not before 7pm at the Friend 86 Caledonian Road N1 1st Sunday of month 'The Fountain' Handcroft, Crawley, West Sussex.

BEAUMONT TRUST
BM Charity, London WC1N 3XX 07777 287878 (7-11 Tues & Thurs). Email: bmonttrust@aol.com Website: http://members.aol.com/bmonttrust . . . . 04 - Educational charity running a helpline two nights a week & providing info & speakers to those interested in all aspects of Gender Identity.

DAGENHAM HELP GROUP (RUBICON)
Tel: 0208 252 2623 . . . . 04 - TS support group meet at Rubicon, Dagenham

DAVID HAWLEY COUNSELLING
London SW18, EC2 and W1 Tel: 0208 871 2273 Mob: 07703 359488 Website: www.gestaltcounselling.co.uk . 04 - Transgender affirmative counselling. Confidential help with gender identity and sexual orientation issues. David is a gestalt therapist & BACP accredited counsellor, UKRC registered independent counsellor.

DEPEND
BM Depend, London WC1N 3XX Email: info@depend.org.uk; Website: www.depend.org.uk. . . . 04 - An organisation offering free, confidential and non-judgemental information and support to all family members, spouses, partners and friends of transsexual people.

DR RUSSELL REID
The London Institute, 10, Warwick Road, London, SW5 9UH Tel: 0207 373 0901; Ask for: Russell; . . . . 04 - Psychiatric assessment, advice, a written report & if appropriate a prescription for hormones. The aim is to facilitate Trannies in their efforts to achieve their full potential whichever gender role the seek to achieve, in their own way, at their own pace.

FTM LONDON
Monthly London Meeting Tel: Maxwell 020 7609 7824 / 0207 278 3294; Email: FTM1000@aol.com Website: wwwftmlondon.org.uk; Ask for: Ben; . . . . 04 - This support group for female to male transsexuals. Meetings on the 1st Saturday of each month 6pm in the Upstairs Room Central Station, 37 Wharfdale Road, London, N1. These meetings provide an opportunity to share information and support each other This very active and large group produce a membership publication 'Boys Own Magazine' available by subscription. Regular group visits to The WayOut Club and other venues. Partners and significant others are welcome to attend from 8pm for social time ONLY.

PENN PSYCHOTHERAPY
Tel: 07973 508664; Ask for: Michelle; . . . . 04 - For pre & post op TS's & people with gender issues. Join a weekly group in West London. A safe environment to work through issues and get support. Ring for more details.

LIFEWORKS
BCM Lifeworks, London, WC1 3XX Tel: Tel/Fax: 0870 1691676; Email: lifeworks3@aol.com; Ask for: Pauline; . 04 - Sellers of books to the transgender community on hormonal therapy, tips on make-up and dressing, voice, relationships and TG fiction.

LONDON LESBIAN & GAY SWITCHBOARD
London Tel: 0207 837 7324 fax 0207 837 7000; Email: admin@llgs.org.uk; Web site: www.llgs.org.uk . . . 04 - Basic information & advice on cross-dressing, gender, sexuality issues & the tranny scene can be obtained from a sympathetic voice on this helpline. The helpline operates 24 hours a day & also includes a minicom facility for the deaf. This is the first call for anyone who wants to understand anything about homosexuality or anything that happens in or around the gay scene.

LONDON TRANSSEXUAL GROUP (L.T.I.S.S.G)
9 Plumstead Road, Woolwich, London, SE18 7BZ. Tel: 02083557413 Tue/Thu eve Mobile: Mob:07763 785602 Fax:0208355 7413; Email: londontsinfo@ntlworld.com; Web site: www.geocities.com/londontsinfo Ask for: Sarah Wilson; . . . . 04 - We are a support group for transsexuals male-female, female-male and the medically formed (post op transsexuals). We meet once a month from 7-10pm on the third Wednesday of the month at the Woolwich Infant Public House, 9 Plumstead Road, London SE18 7BZ. Partners, family members, significant others & social/care workers are welcome. Now able to offer 1-2-1's appointments only.

MIND TRAINING
Mind Conference & Training Unit, Granta House, 15-19 Broadway, London, E15 4BQ Tel:0208 519 2122 Fax: 0208 522 1725; Email: contact@mind.org.uk; Web site: www.mind.org.uk; . . . . 04 - Mind offers various training courses and seminars on mental health some of which relate to LGBT issues. Contact them for more details.

NICOLA BINDER COUNSELLING SERVICES

London Tel: 07947 556143; Ask for: Nicola; . . . .
04 - Nicola has the following letters behind her name
B.A. B.S.W. (University of W.A.). She offers an
empowering, and solution - focused approach to
gender and personal life issues.

RELATE

See Local Phone Directory For Nearest Branch, Head
Office - Herbert Grey College, Little Church Street,
Rugby, CV21 3AP Tel: 0845 130 40 10; Web site:
www.relate.org.uk . . . . 04 - This nationwide
organisation specialises in counselling individuals and
couples in all types of relationships. They are non-
judgmental and are trained to understand cross-
dressing related problems within a relationship. Their
counselling skills are used to help an individual or
couple to resolve or come to terms with their
problems and clearly see their future options. The
service is very highly recommended.

SOUTH LONDON HELP GROUP

Tel: 0208 355 7413 . . . . 04 - Meet 3rd Wednesday of
month, call before 9pm.

Specialist Services

ADAM & EVE DRESSING SERVICE

112a Bethnal Green Road, London E2 7DG (green
shop on corner of Brick Lane) Contact: Liza Tel: 0207
729 7447 Website: www.chrysalistvfashions.co.uk . . . .
04 - A dressing service with an emphasis on social
gatherings that has storage facility and a retail section.
Go to them to change before your night out at the
nearby tranny clubs then arrive back by 2.30am and
change back.

ACADEMY STUDIOS

Greater London Tel: 07802 455 037; Email:
mike.pattison1@btopenworld.com; Web site:
www.theboudoironline.com Ask for: Mike Pattison; . .
. .04 - Highly experienced and professional tranny
friendly photographer who has worked in the
transgendered community for the past 3 years. The
resident photographer for The Boudoir Dressing
Service, Mike will put you at ease immediately and pull
out all the stops to give you the best set of photos
possible. Friendly, discreet and totally professional
Mike is one of the best in the business. Mike can
supply a North London based studio for your shoot
or travel to a location of your choice.

ANN'S DRESSING SERVICE

c/o The Philbeach Hotel, (30-31) Philbeach Gardens,
Earls Court, London, SW5 Tel: 020 7373 4848; . . . .
04 - Ann is a full time TV who welcomes old & new
faces to the Philbeach Hotel. Her comprehensive &
flexible service has been running since 1986. Ann has
wardrobe, wigs, make-up, boots & shoes. A
comfortable space can be provided to change before &
after a night on the town at reasonable costs. All
services are by appointment.

AUNTY YVONNE

London Tel: 0208 316 4639; Ask for: Yvonne; . . . .
04 - A mature TV offering sincere friendship to boys
that want to be little girls. Your party frock is waiting
along with all the accessories.

BOUDOIR EN FEMME

London Tel: 0795 651 9841 Fax: 0870 831 5038 Email:
boudoir@btopenworld.com Website:
www.boudoirenfemme.com . . . .
04 - Dressing service in a discreet luxury riverside
apartment near Richmond with photo's and video.
Offers grooming, deportment and elocution lessons
and escorted shopping trips. Please no withheld
numbers, mutual trust is essential.

COUNSELLOR - DOM

Tel: 07985 185332 . . . . 04 - Gender identity
counselling either at your home or mine. Also
massage and escort services.

DON ALLEN PHOTOGRAPHIC

Central London & Croydon Tel: 07780 668886; Email:
photodonallen@excite.com; Web site:
www.donallen.me.uk . . . . 04 - Has studio facilities in
Central London & Croydon and mobile lighting for
working 'in home'. Very tranny friendly and
understanding to a wide range of subject matter
including TV couples.

DR SUCCAR'S PRACTICE

7 Reptone Avenue, Hayes, Middx UB3 4AF Tel: 020
8848 8288 Mobile: 07956 879083; Email:
dr@natura.org.uk; Web site: www.natura.org.uk. . . .
04 - Qualified in medicine his practice includes
Iridology, Chinese medicine, Detox, Nutrition, Ozone
therapy, counselling, understand your gender & body,
health and safety.

FRASER WEB DESIGN (FWD)

Mobile: +44 (0)7958 277234 Website:
www.fraserwebdesign.com Email:
fraser2003@btinternet.com . . . . 04 - A tranny
friendly web design company, offering you the chance
to get your business or personal homepage on the
web at 'competitive' prices.

GAYS THE WORD

66 Marchmont Street, London WC1N Tel: 0207 278
7654 Website: www.gaystheword.co.uk . . . .
04 -Bookstore that sells many transgender books.
Also do mail order worldwide.

GENDER WORKS ACADEMY LTD

c/o Sam's Hair and Beauty Salon(By appointment only),
169 Old Kent Road, London SE1 5NA Tel: 020 7237
3313 Mel; Email: la-zarus@lineone.net; Ask for:
Mirella Ruggeri; . . . . 04 - Brush up on those all
important feminine skills. Offer hair-care advice, hairdressing, make-up and make-overs, deportment
training, beauty treatments and mail order products.
Not a dressing service but can provide all the
expertise you need to be your feminine best. All
sessions are by appointment only. For free welcome
pack write to Stephenie/Mel, The Gender Works
Academy, c/o Sam's Hair and Beauty Salon, 169 Old
Kent Road, London SE1 5NA She also offer private
consultations for M to F TS's at The London Institute,

HELEN WEBB (SINGING LESSONS)

London, Belsize Park Tel: 0207 916 7016 or 0207 916 706; Web site: www.helenwebb.com. . . . 04 - Helen is a singer song writer with a tried and tested formula for training the singing voice passed down through her family. Having worked on the gay cabaret circuit and teaching Vicky Lee and other trannies Helen is your ticket to self satisfaction. Also on 07966 513954

LIZ DE SOUZA

Tel: Mob: 07968 901840; Email: liz@desouza.fslife.co.uk; 04 - London based photographer with very competitive rates. She works both in the studio and on location whichever is more discreet/appropriate. Her clients are always thrilled with the results and normally come back for more. She's happy to try out any ideas and makes a fun and relaxing environment.

PANDORA DE'PLEDGE IMAGE WORKS

North London Tel: 0207 682 0340 Mob: 07780 914085; Email: glamour@pandoradepledge.com; Web site: www.pandoradepledge.com Ask for: Pandora De'Pledge; 04 - Pandora offers a full dressing service, professional make-over's, top quality photo shoots, accommodation in luxurious premises with all year garden jacuzzi and sun bed. Escorted day or evening trips. Her skill at creating photo images is possibly "The most professional in Europe". Her team can also provide digital services to turn your pictures into CD files, web sites, computer wallpaper. They can even edit video clips of you. All of this is described in massive detail on their web site (see also hair and beauty).

PHOTO EXPRESS

122a Plumstead Common Road, London SE18 2UL Tel: 020 8855 7076; . . . . 04 - Confidential colour film processing service. Photographer available for your personal photographs.

RESPECT HOLIDAYS

89/91 Bayham Street,Camden Town, London, NW1 0AG Tel: 0870 770 0169; Email: info@respect-holidays.co.uk; Web site: www.respect-holidays.co.uk . . 04 - Europe's largest gay holiday company, offering an amazing choice of TV friendly hotels & apartments throughout the Mediterranean, Canaries & further afield at prices to suit any budget. Call or click for a brochure.

SHIP FOR HIRE

Docklands Email: claudianashtv@hotmail.com . . . . 04 - A beautiful wooden ship in a discrete part of Dockland for hire for parties and tranny B&B or tranny flatshare. With 3 double cabins, 2 loos and 2 showers and a sundeck.

SOHO ORIGINAL BOOK SHOPS

12 & 13 Brewer St, Soho, London W1 Tel: 020 7494 1615; . . . . 04 - Wide range of tranny books & videos plus wider range of erotica now with two shops opposite each other, plus 3 new shops in London's east end, 23/25 Leather Lane, EC1 - 020 7404 3594, 124 Middlesex Street E1- 020 7377 5309 & 63 Cowcross Street, London - 020 7251 8020.

SWISH PUBLICATIONS
8 Greek Street London Soho W1 Tel: 0207 437 8132; 04 - The biggest selection of TV TS Magazine titles plus Videos. Looks seedy but is actually very friendly.

THE BOUDOIR (DRESSING SERVICE)
London N22 Tel: 0208 365 7755 Mob: 07967 046669; Email: info@theboudoironline.com; Web site: www.theboudoironline.com Ask for: Jodie; .... 04 - A highest quality dressing service. Dressing appointments with unlimited use of the vast and luxurious wardrobe, professional make-overs, make up tuition, wig styling and tuition, stunning professional photo shoots (in the studio and on location). Jodie Lynn and her staff of bubbly RG's are the leaders in organised outings to events such as: Royal Ascot, The Rubber Ball, Transfandango Ball, Torture Garden. They organise regular group outings to the theatre/musicals,, the Royal Opera house, tea at The Ritz, and many of the London nightclubs (weekly). Personalised shopping trips to the West End are also very popular. This service has a very loyal network of customers and friends who have formed a loose affiliation under the name "The Boudettes" who now have an independent web site to record their various adventures. www.boudettes.com

THE BOUDOIR SHOP.COM
PO BOX 1422, Ilford, Essex IG2 3HF Tel: 020 8365 7075 Email: info@theboudoirshop.com Website: www.theboudoirshop.com .... 04 - A high quality mail order company for the transgendered. sell ing make up, corsetry, body shaping garments, tuitional videos, CD Roms and much more. New products being launched regularly. Part of The Boudoir Dressing Service success.

TRANSFORMATION (LONDON)
52 Eversholt Street, Camden, London, NW1(next to Euston Station) Tel: 0870 741 8877; Email: orders@transformation.co.uk; Web site: www.transformation.co.uk. .... 04 - Open: 9am - 8pm Monday - Saturday. The London branch of Stephanie Anne Lloyds well known chain of shops which provides a comprehensive range of goods and services to cross dressers. See also listing under UK - Manchester, Bristol, Birmingham, Newcastle, Dublin, Berlin and

TRANSGENDER VOICE WORKS
Soho London Tel: 020 7836 4054; Email: garbo.garbo1@btinternet.com; Ask for: Garbo; .... 04 - In Soho the lovely Garbo Roche is a well known character. She has helped some of the biggest name refine their voice for stage radio public speaking. She is keen to help trannies find their most feminine voice & perfect it. Voice-over work one day course bookable.

TV/TS NEWS
PO Box 2534, London, WC1N 3XX Tel: 0207 609 1093; Email: webmaster@tv-ts.co.uk; Web site: www.tv-ts.co.uk. .... 04 - Free information for the TG community. This quirky monthly newsletter is widely distributed. It gives a wide variety of information for the TG community including classified contacts, jobs, buy and sell. For your own free copy send an A5 sae 39p.

U R P LONDON - PHOTOGRAPHY
Ask for: Ulli Richter Email: studio@ullirichter.com www.urphotogrpahy.com www.kinkiprint.com. .... 04 -Photographer take a look at websites, also

VISIONS
P.O.Box 139, Camberley, Surrey, GU15 1UJ Tel: 01276 671116; Email: revisions@iname.com; Web site: www.visions-uk.co.uk Ask for: Peter & Lyn; .... 04 - 10mins from the J3-M3/M25 intersection providing a discreet, complete dressing service with wigs, wardrobe, all the accessories, make-up, plus professional photography on 35mm or digital prints or CD Rom, dress making.

Hair & Beauty

ALICE JAHNS
London Tel: 020 8445 7604; Ask for: Alice Jahns BABTAC. MBAE.C&G; .... 04 - Qualified beauty therapist, British Association of Electrolysists, 20 years of experience with transexuals. Close to M1, A1 North Circular Road.

BARE NECESSITY
28, Maddox St, London W1S 1PR Tel: 020 7499 4904; Web site: www.barenecessity.co.uk. .... 04 - Unisex Clinic specialising in permanent hair removal and skin rejuvination and micro derma-brasion, IPL, botox, facial fillers and vein treatment. Appointment necessary. Trannys welcome.

BLU
London Tel: 0207 481 4801; Web site: www.blu.uk.com Ask for: Pam; .... 04 - Hair dressing and beauty salon. Tranny friendly. Also at Ludgate Sq 0207329 2827, South Quay Plaza 0207538 9000.

CHARLES FOX
22, Tavistock Street, Covent Garden, London WC2E 7PY Tel: 0870 2000 369 / 0870 2001 369; Email: sales@charlesfox.co.uk; Web site: www.charlesfox.co.uk Ask for: Daniel; .... 04 - For over 120 years FOX have been supplying make-up to the industry and has always welcomed customers from the Transgender community. We have a renowned make-over service, understanding staff and a thriving Mail Order Service for the thousands of make-up products and wigs in stock.

CHESSINGTON ELECTROLYSIS
Chessington Tel: 0776 1226749; Email: electrolysis@bustles-and-bows.co.uk; .... 04 - Junction 9 on M25. Uses Blend and regular electrolysis. 15 minute free trial test patch available.

COBELLA
5 Kensington High St 0207 937 8888/1818; Web site: www.cobella.com Email: info@cobella.co.uk Ask for: Andrew Williams; .... 04 - Hair and beauty salon offering laser hair removal using Plasma Light. Free test patch. Full understanding of TG needs.

CRISTIANOS LASER CLINIC (LONDON)
Earls Court Tel: 0800 085 0661; Email:
chris@cristianos.co.uk; Web site:
www.cristianos.co.uk/tg Ask for: Chris Hart; . . . .
04 - by appointment via her Altrincham address Chris
Hart can now offer the same service and price as her
Manchester and Leeds clinics or in her Earls Court clinic
which shares the same building as Dr Russel Reed.

ERICA POOLE I.P.T.I. A.R.M.T.
London & Surrey & Wales Tel: Tel/Fax 01932 867502;
Ask for: Erica Poole; . . . . 04 - Ring for appointment.
With over 24 years of experience treating TVs and TSs
through electrolysis including state of the art computer
controlled electrolysis (almost painless). She also offers
qualified counselling.

FOSTER
108 Stretham Hill, London SW2 4RD Ask for: Mary
Tel: 020 8674 9953 Fax: 020 8674 5855; . . . .
04 - Gentlemens and ladies bespoke wigs and hair
pieces. Also over 1000 modoacrylic fibre wigs in stock.
Also available cleaning, redressing and repairing. Open
Tue - Fri 9.00am - 6.00pm. Sat 9.00am - 1.00pm. Closed
Mondays. Tranny friendly.

HAIR BY JASMIN
187 Fulham Palace Road, Fulham, London, W6 Tel: 0207
381 1742; . . . . 04 - Jasmin and her partner Cielo, run a
hairdressing salon in Fulham. These two lovely ladies are
from the Philippines. They welcome TV customers and
will style your own hair or wig in any style that you
wish. Alternatively, you can leave your wig on a block
for styling, then pick it up later. Ask for Jasmin to make
an appointment and explain that you are a 'transvestite'
and what help you need before visiting this salon.

HAIR DEVELOPMENT
247 Mile End Road, London, E1 4BJ Tel: 020 7790 3996
/ 4567 fax 020 7790 3621; Email: hair@hair-
development.com; Web site: www.hair-
development.com Ask for: Marina or Mike; . . . .
04 - Wigs from around £40 through to more expensive
lace front wigs at their shop or mail order is also
available. This company supplies many other wig outlets
& can often offer best prices as they are the direct
importer. They are manufacturers of custom real hair
pieces & use near undetectable techniques. Visit private
cubicles at their showroom.

HAIR RAISERS
105 Cleveland Street, London, W1P 5FB Tel: 0207 580
7666; . . . . 04 - Glamour fashion and more natural
looking wigs in real hair and synthetic materials. Private
room are available in the shop where wigs can be tried
on. Wigs can be cut and styled on the premises.
Specialists in inexpensive 'character looky-likee' wigs.
They can also be left to be washed and re-styled.
Catalogue is provided for £1.50

HAIR REMOVAL
737 High Road, North Finchley, London N12 Tel: 020
8445 6108; Ask for: Roxanne or Michael; . . . .
04 - Use the Spa Touch System, All skin types, areas and
hair colours treatable. Affordable. FDA approved, EU
approved. Call for more info and free consultation.

HAIRWORLD
31 Stroud Green Road, Finsbury Park, London, N4 3EF. Tel: 020 7272 3370; Email: pak191@netscape.net; Ask for: Jeff Hussain; . . . . 04 - Wigs of all styles & colours.

HEIDI LAWRENCE @ IPL HAIR REMOVAL
London Tel: 07711 317550; Email: heidi.lawrence@talk21.com; Ask for: Heidi; . . . . 04 - TV/TS friendly female offers permanent hair removal using the Spa Touch system. Portable machine, so treatment can be carried out in the comfort of your own home if you wish.

HONKY TONKS WIGS
69 High Street, Egham, Surrey, TW20 9EY Tel: 01784 436349 Website: www.honkytonkswigs.co.uk . . . . 04 - Wide range of fashion wigs from £49.99, expert cutting, colouring and human hair extensions. Discreet entrance from private car park.

HOT HAIR - CROYDON
At Natural Image, The Mall, Allders, North End, Croydon, Surrey Tel: 0208 256 7455; Web site: www.hothair.co.uk. . . .04 - Top quality wig service with friendly service. This shop offers a great range of wigs from 'Natural Image'. They specialise in synthetic fashion wigs cut in the latest styles particularly suited to the younger tranny. Private changing rooms. Help with make-up if required.

ITALIA WIGS
295 High Road, Leyton, London, E10 5QN Tel: 0208 539 4260; . . . . 04 - Tanya recommends this shop who are pleased to help cds with a wide range including real hair wigs, which you can try on in their private fitting rooms. For the perfectionist owner Mike Slade can help you to order a custom-made hair piece. Any wig can be washed and re-styled. You can't make-up in the shop.

JENNY'S ELECTROLYSIS
Hendon, London Tel: 020 8202 4117 or 07850 382950; . . . . 04 - Friendly, professional electrolysis & waxing in discreet & homely surroundings to cross-dressers, TV's & TS's. Also a professional male massage available.

JOHN LESTER WIGS
32 Globe Road, London, E1 4DU Tel: 020 7790 2278 Website: www.johnlester.co.uk . . . 04 - For the complete hair design service - wigs fitted & styled in total privacy. Human hair or synthetic, custom made or ready made. Your own hair styled and colour blended. Experienced hair stylist available to give professional advice. Nearest tube Stepney Green (District Line) 50 yds left.

KARIN TOURNIER
Harrow Tel: 020 8863 0270; . . . . 04 - Semi-permanent make-up. le micropigmentation for eyebrows, eyeliner & lipliner lasting 3-5 years, electrolysis, waxing, facials, acne and peeling treatment. 24 years of experience treating transsexuals.

MAC
107 Kings Road, London, SW3 Tel: 0207 834 6412; . . 04 - Also at Harvey Nichols, Knightsbridge. MAC is the make-up of the 90's. The trendy staff welcome trannies and give good advice. (check the make-up advise pages in this book for testimonials)

MANDEVILLE
Fulham London Tel: 0208 741 5959; . 04 - The ultimate in hand made wigs and hair pieces. A range of luxury real European hair wigs. Ask for a catalogue.

NAILS UNLIMITED
10 Lauriston Street, Edinburgh, EH3 9DJ Ask for: Myra Tel: 0131 477 2633 . . . . 04 - Nail salon & beauty room. Myra offers a full range of treatments, nails, waxing, make-up etc.

N L EPILATION CLINIC
16 Aldermans Hill,London, N13 4PN Tel: 020 8882 2634; . . . . 04 - This clinic offers IPLS and the Epilight laser hair removal machine and is fully aware of Transgender needs. Phone for a free and private consultation. Treating clients with intense pulsed light for the past 4 years. Personal Lifestyle consultations.

NAS'S HOME & BEAUTY THERAPIST
London Tel: 0208 524 5847; . . . . 04 - Nas based in Chingford has a growing tranny clientele all around London and Essex (including Vicky Lee). For those who like to be pampered she provides waxing, electrolysis, lash tinting, body hair bleaching, manicures and pedicures, ear piercing and make-up lessons. Previous to the Beauty Industry Nas ran ladies boutiques and is very good at dressing you from head to toe to get the look. She will also help with shopping trips to buy make-up, shoes, wigs, clothing or a night out. Nas' prices are as friendly as she is.

PANDORA DE'PLEDGE IMAGE WORKS
North London Tel: 0207 682 0340 Mob: 07780 914085; Email: glamour@pandoradepledge.com; Web site: www.pandoradepledge.com Ask for: Pandora De'Pledge; . . . . 04 - Pandora is Vicky Lee's personal hairdresser and Ex Madam Jo's Barbette. She is a qualified & experienced, hairdresser & make-up artiste, who can help you perfect your image while keeping you laughing for hours. Pan offers a unique range of wigs and hairpieces that she customises to create a "ria" unlike any other. Professional make-over's and make-up lessons all in her luxurious premises with all year garden jacuzzi and sun bed. Her skill at creating photo images is possibly "The most professional in Europe". All of this is described in massive detail on their web site.which now has an online shop which includes make-up and a selection of the customised wigs. Pandora also offers dressing service and escorted trips (see specialist services).

POP IN
6 Cleaver Street,(Off Kennington Road), London, SE11 Tel: 0207 735 4371; Ask for: Jackie; . . . . 04 - This is a helpful hair and beauty salon. They invite you to visit the salon for waxing, wigs and hair, sunbed, manicure and make-up. Changing facilities are available with the use of shower, appointment only.

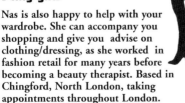

RAOUL'S HAIR & WIGS
34 Craven Road, Paddington, London, W2 3QA Tel: 0207 723 6914; . . . . 04 - In a private cubicle, try on as many wigs as you wish from a wide selection of makes. Prices start from around £85. A reconditioning / re-styling service for any wig is available from £25. Stylists can advise you how to make the best of your own hair with an inbetweeny style. This very popular company has been making human hair wigs & hairpieces since 1899. They are very highly recommended. An appointment is needed as they are always busy.

REENA HAIR EXTENSIONS
17 Connaught Street, London W2 Tel: 0207 258 0022; Ask for: Reena; . . . . 04 - For excellent hair extensions in real hair or monofibre. Reena is very experienced and understanding and produces the best possible results. Recommended by Sarah & Vicky.

ROSIE'S MAKE-UP BOX
6 Brewer Street, Soho, W1R 3FS Tel: 07976 965520 Fax: 0208 390 7773; Email: rosemarie@rosiesmake-up.co.uk; Web site: www.rosiesmake-up.co.uk . . . . 04 - Rosies Make-up Box offers make-up, skincare and wig advice from a top professional make-up designer. Lessons are backed up by a detailed make up chart and telephone helpline. A typical client would wish to pass as a well dressed business girl. Make-up is also available for photographic sessions and Rosie can give advice on photographers.

SCREEN FACE
48 Monmouth Street, Covent Garden, WC2 Tel 0207 836 3955 Website: www.screenface.com (online ordering) . . . 04 - Friendly welcome, full understanding of cross dressing. Wide range of theatrical and daywear make-up including Kyrolan. Also another branch in Notting Hill at 20 & 24 Powis Terrace, Nottinghill Gate W11 Tel: 0207 221 8289.

SARA THOMAS
North West London, Harrow Tel: 020 8933 6487; Email: sarathom@dircon.co.uk; Web site: www.sarathom.dircon.co.uk Ask for: Sara Thomas; . . . . 04 - Sara has very many years experience in beauty therapy specialising in Electrolysis & red vein treatment and works mainly with TV's & TS's. She is highly recommended by many of our contacts. Introducing state of the art technology with soft pulsed light systems. Her qualifications include B.T.E.C. -- H.N.D. -- C&G -- B.A.B.T.A.C.

SELFRIDGES
400 Oxford Street, London, W1 Tel: 0207 629 1234; . . 04 - This famous department store has a superb Perfumery Hall, packed with many famous make-up brands, The store has a wig department with very understanding staff, who are used to cross-dressers. They can offer a facility to try on any wig. Their quality wigs are very natural looking.

SHEPHERDS BUSH MARKET
Under The Arches At Shepherds Bush Tube . . . . 04 - The market has shops either side of the road behind the market stalls and at least four of these sell wigs and specialist products for black hair.

BODY CLINIC
Woodford London & Harley Street Tel: 0845 601 1962; Web site: www.thebodyclinic.co.uk . . . . 04 - Ruby laser hair removal from a company that understands the care and attention that trannies need. 17 other branches nationwide.

THE CARNIVAL STORE
69-85 Tabernacle Street, London EC2A 4BA Tel: 0800 174 114; Web site: www.madworld.com; . . . . 04 - Formerly Stagestruck in Spitalfields London. Make-up, accessories, jewellery, wigs, masks, spangles and bangles plus full costume hire. Every thing for that Madi Gras Carnival - or the Venetian masked ball.

THE WIG BAZAAR
57 Granville Arcade, Brixton Market, Brixton, London, SW9 Tel: 0207 733 3589; . . . . 04 - This is probably the cheapest shop in London for wigs. Run by two ladies in the heart of Brixton Market, off Atlantic Road. This little shop is packed with an array of wigs of all lengths, styles and colours, with a bias towards Afro-hair wigs.

TRENDCO (RETAIL LONDON)
229 Kensington Church Street, Notting Hill, London W8 7LX Tel: 020 7221 2646; Email: trendco@fsbdial.co.uk; www.wigsattrendco.co.uk 04 - They prefer TVs to openly say what they are, so they can give the best help. They have private rooms, and a huge choice of stock including very natural looking, highlight (air brushed) styles. Real hair wigs are also available to order. Trendco will customise, wash and re-style any wig. If you want to try a wig whilst made up, facilities to make-up are available, and the staff are keen to give make-up help and advice.Open Mon- Sat 10am-6pm. A super new catalogue is available. From which you can order by mail order (See Nationwide section)

T & T EPILATION
Tel: 01376 322 109 or 07887 723239 Website: www.ttepilation.com . . . . 04 - Full range of hair removal services using Plasmalite. Fully understanding of transgender needs. Wide range of testimonials. Tina & Tracy are well aware of the community's needs and expectations.

Clothes

AD HOC (KINGS ROAD)
153 Kings Road, Chelsea, London,SW3 5TX Tel: 020 7376 8829; Email: enquiries@adhoclondon.com; Website: www.adhoclondon.com . . . . 04 - A great collection for disco dollys from necklaces to shoes. There is no need to be shy about being a tranny in this shop. One stop shop for theme parties.

AGENT PROVOCATEUR
6 Broadwick Street, London W1 Tel: 0207 439 0229; Email: enquiries@agentprovocateur.com; Web site: www.agentprovocateur.com . . . . 04 - open between 11am-7pm: This shop stocks the most 'come to bed' lingerie around. You will not be allowed to try the underwear on in the shop so please don't ask. They also sell fluffy marabou mules upto size 8. There are two other shops at: 5 The Royal Exchange, London EC3V 3LL and 16 Pont Street, London SW1X 9EN.

ANGELS & BERMANS
40 Camden Street, London, NW1 OEN Tel: 0207 387 0999; Ask for: Emily Lane; . . . . 04 - Extensive costume hire. These are the outfitters to all the movies. Wig Creations is now part of this business offering made to measure plus a range of quality wigs. Highly recommended.

BARE ESSENTIALS
www.jade.co.uk Tel: 0208 902 1292 Mail Order suppliers of stockings and a multitude of sheer and see though garments. Visit their web site for online catalogue and ordering

BERWICK STREET (FABRIC SHOPS)
Berwick Street, Soho London, W1 . . . . 04 - This road has many fabric shops which stock the most glamourous and exciting materials. The very best is Borovics. You won't find better choice & service anywhere. Check out the notice board to see their customers & for dressmakers. Off Berwick St is Klines who can supply trimmings including everything to make corsets. A few minutes away in Beak St there is the most fab shop selling every type of sequins & beads.

BREATHLESS
38b The Stables Market, Chalk Farm Road, Camden, London NW1 8AH Tel: Tel/Fax: 020 7267 3705; Website: www.breathless.uk.com. . . . 04 - Latex clothing, jewellery and accessories, including House of Harlot, Pigalle, Skin Two, Velda Lauder and more.

CAMDEN MARKET
Camden High Street, NW1 Next the Regents Canal. . . . . 04 - Open early until approx. 5pm, Sat & Sun. On Saturdays & Sundays the whole length of Camden High Street is one mass of friendly people. The market is full of new & second hand clothes, ranging from designer wear, through to stage, uniform and historical outfits. Many of the stalls are run by young designers, launching their own designs & careers. The arches are the place to head for to find real gems from every era. The more established units also open 10am to 5pm Thursday and Friday and are fast becoming a tranny haven with names like FU Baby, Cobblers to the World and Black Rose to name a few.

CAMDEN PASSAGE
Runs Beside Upper St, Islington, N1 . . . . 04 - Angel Islington. This market has a wonderful collection jewellery, accessories & antique clothes from all periods of time.

CHARITY SHOPS
Everywhere . . . . 04 - Can be found everywhere but in some London shops great bargains can be found. Try the more expensive areas for some real designer bargains.

CRISPINS
28-30 Chiltern Street, London, W1M 1PF Tel: 020 7486 8924; . . . . 04 - This upmarket shoe shop specialise in larger sizes 8.5 to 12 and narrow fittings size 5 to 8.5. TV friendly but discretion appreciated.

DANCIA
187 Drury Lane, Covent Garden, London, WC2 Tel: 0207 831 9483; Email: dancia@lineone.net; Web site: www.dancia.co.uk . . . . 04 - We are a dancewear shop specialising in all types of dance apparel, we stock capezio hold and stretch tights in Suntan which are useful for drag.

DEBENHAMS
334 Oxford Street, London, W1 Tel: 020 7580 3000; . . 04 - The experienced female staff can be very helpful and individual changing rooms are

DOREEN FASHIONS
644 Leabridge Road, Leyton, London, E10 6AP Tel: 020 8539 4578 fax 020 8518 7771; Email: sales@doreenfashions.co.uk; Web site: www.doreenfashions.co.uk . . . .04 - Open Mon - Sat 9am - 5.30pm. Betty and her staff invite you to their shop in Leyton which features a special tranny changing room. The friendly service & range of goods which cross-dressers have enjoyed for many years is waiting for you. The shop stocks a large range of dresses, coats, lingerie & shoes for every occasion including a new sexy range of clubwear, corsetry, wigs, make-up & showgirl shoes - all in the widest range of sizes. Very highly recommended.

ECTOMORPH
66 Holloway Road, London N7 8JL Tel: 020 7697 8588; Email: sales@ectomorph.com; Web site: www.ectomorph.com; Ask for: Krystina; . . . . 04 - A very exciting catalogue is available that has exciting designs for boys, girls & inbetweenies. Worth obtaining just for the pictures.

EN-TYCE
Leytonstone Tel: 020 8988 0704; . . . . 04 - Friendly service, clothes in larger sizes and lingerie.

ETAM
484 Oxford Street, London, W1 Tel: 020 7629 1430; . . . . 04 - Found country wide this store brings funky clothes in size 8 to 26.

EVANS (SHOPS)
538-540 Oxford Street, London, W1 or 318 Tottenham Court Road. Tel: 020 7499 5372 or 020 7255 2116; . . . 04 - Many stores (branches everywhere). Fashion for the larger woman (sizes 14 - 32). A new trendy line begins to improve. Shoes are available in basic styles all up to size 11 with wide fittings. Changing rooms vary store to store but the newer branches in the new malls have large individual cubicles. There is a good lingerie section in the basement of this shop. Staff attitude varies.

FAIRYGOTHMOTHER
8 East Yard, Camden Lock, London NW1 Tel: 020 7485 0365 Website: www.fairygothmother.com . . . . 04 - A shop of Latex, Corsetry, PVC, Leather and Lingerie in sizes 8-24. Many popular designers stocked. Open Tues-Sat 11-5.30pm

FANTASY SHOES
Unit 44, Barking Industrial Park, Ripple Road, Barking, Essex IG11 OTJ Tel: 020 8594 8555 Fax: 020 8594 8999; Web site: www.fantasyshoe.com. . . . 04 - Manufacturer of boots, and shoes in wild designs.

FEMME BOUDOIR
17b Riding House Street, London, W1W 7DT Tel: 020 7637 5794 fax 020 7637 5796; Web site: www.femmeboudoir.com . . . 04 - Fine lingerie, shoes, hosiery, corsetry, jewellery, rubber, leather, PVC & toys. Visit or call for 36 page catalogue £5.

FENWICK OF BOND ST.
63 New Bond Street, London, W1A 3BS Tel: 020 7629 9161; .04 - The lingerie department and hosiery sections of this department store are particularly good and are well worth exploring. Their range of accessories is excellent. However the seriously upmarket clothing departments will seriously dent your credit card.

FONTHILL ROAD
Finsbury Park, London . . . . 04 - 10am - 3.30pm Sat and some shops are reported to sell to the public on weekdays aswell. This Road is packed with clothing manufacturers and the street is like a market as the 'trade only' showrooms open to the public, selling clothes of every style at around 50% of the retail prices. Cash or cheques only. The staff of these establishments, it must be said, are not, generally, accepting of cds but welcome anyone with cash. Don't expect to try on and find out their exchange policy before you

FOXY 1
18-20 Coldharbour Lane, Hayes, Middlesex, UB3 Tel: 020 8561 6890; Ask for: Bobbie; . . . . 04 - You are invited by host Marticia to a cup of tea and a chance to try on quality clothes from the extensive range of Foxy 1 or order made-to-measure to suit you. Underwear, PVC, boots available. Make-up, wigs & waxing.

GANDOLFI
150 Marylebone Road, London, NW1 Tel: 0207 935 6049; . . . . 04 - Dance belts and dance tights, catsuits and leotards and a healthy attitude towards trannies. Made to measure flesh coloured body suits and tights a speciality.

GILENE
Tel: 020 7608 0362 or 07787 975 452; Ask for: Helene or Gillian; . . . . 04 - Exclusive made to measure clothes for all tastes. Specialising in the sophisticated look of today. Day, evening and cocktail wear. All sizes, alterations undertaken. Confidentiality at all times. Trannies and cross-dressers welcome.

HARRODS
87 Brompton Road, London, SW1 Tel: 0207 235 5000; Web site: www.harrods.com. . . 04 - This world famous department store stocks all that a cross-dresser could possibly wish for. However unless you are very convincing you will be followed about by a security guard.

HONOUR SE1
86 Lower Marsh Road, Waterloo, London, SE1 7AB Tel: 020 7401 8220; Web site: www.honour.co.uk . . . . 04 - A very friendly company which has recently refurbished this shop and expanded its own quality range of PVC clothes in sizes right up to 20. Honour also stocks an extensive range from many other

designers in PVC, leather and rubber. A terrific selection of sexy footwear is also available in a good range of sizes. Shop open mon-fri 10.30pm-7pm, sat 11.30pm-5pm. Everything is available by mail order (don't forget full range of sizes) Honour, Unit 3, 158 Coles Green Road, London, NW2 7HW.

HONOUR (RETAIL AND MAIL ORDER)
Honour, Unit 3, 158 Coles Green Road, London NW2 7HW Tel: 020 8450 6877 fax 020 8450 6899; Web site: www.honour.co.uk . . . 04 - A very friendly company which has recently set up a shop here in their warehouse near Brent Cross. Many items including books & videos. Shop open mon-fri 10pm-6pm, sat

HOUSE OF HARLOT
88 - 90 Holloway Rd, London N7 Tel: 0207 700 1441; Email: robin@house-of-harlot.com; Web site: www.houseofharlot.com. . . . 04 - Extra ordinary designs in rubber. Beloved of Denise van Outen and Posh Becks. Many unusual character themes i.e chauffeur, sailor as well as more common maids etc. Top quality ready to wear or made to measure. Available from many outlets or direct.

HOTHEELS
South Oxhey, Watford, Herts Tel: 0208 428 5635 Ask for: Alan Sowle Email: sales@hotheels.co.uk Website: www.hotheels.co.uk . . . . 04 - A new UK based internet company selling high heels & boots and later in 2004 hotter clothes, as well as the great looking website you can find Alan or Elena at many of the London club's, if you see one of us come and have a chat and find out what great deals we can do for you.

STILETTO SHOES UK
Icon-Shoes, 148 Bedfont Lane, Feltham, Middlesex TW14 9NJ Website: www.icon-stilettos.com Email: russind@hotmail.com . . . . 04 - A great new range of stilettos, shoes and boots. Check out this on-line store. A unique clothes range also available.

JOHN LEWIS
278 Oxford Street, London, W1 Tel: 08456 049 049; Web site: www.johnlewis.com. . . . 04 - Department store where CDs are generally accepted. Do not be afraid to ask about trying on goods. Good source of long gloves on the ground floor along with a super hosiery section. The fabric and Haberdashery section still remains one of the best sources for materials and trimmings for the seamstress.

LA VEY CORSETRY & CLOTHING
Unit 5, Linwood Lane, Leicester Tel: 07941 790976 Website: www.lavey.net . . . . 04 - Made to measure corsets that can be worn on the outside, complete with matching mini skirt.

LITTLE SHOE BOX
89 Holloway Road, London, N7 8LT Tel: 0207 607 1247; Website: www.thelittleshoebox.com . . . . 04 - Manufacturing made to measure shoes in the workshops behind the shop they specialise in very high heels and platforms for all sizes and are completely tranny friendly. They have just undergone a major refit. Well worth a visit.

LOVEBOMB
Studio 216, The Aberdeen Centre, 22 Highbury Grove London N5 2DQ Tel: 020 7281 3513
04 - Wet look skirts and tops that are distinctive for club scene – with top combination from their male range that match their skirts etc.

LONG TALL SALLY
21 Chiltern Street, London, W1 Tel: 020 8649 9009; Web site: www.tallzone.com . . . . 04 - This supplier has a range for the over 30s, specialising in tall women who are size 8-18. The chain has a mail order service from: Long Tall Sally by Post, Unit B, Pioneers Ind. Park, Beddington Farm Road, Croydon. Surrey. CR0 4XB. Branches can be found in cities throughout the UK.

MAGNUS
44 Chiltern St, London, W1U 7QP Tel: 020 7224 3938; Email: info@magnusshoes.com; Web site: www.magnusshoes.com. . . . 04 - Specialises in large sized shoes. Ladies sizes go up to a size 11, both wide and slim fittings. Flats to high heels are available. Also a branch at Hampstead, 63 South End Road, Hampstead, London, NW3 2QB. Tel 020 7435 1792.

MARKS & SPENCER
458 Oxford Street, London, W1 Tel: 0207 935 7954; Web site: www.marksandspencer.com; . . . . 04 - This is the famous chain's flagship store, where their new lines are first introduced. M&S's Head Office say their policy is to train staff to treat all customers with equal respect and that includes men or cross-dressers. M&S is a patron and sponsor of The Gender Trust. M&S is famous for its quality and selection of clothes, particularly lingerie. Larger sizes are stocked now in most styles. The exchange policy at M&S is particularly good. The hosiery department sells M&S own brand, which is excellent quality with a wide range of styles. Shoes in basic styles come in larger sizes and the racks are high enough to hide behind when you try them on. Branches throughout UK.

MIDNIGHT FASHIONS LTD
Unit M, Kingsway Industrial estate, Luton LU1 1LP Tel: 01582 722180 Fantastic selection of pvc and fetish type clothes in sizes that will fit just about any girl.

MICHELLE FASHIONS
105 Epping New Road, Buckhurst Hill, Essex IG9 5TQ Tel: 020 8504 0418 Fax: 020 8559 0999; Email: info@michellefashions.com; . . . . 04 - Aswell as the London shop they have also opened one in Southend at: Unit 2, Warrior Square, Southchurch Road, Southend-on-Sea, Essex SS1 2LZ. Stocking dresses, lingerie, shoes & boots, wigs, gloves, breastforms etc.

PRECIOUS
250 Goldhawk Road, London, W12 9PE. Tel: 020 8762 0625 . . . . 04 - Offers a glamourous range of lingerie for girls & the 1950's woman. Also have ranges of shoes, boots, PVC, items in larger sizes and much more.

MISS SELFRIDGE
40 Duke Street, London, W1 Tel: 0207 629 1234; Web site: wwwmissselfridge-lb.com. . . . 04 - Clothes in this shop cover every need. At the back of the store is a lingerie section. To one side is a section with a good selection of fashionable shoes. The only changing room is communal. Size 14 is generally the largest size available. Branches throughout London and the UK.

MORDEX
22 Brick Lane, London E1 6SA Tel: 020 7739 3586; . . . . 04 - A delightful leather clothes shop selling all styles and colours of dresses, skirts, jackets etc made on the premises. TV friendly. Very competitive prices.

MYTIGHTS.COM
Tel: 020 8400 6270 Fax: 020 8400 6268; Web site: www.mytights.com Ask for: Mariah; . . . 04 - Official retailer of all brands of tights including Aristoc, La Perla, Gio, Jonathon Aston, La Bourgie, Levee, PrettyPolly, Spanks, WoMan tights, and many other brands that suit all shapes and sizes.

NATALIE - DRESSMAKER
Maidstone, Kent Tel: 01622 744 530 . . . . 04 - Natalie is a real lady who offers dressmaking services to cross-dressers at inexpensive prices. She can make anything from cocktail dresses and evening wear to hip shapers tailored to your own measurements. Some ready-to-wear items of clothing are available, as well as her very special Can-Can skirts.

OFFICE
10-59 South Molton Street, London, W1 Tel: 0207 499 8002; . . . . 04 - Office now has shops throughout the country. This independent retailer is exciting in comparison to most high street shoe shops has its has its own styles at the leading edge of fashion. Larger sizes are stocked and if not available they are happy to order them for you at least this branch will.

OMYGOD
38 Frith Street, London W1D 5LJ Tel: Tel/Fax: 020 7287 2662; Email: sin@omygod.org.uk; Web site: www.omygod.org.uk. . . . 04 - Fashion and club accessories.

PANDORA (DRESS AGENCY)
16 Cheval Place, London, SW7 Tel: 0207 589 5289; . . . 04 - This dress agency has designer labelled garments at about a third of their original cost. Both day wear and evening wear items are stocked as well as shoes, bags and jewellery. Staff remain very friendly, understanding and helpful.

PARADISE LINGERIE
105 The Galleries, Eastgate Shopping Centre, Basildon, Essex SS14 1AY Tel: 01268 284411 . . . . 04 - A selection of Lingerie, Hosiery, PVC, Clubwear, Adult Toys, Uniforms and Bad Taste Bears.

PARADISO
Corner of Dean St and Old Compton Street, Soho, London, W1 Tel: 0207 287 6913 or fax 020 8348 9352; 04 - open 11am-7.30pm. Clothing in PVC, lycra and rubber. Satin and lace corsets and French lingerie. Plus a range of wigs, boots and shoes. If there is anything else that you need the staff will do their best to help you. Also at 41 Old Compton Street.

PORSELLI
9 West Street, Off Cambridge Circus, London, WC2 Tel: 0207 836 2862; Web site:

www.porselliuk@aol.com. . . . 04 - Porselli stocks a good selection of dance tights and supports including the very excellent Danskin fishnets and flesh coloured (cover all) tights.

PROWLER SOHO
3-7 Brewer Street, Soho, London, W1 Tel: 0207 734 4031; Website: www.prowler.co.uk; . . . . 04 - Huge expanse of books, clothing, erotica, CD's & gifts. Mon-Sat 11-10pm & Sun 1-9pm.

RAIN LADIES FASHIONS
ol1451 London Road, Norbury, South London, SW16 4AQ Tel: 020 8679 7670 Website: www.geocities.com/persiaqueen2000/rainfashions.html 04 - A tranny friendly ladies boutique located in South London.

SALUTE CLOTHING LTD
162 Holloway Road, London N7 8DD Tel: 020 7700 2354; . . . . 04 - A recommended second hand clothes shop. Open Mon-Sat 10-6pm Sun 11-6pm..

SELFRIDGES (CLOTHES)
400 Oxford Street, London, W1 Tel: 0207 629 1234; Web site: www.selfridges.co.uk. . . . 04 - For the more adventurous, there is a car park, (entrance behind the building), where you can park then enter the shop. The staff are generally very liberal and helpful. Prices and styles vary across the full range to suit everybody, and often in the larger sizes. The staff are well trained, small discreet changing rooms are available. In the hosiery section on the ground you will find the more exotic lines which you can never find in local shops. (see also hair & beauty).

SHE-N-ME
123 Hammersmith Road, West Kensington, London, W14 0QL Tel: 0207 603 2402; Web site: www.she-n-me.com Ask for: Lee Alexander; . . . . 04 - This shop stocks a wide selection of top quality erotic clothing rubber, PVC. Fetish boots & shoes are stocked up to a size 12, lingerie, accessories & lots more. They also stock magazines, videos & marital aids.

SHELLY'S SHOES
Various Branches In Central London Including Oxford St Regent St, Carnaby St, Covent Garden And The Kings Road Tel: 0207 437 5842 (Oxford Street Branch); Web site: www.shellys.co.uk. . . . 04 - The trendiest fashion footwear at very acceptable prices but sorry size 8 max.

SKIN TWO
Unit N306, Westminster Business Square, Durham St, London SE11 5JH Tel: 020 7840 0146; Email: shopinfo@skintwo.com; Web site: http://www.skintwo.com/clothing . . . . 04 - One of the most well known UK fetish shops, stocking rubber, leather, PVC. Catalogue available. Call the Skin Two Nightlife Line for new of clubs anywhere in the UK (60p per minute) - 0906 8299714.

SONJA'S DESIGNS
London Tel: 0208 291 9672; Email: sonjaharms@sonjaharms.free-online.co.uk; Ask for: Sonja; . . . . 04 - Can make any garment you are either able to describe or have a picture of to your personal measurements. They are an established company & work for a wide range of clients, including the Royal Opera House, Covent Garden. Prices start at approx £180 plus materials.

STEINBERG AND TOLKEIN
193 Kings Road, London, SW3 Tel: 0207 376 3660 Fax: 0207 376 3630; . . . . 04 - Open: 11am-6.30pm Tue-Sat.12-6pm Sundays. The ground floor of this unusual and very friendly second hand shop is like Blackbeard's treasure chest. There is sparkling jewellery from many famous couture houses like Channel. They stock the 'worlds largest' range of vintage haute couture including vintage shoes & accessories. Specialise in period costume jewellery.

STILLETOHEELLTD.COM
Web site: www.stilletoheelltd.com. . . . 04 - A new footwear service wide range of sexy styles at value for money prices.

TOP SHOP
214 Oxford Street, London, W1 Tel: 0207 636 7700; Web site: www.topshop.co.uk . . . 04 - A great selection of young fashion. You can find something for every occasion. Be careful, but do not be afraid to ask about trying on goods, as they have a good selection of changing facilities. Sizes are limited.

ULTIMATEFOOTWEAR.COM
8 Exchange Way, Chelmsford, Essex CM1 1XB Tel: 01245 268 400; Email: sales@ultimatefootwear.com; Web site: www.ultimatefootwear.com . . . . 04 - Sexy, glamour and fetish footwear in sizes 3-12.

Transport

EXPRESS CARS
1-20 Spurgeon Street, SE1 4YP Tel: 020 7403 3333; . . . . 04 - This is still our favourite cab company. It is a very large mini cab company covering all areas of London, which is extremely professional in its operations. All their cars are virtually new, their drivers are polite and tranny-friendly, & are very unlikely to 'take you for a ride'. To top it all they are one of the cheaper cab companies in London.

LIBERTY CARS
297 Old Street, London EC1 Tel: 020 7734 1313; . . . . 04 - London's lesbian & gay cab company offers a tranny-friendly service to any destination. If you really want to arrive in style they have various 'super' vehicles to hire.

HYDE PARK CARS
16 Hogarth Place, London Tel: 020 7244 6555; . . . . 04 - This company uses only smart drivers, & large good quality clean cars, such as Mercedes & Volvos. Limousines are also available. They are a little more expensive than other taxi companies, but all their drivers are understanding & welcoming of cross-dressers. They will look after you & treat you like a proper 'lady'.

MR BOX

London Tel: Freephone 08009562389 Mob. 0795 6220408; Email: enquiries@mrbox.biz; Web site: www.mrbox.biz; Ask for: Silburn A Daure; . . . .
04 - Tranny friendly storage, house clearance, all removals catered for - home or office. International shipping, deliveries & collections. Man & van. Packing materials for sale - delivered to you. 7 days a week.

OLD COMPTON CARS

20 Old Compton Street, Soho, London, W1 . . . .
04 - In the heart of Soho opposite Eds Diner, is this mini cab company. They operate evenings only, until around 5am. If you walk to their kiosk you are likely to be greeted with a friendly smile. You are given a quote at the kiosk before you take your cab, so you know exactly how much you will pay for your journey. Don't expect a limousine - in fact you will be lucky to get anything but a wreck. However, the drivers are generally good & prices are fair.

Hotels & Restaurants

BALANS

60 Old Compton Street, Soho, London, W1 Tel: 0207 437 5212; Email: info@balans.co.uk; Website: www.balans.co.uk . . . . 04 - Alcohol until 2am, (small late door charge) Breakfast from 2am-5am. This is a very friendly mixed gay establishment in the heart of Soho. The staff are great and are very welcoming of drag queens, TVs and TSs. Open 8am-4am Mon Tue Wed & Thu. Open Sat 8am -6am, Sun 8am-2am.

BARKING HOTEL PLAZA

04 - About 15 mins from city at the junction of the A13 and A406 (leave A406 at Highbridge Road, Barking) you will find four NEW hotels - Local taxi service from these hotels to city is aprox £14 ... 0207 503 5555 Ibis - £60 per room Premier Lodge £42 per room 0807 7001444 Etap £37 0208 283 4550. Formule 1 - just £25 per room A good room for up to three people with sink & mirror (shower off shared corridor) 0208 507 0789 This may be the cheapest hotel in London.

BEAVER HOTEL

57-59 Philbeach Gardens, West Kensington, London, SW5 9ED Tel: 0207 373 4553; Email: hotelbeaver@hotmail.com; Website: www.beaverhotel.co.uk Ask for: Richard; . . . .
04 - The Beaver Hotel has 38 rooms over four floors of a charming converted Victorian Townhouse. The hotel staff and management are very TV/TS friendly and understanding of clients needs. Ample mirrors and good lighting make this the ideal place to stay for a night on the town, a days shopping or a short away break to the capital.

CHAMBERLAIN HOTEL

130-135 Minories, London EC3 1NU Tel: 020 7680 1500 fax 020 7702 2500; Email: chamberlain@fullers.co.uk; . . . . 04 - All rooms equipped with air-con, TV, hair dryer, tea & coffee making equipment & so on. Rooms can have Continental breakfast or full English Breakfast. Couple of minutes walk from Algate and Tower Hill tube

UK London ■ Hotels & Restaurants

stations & The Way Out Club. Ask for wayout weekend rates and at some times of the year you may achieve 1/2 price £60 - £70.

COMPTON CAFE
34 Old Compton St, Soho, London, W1 Tel: 0207 439 3309; . . . . 04 - Open: 24 hours every day: This gay run cafe serves the most delicious hot and cold snacks made to your specifications with no questions asked. If semolina and gherkin sandwiches are your fancy at 4am in the morning - no problem. Particularly late at night as the clubs wind down, you are very likely to catch drag queens and trannies grabbing a bite to eat on their way home. A great place to hang out while waiting to meet somebody. Always busy.

EXPRESS BY HOLIDAY INN
The Highway (nr The Lime house link Tunnel) 0207 7540 0800 434040 www.hiexpress.co.uk
04 - advertising £69 advertised weekend rate

LA PERLA RESTAURANT
28 Brewer Street, London W1 Tel: 0207 437 2060; . . . 04 - Italian menu, tranny friendly, polite service. Private room for parties. Mon-Sat 12-3pm 5-11.15pm last orders. Waiters see a steady and regular tranny trade and make you completely at ease.

NOVOTEL HOTEL (LONDON TOWER BRIDGE)
10 Pepys Street, London, EC3N 2NU. Tel: 0207 265 6000 fax 020 7265 6060; Email: h3107@accor-hotels.com; . . . . 04 - 203 spacious en-suite bedrooms,phone, mini bar tea & coffee facilities, hairdryer,movies & playstation. 24hr room service. Hotel is 2 minutes walk from Tower Hill tube station & The Way Out Club.

PHILBEACH HOTEL
30\31 Philbeach Gardens, Earls Court, London, SW5 Tel: 020 7373 1244 fax 020 7244 0149; Email: 56.3112@compuserve.com; Web site: www.philbeachhotel.freeserve.co.uk. . . . 04 - This is probably the most popular hotel in London for cross-dressers. Principally a gay hotel, it has become quite infamous as 'the place' to stay in London. All cross-dressers can feel free to share the communal lounge breakfast room & bar (which includes use of the newly extended bar & garden patio), with the other guests. The lounge has an internet terminal for discreet surfing. You can treat the place like home, dressing throughout your stay. The hotel, together with the Restaurant (see listing for Wilde about Oscar) offer a special welcome to TVs on Monday nights - called 'Lipstick' See separate listing. The friendly staff & 'almost anything goes' atmosphere of this hotel coupled with the extensive renovations always in progress, including better lighting & more mirrors, makes this the only place to stay in town. A good breakfast is served in the restaurant and is included in the room rates which, lets face it, are still very reasonable for the warm welcome you receive.

STEPH'S
39 Dean Street, London, W1 Tel: 020 7734 5976; . . . . 04 - Open: noon to 12pm: Door policy: Very Welcoming. One of the most tranny friendly restaurant in town. This is a busy mixed gay restaurant

in the heart of Soho & is frequented by a diverse clientele. The very lovely Steph, the owner, will soon make any new 'girl' feel at ease. The menu has a wide selection of meals ranging from quarter pounders to smoked salmon & sirloin steak.

THAI PRINCESS
At The Philbeach Hotel, 30 Philbeach Gardens, Earls Court. London, SW5 Tel: 0207 373 9046. . . . 04 - Situated in the Philbeach Hotel is this pleasant restaurant which has always been popular with cross-dressers. The style of food is now prepared by a team of ladyboys. The quality of the food is good & the presentation & service is always pleasant. The friendly bar in the basement is available before & after a meal, where you will often have the opportunity to meet other trannies. In the Summer the lovely garden is available for dining alfresco.

TOWER THISTLE HOTEL
0207 481 2575   04 - Ask for weekend rates which at some times of the year can be £60 - £70. (5mins from the club and overlooking Tower Bridge)

TRAVEL LODGE
04- This has become popular Corriander Ave, (off East India Dock Road) near Canary Wharf 0207 531 9705.

TREBOVIR HOTEL
Trebovir Hotel, Trebovir Road, Earls Court, London Tel: 0207 370 3310; Ask for: Mr Yousuf - Hotel Manager; . . . . 04 - Tranny friendly Hotel newly upgraded. Standard room starts at £30.

Bars & Nightclubs

APPLEBY'S BAR
30 Philbeach Gardens, Earls Court, London, SW5 Tel: 0207 373 1244/4544; . . . . 04 - James Appleby always has the latest news and gossip from around London's tranny scene from behind the bar named after him, in the basement of the Philbeach Hotel. The bar has a summer patio and is particularly busy on Monday & Friday nights.

BLACK CAP PUB
171 Camden High Street, London, N1 Tel: 0207 428 2721; Email: jimmy@theblackcap.com Website: www.theblackcap.com. . . . 04 - Open till 2am: Open til 3am Fri & Sat. £2 Entry charge dependent on act: Door Policy: accepting: Dress Code: casual. This venue has long and strong associations with drag. Now completely refurbished with a super roof garden. The emphasis on resident and local acts which attract a local crowd who know the acts so well they become part of the shows, can be great fun if you are in 'the clique'. The main entertainment is the disco which is particularly good, with award winning DJs playing 'house' and 70's & 80's chart music. Have drinks promotions.

CENTRAL STATION
Kings Cross Tel: 0207 278 3294; Web site: www.centralstation.co.uk Email: info@centralstation.co.uk 04 - Open till 2am: Door Policy: welcomed: Dress Code: casual. A small independent gay owned bar with a loyal crowd that

302   The 'portal' to everything tranny on the Internet **www.wayout-publishing.com**

raises lots for charity. On Fridays, Saturdays and Sundays drag cabaret graces the bar, whilst in the basement there is room to boogie (and they do). Now with air conditioning. Changing facilities are available. Ask for manager Martin for details of the basement promotions, which are often drag themed.Also @ 80 Brunner Road, Walthamstow, E17 7NW, 0208520 4836.

FAUX
Faux@Heaven Nightclub, Under the Arches, Villers Street WC2N Tel: 020 7930 2020 Email: faux_elle@hotmail.com Website: www.heaven-london.com . . . . 04 - London's midweek venue once a month lounge extravaganza hosted by Darcy with DJ Tallulah. A night dedicated to those who love to dress in drag and admirers. Live cabaret. 11pm-3am. Door Charge £2 B4 11.30pm with flyer £6 after. Email for details.

GOOSE & CARROT (EX HORSE & JOCKEY)
128 Wellesley Road, Croydon CR0 2AH Tel: 020 8689 3473; . . . . 04 - TV/TS warmly welcomed - changing available. Late License Fri - Sat till 02.30am. Sun - Thu 12.30pm. Two bars - full range entertainment. Food available.

HEAVEN
Under The Arches,Villiers Street, London WC2N 6NG Tel: 020 7930 2020 ext 210 Fax:020 7930 8306; Email: info@heaven.virgin.co.uk; . . . . 04 - Open till 3.30am; Entry Fee: £7 (can vary): London's largest gay disco with three floors. These days, girls (and that includes us) feel more at home as the club is more mixed. The main floor is hot and sweaty, playing 'high energy' dance music on its amazing sound system, with some of the best lighting effects in London. The main stage in the cavernous venue plays host to many drag extravaganzas, & personal appearances from scene queens, such as Rupaul Elvira, Lady Bunny & Grace Jones. This is the place where the trendy trannies & drag queens throw 'shade' with attitude. Catwalk & fetish fashion is the order of the day. This bar is not ageist by any means, but you do need the right attitude to feel comfortable.

KUDOS
10 Adellaide St, London, WC2 Tel: 020 7379 4573; . . 04 - smart-casual gay bar just off Leicester Sq. This is still one of the smartest, trendiest & friendliest of London's gay bars on two levels with lots of intimate corners & a great selection of drinks & snacks. A nice place to meet friends & start the evening.

QUEENS ARMS
223 Hanworth Road, Hounslow Tel: 0208 814 2266 04 - Saturday nights Tranny friendly.

REFLEX (KINGSTON)
184 London Road, Kingston Tel: 0208 549 9911; Web site: www.reflexnightclub.com. . . . 04 - Gay nightclub open on Fridays Saturdays Sundays 9pm-3am Good venue variable atmosphere. Worth a try specially in a group. Ring web for cabaret and theme party

THE FRIDGE
Town Hall Parade, Brixton Hill, London, SW2 1RJ Tel: 0207 326 5100; . . . . 04 - The themes for each night keep changing at this fabulous night club. Don't expect glitz what they have is style. Mixed nights are great for trendy trannies.

THE GLOUCESTER
1 King William Walk, Greenwich, London, SE10 Tel: 020 8858 2666; . . . . 04 - Train BR: Greenwich: Dress Code: casual. This gay pub situated near the 'Cutty Sark' gets trannies here on a regular basis. The tough clientele are not afraid to call a spade a spade, so be prepared to stand up for yourself & you will end up with friends for life. Drag entertainment at weekends.

THE SHADOW LOUNGE
5 Brewer Street, London, W1 Tel: 020 7287 7988; Web site: www.theshadowlounge.co.uk . . . 04 - New and very stylish gay club in Soho that is 'girl' friendly. Although membership is £300 pa you can usually still get in midweek without too much problem but best to phone first.

THE SPIRAL
138 Shoreditch High Street, London, E1 Tel: 01721 613 1351; . . . . 04 - Open 5 days Wed-Sun. Wednesday Drag karaoke alternate weeks. Thur up to minute disco, brand new light and sound system. Fri Grand Karaoke night. Saturday back to the dancefloor DJ Darren G. Sun the infamous piano bar resident pianist Ian Parker & guest presenters.

THE WHITE SWAN
556 Commercial Road, London E1 Tel: 020 7780 9870; . . . . 04 - The White Swan presents drag acts and accepts with indifference the odd tranny in the audience. On Sundays 5.30 - Midnight "Legend" Jo Purvis presents her line dance disco. £2 entry - tea, sandwiches and biscuits until 7.00pm.

TWO BREWERS
114 Clapham High Street, London, SW4 Tel: 020 7498 4971; . . . . 04 - Open till 1am: Door Policy: accepted: Dress Code: casual. Offering two bars, one with cabaret every night with a diverse mix of the best acts, the other a newly equipped disco. The opportunity for a group of trannies to enjoy a show & a dance is great.

Clubs & Events

DENNIS'S DISCO (LOVEJOY)
Hackney United Service club, Almack Road, Hackney , London E5 Tel: 0788 060 7785 . . . . 04 - Fortnightly on Fridays. Large free changing room available. Entry £5 (including raffle)

EXCLUSIVE NIGHT CLUB
West Lodge, 67 Corbets Tey Road, Upminster RM14 2AJ Tel: 0170 822 0730 Fax: 0170 822 4724 Website: www.geocities.com/lodgeeo . . . . 04 - 1st Wednesday of month in Londons leafy suburbs. Changing ok.

G.A.Y.
The London Astoria, 157 Charing Cross Road, London, W1 Tel: 020 7434 0403; . . . . 04 - Saturday only: 10.30pm-5am: Door Policy: OK welcomed if you look trendy: Dress Code: young clubby The very successful night with a formula of soap & dance chart stars live on stage, with an unpretentious young lesbian & gay crowd with their cool friends. This is a good venue for young trannies with a bit of attitude.

HOUSE OF DRAG (CLUB NIGHT)
32-38 Dukes Place, behind Aldgate tube station London EC3Tel: 0797 643 4302; www.houseofdrag.tv. . . . 04 - After 4 years in Mayfair Steffan entertainer & co host of The WayOut Club now now hosts his midweek night near Aldgate tube station every Wednesday from 9 till late. This is a great opportunity to chat, dance, mix and single guys are very welcome. Cabaret is presented every week Steffan is joined by the oriental "Muse Girls" Dee and Penny first Wed of month for live singing. Brazilian she-males second Wed. Sissy maids with Mrs Silk third Wed and fetish fashion with Miss Rani last Wed. Entry £5 members & £7 others. www.clubmuse.co.uk for more on first Wed.

LEGS
800 Lea Bridge Road, London E17 Tel: 0208 558 1331 Website: www.legs-800club.co.uk . . . . 04 - Every Thursday from 9 til 2am. For TV's (RG partners also welcome) TS's and the men who like them. Admission £10. Excellent dressing/make-up facilities, storage lockers, dark rooms and private cabins.

LONG YANG CLUB
London Information Line Tel: 020 8311 5835; Web site: www.lyclondon.com; . . . . 04 - The Long Yang Club has branches throughout the UK holding meetings, parties, & events for Oriental gays & their admirers. Club nights in Thai Square (off Trafalgar Square) every Sunday. Weekly events include Authentic Oriental Karaoke, Disco, Badminton every Sunday. Tennis group every Friday evening. Parties: Chinese New Year party every February. Thai New Year party every March. Mr LYC & Miss LYC Contests every November

LIPSTICK
at The Philbeach Hotel, 30-31 Philbeach gardens, London, SW5 9EB Tel: 0207 373 1244; . . . . 04 - Every Monday night in Appleby's Bar at the Philbeach hotel host 'Lipstick' a popular night for trannies and friends. 60 people on average. A small cover charges includes a buffet and late bar. For those that want help to dress Anne's dressing service that operates at the hotel can help. Other nights of the week are also welcoming but not so busy yet!

POPCORN @ HEAVEN
Heaven, under the arches, off Villiers St, London WC2N 6NG Tel: 020 7930 2020 Email: popcorn@heaven-london.com Website: www.heaven-london.com . . . . 04 - Popcorn every Monday night at Heaven 10.15pm - 4am. All drinks £2 (excluding bottles, cocktails & champagne). 5 different rooms each with a different sound.

THE LONDON FETISH FAIR
Shillibeers.Carpenters Yard North Road,Islington London N7 4EF. Tel: 020 7916 8360; Email: INFO@LONDONFETISHFAIR.CO.UK; Web site: www.londonfetishfair.co.uk. . . . 04 - Every 1st Sunday of the month 11.00am - 5.00pm, £5 entry. Over 18's only, NO dress code, street clothes cool or dress to the 9'S.Corsetry, high heels,uniforms, leather clothing,scintillating clubwear,mag & video's. Bar & restaurant with Sunday lunch.

STUNNERS
Limehouse, Cable Street Studios, 566 Cable Street, London E1W 3HB Tel: 020 7423 9145; Email: admin@stunners.tv . . . . 04 - Private party club, fetish theme for TV's-admirers with fun rooms that leave nothing to the imagination. Thurs, Fri & Sats 10pm-10am Sundays 1pm -11pm. Admission £10 members £15 guests.

TED'S PLACE
305a North End Road, London, W14 9NS Tel: 0207 385 9359; . . . . 04 - Thurs only 7pm-Late. Entry £2 non members: This is a very friendly basement bar / club. Ted was one of the first London venue to promote a night directly for TV and TS girls. Ted (who is a really nice guy) and his staff welcome TVs and TSs every Thursday night, TVs can change when they arrive, although the space is limited. This is a good opportunity to meet other 'girls' and guys that like 'girls' in a discreet and friendly atmosphere. A good place to go for your first night out - but be prepared to say no to advances (you wont offend - and then you can get on with just having fun). Mon/Tue/Wed//Fri/Sun - Gay Men only cruise sessions 7.00pm-late.

TONY GLOBAL VILLAGE DANCE
The Space, 269 Westferry Road, Isle of Dogs, E14 Tel: 020 7515 7799 or 020 7538 3852; Ask for: Tony; . . . . 04 - Ballroom, Argentine Tango, Latin, Rock & Roll, Jive, Swing, Salsa, Merengue, Line Country, Disco & Party Music. For dates of events call Tony.Fetish Clothes

TRANS-MISSION
Monthly First Saturday of every month - 8pm to 2am. DJ's Jasmine and Vicky Valentine put on this club with 3 floors at 1- 5 Long Lane, Barbican, London EC1A (just around the corner from Barbican tube station). This busy club attracts almost exclusivly transgendered girls and a few male and female friends. The girls range from first night out to can't get enough. The atmosphere is friendly but can feel a little clikky and very white. Most regulars know each other through the internet before they visit the club so the club is almost an extension of chat rooms and the ground floor is chat central. The club attracts a dancers and DJs spawning a gaggle of tranny DJs. What the club does not attract is she-males and men looking to meet t-girls therefore there is little (if any) sexual tension and what there is, could be described as t-girl-lesbian. Great as a stepping stone out of the closet. Entry £7.00 www.trans-mission.org

WAYOUT CLUB

At Charlie's, 9 Crosswall, EC3N (off Minories near Tube Aldgate/Tower Hill) Tel: 0208 363 0948; www.thewayoutclub.com. . . . 04 - The club is open: 9pm-4am, Saturday only: Entry: £10 - £8 BUT before 11pm - trannies just £ 5 including a free cocktail. (Membership offers tranny members £5 - other members £8 discount after 11pm for £25 per year saving the rush to get to the club before the make-up has set). Easy parking, changing facilities with £15 make-up service, secure cloakroom. The WayOut Club is possibly the most consistent, unique night out on the transgender scene in the world. Vicky Lee & Steffan Whitfield have run this club for 11 years with cabaret extravaganzas with numerous drag queens costumes and scenery or a talent search to give you the opportunity to join the show every Saturday. The club also holds occasional bigger events like 'The Alternative Miss London Contest' and Drag Olympics. The ever changing crowd plus loyal regulars averages 200 to 300 people. About half are cross-dressed and range from 'first out' to 'always out'. The cream of London's beautiful transsexuals are regulars along side groups from every culture including sari clad Indian 'girls' and silk clad oriental 'girls'. If you are not ready to dress in public you can go as a guy, as many do. The dance floor has a great sound and lighting system with giant video screen running tranny television and home videos. The venue also has a second area with sofas, dining chairs and tables, food served all night. Prices at the bar are fair. WayOut always aims to attract a mixed crowd of all ages, backgrounds, genders and sexuality's - 'boys, girls and inbetweenies' not just trannies. There is no dress code anything goes and wives, girlfriends are encouraged to dress to excess too. Visitors come back time after time because the atmosphere is so relaxed, such fun and because it really does not matter who or what you are. The club is stylish but not intimidating. The hosts look forward to meeting YOU soon.

WAYOUT WINE BAR

At Lovatt Lane, (off Eastcheap), London EC3 nearest tube - Monument Tel: 0208 363 0948 Email: wayout@wayout-publishing.com; Website: www.thewayoutclub.com/winebar.htm
04 - Every Friday 8.30 til late. no dress code but smart preferred. Exclusively for T-Girls and guests. Single guys are not encouraged unless invited as personal guests. Changing facilities, easy parking. Meet and mingle, dance and dine recreating the classic formula of the original WayOut Wine Bar. Small dance area in the basement bar. Comfort area with dining available snack and full a la carte meals on the ground floor. A private first floor room is available for celebrations and dinner parties.

WIGS @ THE WOOLWICH INFANT

EVERY Tuesday TVs, TSs, CDs and admirers are welcomed at this friendly SE gay bar 8pm till 2am. Music is by their resident DJ Kevin Saint. Woolwich Infant 9 Plumpstead Rd, Woolwich London SE18 7BZ

Fetish clubs and events

CLUB RUB
At Dukes 18-22 Hounsditch EC3 City of London 0709
119 3146 www.club-rub.com Email:
kim.clubrub@virgin.net . . . . 04 - Location very close to
Liverpool Street Station in the city (3 mins walk). Write
for news letter info about their monthly club to this
address Chancery House, 319 City Road, London,
EC1V 1LJ.

SKIN TWO RUBBER BALL
At Le Palais, Hammersmith, 242 Shepherds Bush Road,
London, W6 Tel: 020 8968 9692; Email:
rubberball@skintwo.com; Web site:
www.skintwo.com/rubberball. . . . 04 - Dress Code:
kinky drag. The annual Skin Two Ball is attended by
hundreds of fetish fashion followers. The huge dance
floor has a stage where various events take place
throughout the evening, including live bands & fashion
shows. Side-shows include portrait studios, clothes &
other products. Possibly the best fetish fashion event of
the year.

SKIN TWO CABARET
Red Rose Comedy Club, 129 Seven Sisters Road,
Islington N7 Tel: 020 7281 3051 Website:
www.redrosecomedy.co.uk . . . . 04 - Top acts from
the London comedy scene along with pervy stars from
the world of fetish. Also resident live house music band
Kinky Sax and usual late bar at pub prices and good hot
food on sale too. Doors open at 8pm. Shows starts at
9pm. All ticket £10 (includes free red rose
membership).

TORTURE GARDEN
Various Venues Around London Tel: 0207 613 4733;
Email: tg@torturegarden.com; Web site:
www.torturegarden.com. . . . 04 - Torture Garden is
the largest monthly fetish club in the world with regular
attendances of 1000 people or more.

WICKED GIRLS
100 Tipworth Street, Albert Embankment Vauxhall
SE11 www.wickednightclub.com . . . . 04 - Nightclub for
TV's, TS's CD's, TG's and admirers with cabaret.
Glamour studio and photo suite. Also a Pole for
dancing. See www.wickedgirls.tv for dates of these
Wicked Girls nights.

Photos with thanks James Stafford
"No Dress code at The WayOut Club"

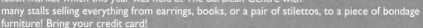

For a night out like no other, then you should head for the Skin Two Rubber Ball! (www.skintwo.com) Don't let the 'Rubber' bit put you off though. The dress code is wide and varied.

NO street clothes, but you can wear Rubber, Leather, Drag, Clingfilm(?), or anything else that can be described as 'Fetish'. Kitty and I travelled down from Birmingham, and stayed in a hotel very close to the event which runs over a weekend in October, with the main party on the Monday evening. There are many things to do before the actual ball though. There are other 'pre-party' parties that can get quite 'intimate'. You can chat to others, and find out the standard of dress that you can expect to see on the Monday night. I thought I was broad minded, but !!! There's also a fetish market which this year was held at The Barbican Centre with many stalls selling everything from earrings, books, or a pair of stilettos, to a piece of bondage furniture! Bring your credit card!

The night arrives, and we glammed up for the occasion. After spending hours having a nice long soak in the shower, and make-up it was time to get dressed and go out. I love the reaction of people in hotels. We breezed through the hotels reception where we generated our fair share of jaw dropping looks. I love my nights out! We then walked to the club, which was a short distance away.

Once at the event the music is loud, and the people are friendly., there is always a bit of a queue. We jumped most of it as we had tickets. It's always best to buy your ticket before the night. If you can leave your coat behind, as we did, you'll save time at the cloakroom, as the queues here tend to get quite long. We chatted to people that had come from Germany, Sweden, USA, and Mexico. People here are into diverse things, and all were very tolerant of each other. You must respect people there though, just because a lady has her boobs out, doesn't mean she wants anyone to touch her! You will get kicked out-Pronto! One chap I spoke to just liked women to walk on him, and many people enjoyed bondage in various guises. People really do let themselves go – and it's great to see that there were so many drag queens, trannies, sissy boys, and 'gender benders' there.

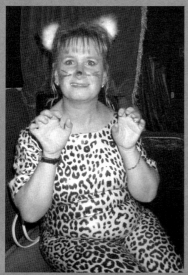

The stage show was about to start, and people made the last dash to the bar before the lights went down (even more). The fashion show featured many leading fetish clothing designers, such as House Of Harlot, Skin Two, Murray & Vern etc etc. Fantastic choreography, and special effects made this a tiptop extravaganza! Some top celebs could be seen milling around the club, but believe me, they paled into insignificance compared to the party goers.

The night was drawing to a close (at 4am!) but for some that wasn't enough. There was an after party – party at Club Rub, which we didn't go to (I'm getting old-music today etc etc). Kitty and I walked the short trip back to the hotel. Fantastic night out.

What to wear next year? Hmmmmm?

Stacey Christie
staceychristie@blueyonder.co.uk

Picture of Kitty at the ball as a Kitty :)

A Personal Report

WayOut CLUB ■ FAQ's

SATURDAY NIGHT
at The WayOut CLUB

Q - IS THERE A DRESS CODE? Wear whatever you want amongst over 200 you will always be in good company and feel comfortable with what you choose to wear.

Q - CAN I DRESS MALE ? Dress as a man or a woman we have a very mixed crowd - Many women partners and men friends enjoy the club and many say that they find the club more relaxed and fun to be at than "straight" clubs. Many of our male guests are men who 'dress' in private but not in public. Other men enjoy the chance to meet girls that have that little bit 'extra'. Respect and politeness is respected from all and those who do not understand the meaning of this and cause offence may be asked to leave by Vicky, Steffan or our security. Some of our men and women guests have been regulars since we first opened in 1993. As have many of our Tranny regulars. We have new faces EVERY week who we all enjoy meeting and making welcome.

Q - DO I HAVE TO BE A MEMBER ? No, WayOut is open to any one. Membership provides a £5 discount for an annual fee of £25 saving plenty for regulars who arrive after 11pm.

Q - HOW MUCH IS ENTRY ? From 9pm to11pm standard entry is £8.00 but just £5 for trannies who also receive a free drink and free storage for bags (if changing). After 11pm stndard entry is £10 and £5 for members.

Q - IS IT EASY TO FIND ? Our address is WayOut at Charlie's 9 Crosswall (off Minories - a name better known by cabbies) London EC3N. We are on the London A to Z but Crosswall is less obvious than Minories on the map. The City Police are well aware of The WayOut Club and are very supportive to trannies on their way to the club. All routes end up at the roundabout at Aldgate East tube station - from which you turn into Aldgate and immediately left into Minories and then right into Crosswall at the traffic lights.

Q - IS IT EASY TO PARK ? Very Easy - There is ample free parking available on single yellow lines and parking bays very close to the club. Parking on double yellows, with your wheels on the pavement or in a designated parking space may still result in a fine even very late. This is a very safe and discreet area on Saturday nights.

Q - WHAT WILL TAXI DRIVERS THINK IF I DRESS ? London black taxi drivers are the best in the world and have seen everything. It is very unusual to find a driver that does not treat trannies with respect. - We also recommend private companies Express Cars ...0207 403 3333 Freedom Cabs ..0207 734 1313

Q - CAN I GET A TAXI EASILY WHEN I LEAVE ? Yes we have a licensed cabs that our reception will call for you who will normally have a car for you immediately (prices are average for late night Saturdays).

Q - WHEN IS THE BEST TIME TO ARRIVE ? We open at 9pm and up till 11pm we have a great deal to offer early birds - FREE welcome cocktail or soft drink and reduced entry for all trannies - All drinks are reduced to city bar prices until 11pm - The party builds up from 10.30pm to 1am and goes on till 4am with show time at 1.30am

Q - WHERE CAN I CHANGE ? ...and get help with make-up? At The WayOut Club - We offer 800sq ft of FREE changing space with mirrors and lights from 9pm - 1am and 2.30 - 4am nearby toilets have washing facilities. We offer secure storage of bags this is FREE if changing. You may like to take advantage of help with make-up by one of 'the wayout girls' to boost your confidence £15.00 please book ahead by ringing Vicky Lee 07778 157 290 Jodi at The Boudoir offers support, wardrobe and make-up and escorting. Details on 0208 365 7755 Pandora at Image Works offers support, wardrobe, escorting and accommodation. Details on 0207 684 0340 Adam and Eve close by off Brick Lane provide help support make-up and escorting 0207 729 7447. Ann's Dressing Service may be booked for Saturday preparation at the Philbeach Hotel 0207 373 4848

Q - WHAT IS THE WayOut CLUB Like ? When you arrive at the club you are magically spirited into our subterranean, WayOut world, from the smart street level reception by lift, (or staircase). This super venue, is in a discreet location, with easy parking and taxis waiting at the door. We have wheelchair access. There is a separate changing area. The venue is air conditioned. The single level has two areas - a full on dance and cabaret room, plus a quieter room with plenty of seating. In the main room WayOut's DJs mix music and lights to suit the mood of the night, from 70's & 80's camp and the latest commercial dance music, to a wild 'uplifting house' dance party. Video screens and televisions provide a constant visual feast in both rooms. We encourage gorgeous 'girls' (and boys) to get up and strut their stuff on the WayOut dance podiums (and they DO). A good menu of tasty food is always available throughout the night.

Q - IS WAYOUT INTIMIDATING ? For over 450 nights over 9 years 'The WayOut Club' has brought together newly 'out' transvestites, full time trannies, transsexuals, drag queens, tranny admirers and friendly party people of all ages, cultures, sexuality's and genders.... Each week 200 to 300 visitors come from all over the planet and are never disappointed, reporting it to be relaxed, friendly, and without doubt the best of its kind in the world.... WayOut always has super looking 'girls' but they all had to start somewhere and are very supportive to newcomers. Steffan and I are always pleased to meet new visitors and encourage you to come early when we have time to chat with you before the club gets too busy.and we get involved with putting on the nights entertainment. Every one that comes to the club loves to chat as most do not have the opportunity to express their thoughts and feeling in every day conversation so the club is verbal release as well as visual release. Our venue at Charlie's is such a good shape that you can comfortably watch others without feeling that every one is looking at you. Of course if you are a confident party animal and want to get up and dance on the podiums we will encourage you.

Q - WHAT ENTERTAINMENT IS THERE AND WHEN IS IT ON ? Steffan and Vicky Lee present at 1.30am, a unique WayOut show directed by Steffan, featuring the WayOut 'Girls' and 'House of Drag Girls, plus guests, and PA's from the best of the gay and alternative cabaret circuit. with sets and costumes to rival any floor show. Alternatively we present an events like The Drag Olympics and Alternative Miss London. The last week in each month we feature Star Search. The club has provided many performers the opportunity to develop their talents over the years and a 'talent search' on the last Saturday of the month is a popular night... with a £150 prize To enter just be at the club before 1am with your music and a smile and ask for Vicky or Steffan to register.

Q - WHERE CAN I GET A BITE TO EAT ? FROM 9pm - 4 am - that's a long time At the WayOut Club tasty food is served all night long.. Snacks such as French-fries, Nachos, Potato wedges, Onion rings, Potato skins, Chicken dippers, Scampi start from £1.60 Burgers (meat or veggy) with all the tangy trimmings from £3.50 "Try it with sweet & sour" says Miss Sarah Lloyd Curries with rice from £6.50 Pizzas made freshly just for you - from £7.00 There is a wide choice of your favourite topping plus some that may be new for you.to try "The best Pizza's ever tasted and I know Pizza" says Miss Vicky Lee

Q - WHERE CAN I FIND suitable **ACCOMMODATION ?**
The following are ALL regularly used by visitors to WayOut HOWEVER not all encourage "dressing" for breakfast! You can negotiate "weekend" rates at about £70 if the hotel is not too busy. The Philbeach Hotel, (the most tranny friendly hotel), Philbeach Gardens in Earls Court 0207 373 1244 The Beaver Hotel Philbeach Gardens in Earls Court 0207 373 4553 Trebovire Hotel, Trebovire Road, in Earls Court 0207 370 3310 Local taxi service from these hotels to WayOut is aprox £14 The Chamberlain Hotel (just around the corner from WayOut) ask for special weekend rates. 0207 6801500 Novotel Hotel Again just around the corner free street parking Saturday and Sunday 0207 265 6000 The Tower Thistle Hotel ask for weekend rates. 0207 481 2575 (5mins from the club and overlooking Tower Bridge) Express by Holiday Inn The Highway (nr The Lime house link

Tunnel) 0207 7540 0800 434040www.hiexpress.co.uk advertising £69 weekend rate The Travel Lodge has become popular Corriander Ave, (off East India Dock Road) near Canary Wharf 0207 531 9705. About 15 mins from WayOut at the junction of the A13 and A406 (leave A406 at Highbridge Road, Barking) you will find four NEW hotels - Local taxi service from these hotels to WayOut is aprox £14 ... 0207 503 5555 Ibis - £60 per room Premier Lodge £42 per room 0807 7001444 Etap £37 0208 283 4550. Formule 1 - just £25 per room 0208 507 0789 This may be the cheapest hotel. A good room for up to three people with sink & mirror (shower off shared corridor) Pandora De Pledge offers accommodation plus escorted visits as well as a full range of makeover and wardrobe. 0207 682 0340 Q - FROM 9pm - 4 am - that's a long time

311

My WayOut year ■ by Miss Sarah Lloyd

Can you believe it, yet another year has whizzed past so quickly, as I am writing this, it's Christmas. I've moved home a few times around London and now settled near Sadlers Wells Theatre and have been with WayOut now for a good solid 6 years and it is still as fantastic as ever. So what are my highlights for 2003?

Yet another successful trip to Ascot with the Boudoir team, organised by Jodie. Getting photographed again, in tow with Michaela Marbella . Perfect weather and good food, a good day had by all.

The WayOut CLUB birthday celebrated 10 years clubbing, now that's a huge milestone, considering that it started out in a tiny basement bar all those years ago. It goes to show, more of you girls are stepping out of the closet, making dressing services and clubs in London busier than ever.

Again this year I returned with Steffan to perform at G.A.Y. This time for Ashley Hamilton, and again to launch the Chicago DVD with our never to be forgotten live rendition of "All That Jazz", Considering we both had colds at the time, we pulled it off to great applause.

Then on to the second Transfandango Ball in Manchester, which was sold out and even better organised this year. I awas pleased to give my time to produce a new set of costumes for an eye popping floor show from the WayOut Girls. Big thanks to Davina Diamond from Liverpool for being our 'bee'.

Transfandango raised another £25,000, which was fantastic. Sadly shortly after the ball one of the founders of the charity Foo Foo Lamar died of cancer, a true showman, who will be sadly missed by all.

I joined Davina again in my adopted city Liverpool to help with the opening of the 'Superstar Bar'.

To crown the year off, it was good to see the ever so talented 'Miss Rossita' crowned Alternative Miss London and the ever so talented 'Miss Lynn Daniels' crowned 'Miss House of Drag' with her rendition of 'Miss Spectacular', complete in feathers and diamonte - a true showgirl.

I have enjoyed getting to know more of you while helping you to find your feet with one of my makeovers and I am looking forward to welcoming you to the new WayOut Wine Bar for a relaxed "girls night out".

So as 2003 gradually comes to a close, and 2004 is upon us, join me and take your hats off to the rest of the team that is WayOut and also all those close friends in the background who support and help tirelessly all year round.

Who knows what else the new year will hold? I just know that I personally will still be producing fabulous scenery, costumes etc. Adding to the glitter and glam in our WayOut shows.

FRIDAY NIGHT
at The WayOut Wine Bar

Q - IS THERE A DRESS CODE? This is an intimate smart venue.

Q - CAN I DRESS MALE ? Males dressed male are welcome as friends of T-Girls who are attending

Q - DO I HAVE TO BE A MEMBER ? No

Q - HOW MUCH IS ENTRY ?
£5 for T-Girls and £7 for friends

Q - IS IT EASY TO FIND ? No to be honest-There are one way road systems so you need to approach from Monument tube station. on Eastcheap. Lovatt Lane is a pedestrian lane off Eastcheap near to the tube station. You will see our name board on the pavement from Eastcheap.

Q - IS IT EASY TO PARK ? Very Easy - There is ample free parking available on single yellow lines and parking bays very close to the club. Parking on double yellows, with your wheels on the pavement or in a designated parking space may still result in a fine even very late. This is a very safe and discreet area on Friday nights.

Q - WHAT WILL TAXI DRIVERS THINK IF I DRESS ? London black taxi drivers are the best in the world and have seen everything. It is very unusual to find a driver that does not treat trannies with respect. - We also recommend private companies Express Cars ...0207 403 3333 Freedom Cabs ..0207 734 1313

Q - CAN I GET A TAXI EASILY WHEN I LEAVE ? Yes we have a licensed cabs that our reception will call for you who will normally have a car for you immediately (prices are average for late night Saturdays).

Q - WHERE CAN I CHANGE ? ...and get help with make-up? At The Way Wine Bar - We offer a large area that has sinks and mirrors. We offer secure storage of bags this is FREE if changing. Jodi at The Boudoir offers support, wardrobe and make-up and escorting. Details on 0208 365 7755 Pandora at Image Works offers support, wardrobe, escorting and accommodation. Details on 0207 684 0340 Adam and Eve close by off Brick Lane provide help support make-up and escorting 0207 729 7447.Ann's Dressing Service offers make-up preparation at the Philbeach Hotel 0207 373 4848

Q - WHAT IS THE WayOut Wine Bar Like ? When you arrive at the club you are met by our receptionist who can look after your bags and coats in a secure room. There is a charge of £1 per item. At the begining of the night every one is directed to the Basement Bar unless dining . After 10pm or when it is busy the groundfloor is available for everyone with ample seating to rest your feet and talk with a lower music level than the basement provides. This is where where DJiMac our computer juke box selects from its libary of disco classics from the 70's 8o's and 90's. The dance foor awaits.The venue is air conditioned

Q - WHAT ENTERTAINMENT IS THERE AND WHEN IS IT ON ? There is no entertainment (For that you need to visit the WayOut CLUB). But we do encourage budding DJs to give DJ iMac a break and show what they can do..

Q - IS WAYOUT INTIMIDATING ? We aim for The WayOut Wine Bar to be the safest and friendliest of environments for anyone to explore the transgender world and to meet up with like minded friends.

Q - I HAVE NEVER BEEN OUT OF THE HOUSE "DRESSED" SO WHAT SHOULD I WEAR ON MY FIRST VISIT TO THE WAYOUT CLUB? For your first time there is no place better or safer to take your first steps. IF I WAS going to recommend a style to make you feel comfortable on your first visit I would say - Good hair / wig and a black dress (long, short or knee length) with some nice accessories. When you see what others wear you will be inspired to follow your feelings on your next visit - be that flamboyant, tarty, glamourous, clubby or even MORE sophisticated. That's what it's all about.

Q - WHERE CAN I FIND suitable ACCOMMODATION ? See the accomodation sugesstions for The WayOut Club because the Wine Bar i in the same area

BOOK & MAGAZINE Reviews

The quality of content in all the magazines continues to improve year over year as we all receive more inspiration and amazing material from ALL parts of the transgendered community

There is a constant new supply of books coming from a wide range of authors addressing all areas of interest. I hope you will be inspired to find a copy of these reviewed here from the library or your local store.

If you want a WayOut Stock List

phone 07778 157 290

fax 0208 366 0517

write to

WayOut Publishing

P.O.Box 70

Enfield

EN1 2AE - UK

or log on the web
www.wayout-publishing.com

look for WayOut Products

BOOKS available from WayOut

THE THIRD SEX
Available from WayOut £18.99 inc UK p&p
ISBN 0-285-63668-5 by Dr Richard Totman Published by Souvenir Press.
The 'kathoey' phenomenon has been part of Thai culture for generations it is the subject of a fascinating new book by Dr Richard Totman, a prize research fellow at Oxford University's Nuffield. Dr Totman, who is also a widely-travelled theatre director, became probably the first "farang" (Thai for Westerner) to infiltrate the mysterious world of the ladyboys. He lived for months with kathoey girls and their families, learnt the language and spent much of his time talking to dozens of them and sharing their unique lifestyle.

TRANSVESTISM AND CROSS-DRESSING
Available from WayOut £ 10.50 inc UK p&p
Edited by M T Haslam for the Beaumont Trust with contributions by 14 respected writers including pshyciatrist Russell Reid ftm champion Stephen Whittle, Rev David Horton, women of the beaumont leader Diane Aitchison and chair of the Beaumont Jannett Scott Subtitled "towards an understanding" this book brings together a cocktail of subjects and view points that are well grounded and invaluable for any tranny or partner trying to learn more about the subject.
"Why do I like dressing in women's clothes?" Why does my husband want to dress in my clothes, use my jewellery - my make-up?" These and hosts of other questions are asked by transvestites themselves and by their loved ones. Public perceptions are formed by a generally unhelpful portrayal by the media, while textbooks inevitably approach the subject from a pathologising viewpoint.

Towards an Understanding

Transvestism &
Cross Dressing

Edited by M.T.Haslam
The Beaumont Trust

SEX, GENDER & SEXUALITY
Available from WayOut £15.99 inc UK p&p
ISBN 0-9529482-2-2 by Dr Tracie O'Keefe DCH Edited by Katrina Fox Published by Extraordinary People Press.
Tracy is a well respected Physiotherapist and Clinical hypnotherapist and friend of myself and WayOut who is much missed after her departure from London to live in Australia. This book I feel is her legacy of good sense and wise interpretation of study for those who cannot consult with Tracey in person. She writes a readable book providing a good mix of scientific personal experience and interviews with others. Half the book contains the many papers that she has presented internationally along with never before published papers. For those studying or experiencing or those just plain trying to get your head round gender, sex and sexuality this book is an excellent place to start to put all three into context.

SEX, GENDER
& SEXUALITY
21st Century Transformations

By Dr Tracie O'Keefe DCH

LAZY CROSS-DRESSER
Available from WayOut £ 11.50 inc UK p&p
By Charles Andres, Charles a writer and cross-dresser with many years experience shows here how he built his confidence and skills. Tips hints, ideas and stories are plentiful along with illustrations. Unlike crossdressing manuals that insist on nothing less than perfect passable femininity, the pages give you permission to experiment! You'll learn how to achieve the results you desire with... Make-up ("The Televangelist's Finger Test") Body Image ("Fat is a Feminine Tissue") Undergarments ("Mr.Sad is Mr Happy Upside Down") Shoes & Accessories ("Man the Pumps!") Fashion ("Yuppie Riot Grrl Barbie") Shopping ("Your own Executive Personal Shopper") Dating & Relationships ("T and Empathy")

The LAZY
CROSSDRESSER

CHARLES ANDERS

The Modern TV
a NEW video
available from
WayOut Publishing

 Whether you are new to the scene or already finding your way, this new video offers a supportive and encouraging insight, clearly proclaiming "It's O.K. to be TV."

 The video features cross-dressers from various situations and age groups who speak to the camera with honesty and frankness about real life experiences,

 Single and married cross-dressers express their views and offer tips on make-up, clothes, developing confidence, relationships and life style, openly discussing difficulties often encountered by TVs and how they have found solutions.

 Includes an exclusive interview with Vicky Lee about producing "The Tranny Guide", her lifestyle and her exciting involvement with The Way Out Club.

 Dynamically and sensitively filmed, "The Modern TV" will encourage you to come out with confidence and style.

Professionaly made - television documentary quality
Available in PAL and NTSC

318

BOOKS available from WayOut

CROSSING THE LINE

Available from WayOut £17.99 inc UK p&p
ISBN 1-899235-39-6 by Sara Davidman Dewi Lewis
Publishing.
Sara is a photographer who has collected picture
on the London cross-dressing scene for many
years. Her book now documents her vision of a
third gender as captured by her camera. 100 full
colour pages in a hardback book. For those on
the UK scene many faces will be familiar many
pictures were taken at The WayOut Club.
Maybe your picture is in this book.

GINA THE WOMAN WITHIN

Available from WayOut £10.95 inc UK p&p
ISBN 0-95443544352-0-6
Interactive Promotions and publishing.
Gina Large reached her 54th birthday before she
realised what was wrong with her life. She
believes the widespread prejudice, ridicule and
blind ignorance which still persists against
transsexuals is based in a basic lack of
understanding. Maybe this is why Gina reached
54 before she took steps to rebalance her life and
herself. This moving book documents every
tearful and smiling step along the way.
This real life transsexual relates her traumatic and
very reluctant transgender journey of self-
discovery, at it really happened.

TRANSGENDER UNDERGROUND - LONDON & THE THIRD SEX

Available from WayOut £13.99 inc UK p&p
ISBN 1-902588-11-8 by Claudia Andrei glitter
books.
While Sara Davidman was at The WayOut Club
collecting pictures for her book, German freelance
illustrator Claudia was discovering the our
underworld at the late Ron Stormes club in his last
two years. 100 B&W pages and a colour centre
spread not only capture the images but Claudia has
also has gathered the thoughts
of many of the regular faces around London in
early new millennium. Again many faces will be
very familiar to you.

TRANSACTIONS

Available from WayOut call or check website for price
ISBN91-89443-01-2 By Erica Zander
Erica Zanda is a Swedish, Lesbian, male to female transsexual.
She transitioned at age 48 and lives with her wife of 30 years and 2 adult
sons. In this candid autobiography, Ms Zander discusses a wide range of
topics related to gender and search for wholeness. Her text has an
immediacy that is only possible because it was written throughout her
transition , not years after through rose tinted memories.

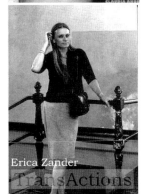

Erica Zander

"The best lifestyle magazine from the UK." (Tranny Guide)
But don't take their word for it -

WATCH THE MOVIE!

New CD Rom Audio-visual Presentation
giving full details of *Rose's Club* and
TV Repartee magazine. (Inc. video footage).
Send A5 SAE to address below for your copy (UK only)

Interactive Web Site, 24 hour on-line shopping
for magazines, cosmetics, wigs, silicone breast forms
and much more: **www.repartee.tv**
Sample magazine £5, Subscription £24 (UK)

Rose's (TG4) PO Box 186,
Barnsley, South Yorks. S73 0YT
Tel: 01226 754252

MAGAZINES available from WayOut

UTTERLY FABULOUS

Available from WayOut £7.95 inc UK p&p
for three issue over 12 months

Also available for free as a download from
www.wayout-publishing.com/fabulous.htm. And
free to collect from many clubs bars shops and
services. If not stocked near you let us know.
This is a lifestyle magazine aiming to spread
confidence and pride in an Utterly fabulous
lifestyle. Full of great pictures, positive stories and
fun. With reviews and news of events and regular
opportunities to share this utterly fabulous
lifestyle with others.

GIRLTALK

Available from WayOut £ 9.95 inc UK p&p
(many collectible backissues)

Calendar Girl, PO Box 4915,
North Hollywood, CA91619-1915, USA.
Subscribe online: www.calendargirlusa.com.
Quarterly, high quality, glossy lifestyle magazine.
The Cadilac of tranny magazines. Featuring top
class Hollywood photo shoots. Unique well
written reports and interviews. Despite the oh
so confident gloss the magazine keeps in touch
with the sensitive closeted end of the market.
Growing to be a major influence on straight
people to accept that there are alternative ways
to look and behave.
"Listen up George your time is drawing to a close".

REPARTEE

Available from WayOut £ 12.00 inc UK p&p

Rose's, P.O Box 186 Barnsley, South Yorks, S73
0YT. Tel/fax 01226 754 252.
www.repartee.co.uk
A quarterly glossy magazine for TVs and T-Girls
from Bella Jay, Debbie, Martine Rose and team.
The magazine is packed with features, stories,
news and details of social events plus readers'
letters, contact adverts, etc. Now reflecting a
wider age range of style and activity. In a
colourful A4 format. We vote this mag the best
lifestyle magazine from the UK.

TRANSGENDER COMMUNITY NEWS

Available from WayOut £ 12.00 inc UK p&p
(many collectible backissues)

The Renaissance Transgender Association Inc.,
987 Old Eagle School Road, Suite 719, Wayne,
PA 19087 -USA. Tel: 610 975 9119.
Website: www.ren.org. Monthly publication featuring regular
contributors columns, TG news from across the states and special
features. Backed up by a super resource web site
www.tgforum.com

More MAGAZINES

CROSSTALK
P.O Box 258, Manchester M60 1LN England. E-mail: JennyB@northernconcord.org.uk. The magazine of Northern Concorde Group. This well produced A5 size book is published quarterly. Typically full of articles, letters, pics and reports from members. Cost is included in membership to the group, or £3.50 each inc p&p

FORUM
P.O.Box 381, City Harbour, London E14 9GL. Te:l 0171 987 5090. E-mail: forum@norshell.co.uk. Price £3.60 Available on most newsagents top shelf. This magazine is a general sex mag with articles on all aspects of sex. However the tranny content is consistently high with letters and articles. A good mag for those that dare not take a specialist mag home. Plus an opportunity to try cross-dressing at home after trying every other option in the book as a cover up. Guess who is Forum's Tranny Agony Aunt, yep, Vicky Lee.

F.M.I. FEMALE MIMICS INTERNATIONAL
F.M.I. PO Box 1622, Studio City, CA91614, USA. This long running magazine has pictures and reports on USA drag events. However, more recent editions have moved more towards explicit she-male pictures.

GEMS NEWS (SOON TO CHANGE NAME)
BM Gentrust, London WC1N 3XX. E-mail gentrust@mistral.co.uk. Website: www.gender trust.com. This is a members magazine sent out quarterly. The cost is included in membership which can be full or a friends membership. The mag is packed with personal and detailed accounts from transsexuals, articles on political and other gender based issues generally and is recommended to those that want to understand this area in more detail. A serious little mag.

LADYLIKE
Creative Design Services, P.O. Box 61263, King of Prussia, PA 19406-1263 USA. Website: www.cdspub.com. Price US $12.00 per copy. LadyLike is a popular magazine from the USA for cross-dressers, which contains a lot of information about the practicalities of cross-dressing, such as make-up tips and deportment. Many readers' pictures and photo reports throughout.

SKIN TWO
Skin Two, Unit N 306, Westminster Business Square, Durham Street, London SE11 5JH, Tel 020 7840 0146, fax 020 7735 0355 E-mail info@skintwo.co.uk Website www.skintwo.co.uk
This quarterly fetish magazine. Available from Tower and Virgin stores or direct for £10.00 each issue. A quality magazine that has set a standard for the worlds fetish scene. News reviews, party reports art photography plus an exhaustive directory.

SILHOUETTE
ISSN1473-9658 D Daniels, P.O.Box 3, Basildon, Essex, SS13 3WA. £5.95 inc delivery. This magazine Danielle produces in association with Translife. Containing stories, history, letters, directory plus reports and details of events for trannies that like to be 'tight laced' in corsets and those that hanker for the stout underwear of all past eras.

TRANSGENDER - TAPESTRY
I.F.G.E., P.O. Box 540229, Waltham, MA 02254-0229, USA. Price: US$12.00 or c.£12.00. E-mail: info@ifge.org. This is possibly the leading Transgender community magazine. It is an international magazine, which is published in the USA. It contains a large contact section, excellent articles and news, which are at the front edge of politics and a new understanding of the diversity on the scene both f2m and m2f. It has a very comprehensive listing for support groups throughout the USA and much of the world.

TRANSFORMATION
Vista Station, PO Box 51480, Sparks, NV89435-1480 USA. Tel: 775 322 8995. Fax: 775 322 6362. Website: transformationmag.com. Price: US $8.95

More MAGAZINES

+p&p. UK £5.50. Jerri Lee from California publishes this good quality colour magazine for TVs, TSs, drag queens, etc. Packed with photospreads (many of explicit she-males showing tits and testicles), articles, stories, fashion news and advice, hormones, surgery, make-up tips, and movie and book/magazine reviews. This is possibly the leading US scene reportage for the more glamourous side of the scene and will certainly suit tranny admirers of all persuasions. The pictures are 'hot'.

TRANSGENDER LIFE
Lauter Bunte Schmetterlinge
ouchstoC/O Charis Berger, Postfasch 86 08, D-81 635 Munchen Germany. Tel 089-472454 order 0177 5520699 faX 080741453 E-mail: charisberger@gmx.de website www.geocities.com/westhollywood/6687 This photocopy quality magazine produced in German language is full of information advice and news for those visiting or living in this country full of cross-dressing history and future opportunities.

TRANSLIFE INTERNATIONAL
PO Box 3, Basildon, Essex, SS13 3WA. Tel/Fax and Helpline: 01268 583761. £10 per issue. Through ups, downs and changes of staff this is still one of the UKs top quarterly tranny lifestyle magazines leaning towards those that would like to become full time women. Typically loaded with media watch, members photo's, letters, agony columns and tips.

TV CONNECTION
DM International, PO Box 35010 Phoenix, AZ 85069-5010 USA.US $8. Quarterly publication from Deena Moore. Features include TVC Girls of the Month, personal ads, features, back issues available.

TV/TS NEWS
PO Box 2534, London, WC1N 3XX Tel: 0207 609 1093; Email: webmaster@tv-ts.co.uk; Web site: www.tv-ts.co.uk. . . . 04 - Free information for the TG community. This quirky monthly newsletter is widely distributed. It gives a wide varity of information for the TG community including classified contacts, jobs, buy and sell. For your own free copy send an A5 sae 39p.

MORE BOOKS fiction

(EXAMPLE) MAGS INC FICTION - THE PINK SATIN RIBBON
Order by EMAIL: magsinc@wgn.net. 1-800-359-2116 FAX line (1-818-784-9563) A long list of titles published by Mark at Mags Inc containing very sexy stories by various writers illustrated by Lizzie. Enforced feminisation and sissy stories all of the highest quality.

CONTEMPORARY TV FICTION
Thomas Publications; Virginia Prince, Box 36091, Los Angeles 90036, CA, USA; Founder member of UK Beaumont Society, FPE-USA, FPE/NE Sweden, Virginia Prince has written a number of books. She offers these books plus an extensive list of titles priced between $7.50 and $15.00.

CROSS DRESSING BETWEEN THE WARS
ISBN 0 9512385 90 Farrer Peter Karn Publications, 63 Salisbury Road, Garston, Liverpool L19 0PH. £25.00. Maybe fact maybe fantasy. This is new collection of letters and articles sourced from Peter Farrers extensive research into the archives of 'London Life'. The period 1923 - 1933 was a period of change and reform due to the loss of 1000,s of men in the First World War and the newly acquired votes for women. A change in attitude to cross-dressing can be easily detected for those that have followed Mr Farrer's historical journey through these popular press cuttings. Peters best yet for my money.

CONFIDENTIAL CORRESPONDENCE ON CROSS DRESSING
PT.ii 1916 - 1920 ISBN 0 9512385 6 6 Farrer, Peter; Karn Publications Garston, 63 Salisbury Road, Garston, Liverpool, L19 0PH Peter has furthered his collection gathered a wealth of letters from the pages of a newspaper published under a variety of names ending in 'Fun' between 1911

Writing your own Stories (and getting them published) By Deena Gomersall

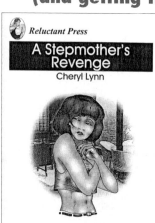

Reluctant Press

A Stepmother's Revenge
Cheryl Lynn

ILLUSTRATIONS BY CHAS

A 'NEW WOMAN' NOVEL

EVER THOUGHT ABOUT WRITING TRANSGENDER FICTION NOVEL?

Reluctant Press are always interested in seeing new material and pay $2.00 per printed page (Books usually range from around 80 to 120 pages) and offer want-to-be authors the opportunity to experience professional publishing and receive genuine recognition for their accomplishments.

You will get your story / stories professionally edited, illustrated and printed as well as being paid for your effort plus you will receive three finished copies of your story plus a copy each of the accompanying stories by other authors released that month.

If you have an idea for a story then try to make it as interesting to a reader as possible, try to emphasis the emotional stress of learning to live in a woman's world, try to explain how the 'subject' arrives at this point of their life and, if being enforced into femininity/womanhood, try to illustrate the trauma the subject is likely to go through. If the subject is being force fed feminizing hormones then take time in writing, step by step, the changes that occur and the slow acceptance of his burgeoning womanhood.

Stories that are merely based on a cross dresser slipping in and out of various feminine garments and going here and there having fun does not tend to hold a readers interest so try add some excitement or adventure, feed in the emotional changes and present a strong story line.

WHO ARE RELUCTANT PRESS ?

Reluctant Press are probably the largest publisher of full length, professionally illustrated, transgender material, in the world. They release three new titles each month and currently has just under five hundred titles to choose from, written by over one hundred different authors from around the globe including;

Continued on page 328

MORE BOOKS fiction

to 1920. Stories fall into enforced feminisem (of all ages) and tight lacing and female impersonation. Line drawings of the fashions of the time complete a fascinating study. I didn't know whether to put this in fiction or fact section and I get the feeling that Peter Farrer doesn't know either.However I am sure there is no smoke without fire.

FANTASY FICTION GROUP (FFG)
PO Box 36, Chesterfield, S40 3YY UK. Tel/Fax: 01246 551196. E-mail: info@tvfiction.com. Website: www.tvfiction.com. Kate Lesley, editor and publisher, brings you Tales of Crossdressing, Tales of the Maid, Tales of Sissy School. These books run in series and have a number of different well written stories in each edition that usually flow into the next edition. The themes of enforced dressing and blackmail leading to full time femininity and enforced transition fill these titles.

FREDERIQUE
ISBN 0-7499-3080-2 Piatkus A story with shadows of blackmail, fear, gritty realism, which twists and turns. The central character is so well studied it is hard to believe the author has not experienced the life of a closet tranny but she is a woman and this is her first book.

MY FIRST PARTY DRESS
ISBN 0 9512385 8 Farrer, Peter; Karn Publications Garston, 63 Salisbury Road, Garston, Liverpool, L19 0PH. The content gathered by Peter and Christine Jane Wilson includes a mixture of fantasy stories and Peters favourite historical references.Write for a full list of many more fascinating books full of historical pictures and references to period cross-dressing.

TRANS-FICTION EROTIC FICTION
ASSQ P O Box 23893 London SE15 2WQ Alex Shelley and a variety of other writers produce a series of novels that are pretty sexy.with plenty of explicit sexual detail. The formula of change from male to female after an awakening through sexual experimentation is the type of gendre.

MORE BOOKS non fiction

ARMOUR PLATED
ISBN0-595-29523-1 By Jill Devine www.JillDevine.com
Female impersonator, father, husband, author and motivational speaker. Jill has faced contradiction and moved from victim to victor. In this book Jill provides a six step process to discover your personal calling and to achieve it. The

CHANGING CHANNELS?
ISBN 1 85174 258 1 A Christian Response to the Transvestite and Transsexual. Horton, Rev. David. £2.25 + p&p. Grove Books, Ridley Hall Road, Cambridge CB3 9HU. Stocked in many Christian bookshops. More of a booklet than a book, as the title suggests, this well thought out guide covers the interaction of religion and transgenderism. It includes a sensible introduction to transvestism and transsexualism and as such makes a good starting point for any Christian friends or relations as well as being of direct use to those who feel their own TV or TS nature is in conflict with their Christian beliefs.

DRAG QUEENS OF NEW YORK
ISBN 0 04 440994 Fleisher, Julian, Pandora books. This is a very modern all out description of the Ru Paul / Lady Bunny school of drag. Subtitled 'An illustrated field guide' the writer categorises and profiles 27 of the most darling dragsters of 1996 using his Plumageometer on a scale 'glam to clown'. Highly recommended reading for any Queen.

FINDING THE REAL ME
ISBN 23812-43795 Wiley books by Dr Tracie O Keefe & Katrina Fox. A collection of real life stories by a wide range of sex and gender diverse people. These are healing tales of struggle and transformation. The book helps us not to fear difference and to indeed be in awe of possibilities.

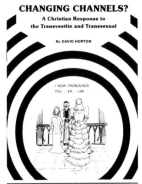

Grove Ethical Studies No. 92

CHANGING CHANNELS?
A Christian Response to
the Transvestite and Transsexual

By DAVID HORTON

I NOW PRONOUNCE
YOU ... ER ... UM ...

Jill Devine
with Julian R. Quinton (DMS) Dip PTM, BA, MBA

Armour Plated
Become supercharged
and successful beyond your wildest dreams.
Wealth, health and prosperity to you.

Why were you born?

Finally...A book that allows you to answer life's most critical question.

the Drag Queens of New York
AN ILLUSTRATED FIELD GUIDE

JULIAN FLEISHER

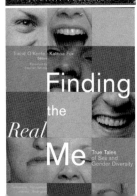

Tracie O'Keefe   Katrina Fox
Editors

Finding
the
Real
Me
True Tales
of Sex and
Gender Diversity

327

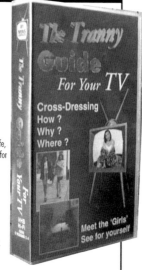

The USA, Canada, South America, Australia and Europe as well as the UK, each contributing to offer a wide variety of interesting and exciting stories.

What makes Reluctant Press stand out from similar publishers however, is that their editing staff care so much about what their readers want to read. They regularly post out opinion polls with their flyers to check the market. They also like to offer stories that cater for a diversity of tastes and, as such, the well bound, illustrated books come in five separate categories to ensure the reader gets what they want to read:

YOUNG ADULT STORIES These involve young people, up to early teens who, as part of discipline, petticoat punishment or a variety of other reasons, find themselves forced to live a feminine lifestyle. The stories do not have any sexual overtones.

NEW WOMAN STORIES Mostly involve enforced or Coerced feminization which leads to the total sex change of 'hapless' males who must, from thereon in, live in a female world. These stories often include explicit sex, bondage etc. The majority of Reluctant Press' readers favour this classification.

HER TV STORIES Do not involve a sex change but the male is led into dressing as a woman and living a female lifestyle by real women (lover, Wife, Mother/ 'in-law', relative or complete stranger) with whom they often have a sexual relationship.

ADULT TV STORIES These, again, are stories where a male is either forced or helped along into living as a female, often by other males, and where they may end up having a relationship with a man.

SPECTRUM OF STORIES For those readers who like variety of the above - The Spectrum range each have a collection of shorter stories or one long story which contain two or more of the above classifications.

Your completed manuscript should be set in one of these genres and sent on computer disk to the following address or sent, online, as an attachment, to: editors@reluctantpress.com

The Reluctant press website is at: http://www.reluctant press.com. To write, Reluctant Press' address is: Friendly Applications, P O Box 5829, Sherman Oaks, CA 91404, USA Or E-mail: sales@reluctantpress.com

BCM Life Works carry a selection of RP Titles, their address is 27 Old Gloucester Street, London WC1N 3XX. See their web site at: www.bcmlifeworks.co.uk

MORE BOOKS non fiction

GENDER LOVING CARE
ISBN 0-393-70304-5 By Randi Ettner. This is the book is an excellent guide to counselling transgendered clients. Obviously it is good for trannies to read as it helps to understand not only themselves but also those trying to get to grips with them whether in day to day contact or in therapy.

INSIGHTS
ISBN 0-9543821-0-2 byTranliving POBox 3 Basidon Essex SS13 3WA
A dense read with a very wide collection of subjects covered in a frequently answered questions style answered by Stacey Novak (RG - Transliving), Dr Russel Reid (Leading Tg specialist)

LESSONS FROM THE INTERSEXED
ISBN 0-8135-2530-6 bySuzanne J Kessler. Her is book densley packed with the exploration of intersex children (also referred to by some as hermaphrodite). The book concludes with a rethink of genitals and gender.

MALE FEMAILING
ISBN 0-415-10625-7 Ekins, Richard: Routledge: The latest academic book from Richard is easier to read than previous. There are interesting case histories supporting his look at "A grounded approach to cross-dressing and sex-change".

MY GENDER WORKBOOK
ISBN 0-415-91673-9 By Kate Bornstein. Kate is a celebrated Transgender activist and this book though serious in intent is fun to "play" with. It is also the kind of book to dip in and out of. Well when you have finished your workbook let us know just how transgendered you are ??

MY HUSBAND BETTY -
By Helen Boyd
Available from WayOut price on application
Shortly after Helen Boyd met the man who was to be her husband he told her that he cross-dressed. It has cost her some struggle and pain to come to an accommodation with this side of his nature. The book begins as a journey of self-discovery. Helen Boyd explores with clarity and modernity, mixing academic rigor with intimate detail. Through Helen we meet other trannies and their partners, transsexuals, drag queens, fetishests. Helen pulls no punches in discussing everything including the much avoided sexual practises of these people. She concludes 'My husband is beautiful as a man or a woman, but unbelievably beautiful when he's something in between.' And goes on to say that other minorities like black, gay, women, struggle for civil rights and the next group to join that struggle is the transgendered.

NORMAL
ISBN 0-7475-6456-6 By Amy Bloom Bloomsbury Books
Novelist and psychotherapist Amy Bloom takes on a well researched, intimate and humourous journey into the world of transsexuals, Cross dressers, and Hermaphrodites. In this modern book she pulls apart the fibers of hers and maybe our assumptions describing a revised contemporary view of happiness, human nature, identity, self and above all what is normal.

THE OTHER WOMAN
ISBN 0-595-30250-5 By Pamela Hughes
Pacey witty fiction based on well researched fact, this is a character story about three very unique women who are transsexuals. Each of these three have their own very different expectations, needs and wants. Each has a different way of living with, coping with, enjoying their gender gift. All experience rejection, pain and yearning. Together they find strength and support in their shared experiences and differences becoming a "family" providing the emotional support that so many in this situation struggle to find.

PERSONA
ISBN 0 -8478-2046-7 By Susan Brown. A book full of interviews and photographs. The style covers female impersonators and drag so pictures vary from to characterisations to stunning glamour and unbelievable femininity

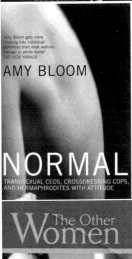

MORE VIDEOS - DVD - CDRom available from WayOut

TRADING FACES VIDEO OR CDrom ...
Available from WayOut £ 22.95 inc UK p&p
By TJP Professionally shot and edited, aprox 48 mins,
PAL & NTSC video or CDrom to run on any computer

This complete tutorial to show you how to achieve a stunning change from male to female, using only the techniques of make-up. Watch and learn as top TG stylist Pandora De Pledge talks you through each stage showing all the secrets in super detail. See for yourself how to choose products and apply them professionally to create a natural feminine look. The video (or CDrom) includes before and after comparisons, computer generated illustrations and "quick info" pages between each section. This is a brilliant and very popular program for all who wish to master male to female make-up application for themselves.

TRADING SHAPES VIDEO OR CDrom ...
Available from WayOut £ 22.95 inc UK p&p
By TJP Professionally shot and edited, aprox 48 mins,
PAL & NTSC video or CDrom to run on any computer

A complete guide to show men how to achieve a feminine shape using readily available foundation garments. Watch and learn as model "Emma" is transformed from her usual masculine shape into a shapely female. Numerous alternatives of each garment are explored to show how to cope with various styles of outer clothes and to also show what can go wrong when using foundation garments. The advice is based on The WayOut of the Closet and Jodie Lynn's vast experience with her customers at 'The Boudoir'. The voice over is by Vicky Lee takes you step by step through the choice of foundation garments that create a convincing female shape for either studio shoots or stepping out on the town. WayOut 'baby spice' Miss Debonair models showing every trick and mistake. The video (or CDrom) includes before and after comparisons, computer generated illustrations and "quick info" pages between each section. This is a brilliant and very popular program for all who wish to master male to female body shaping for themselves.

MORE BOOKS non fiction

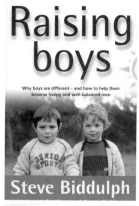

RAISING BOYS
ISBN 0-7225-3686-0 by Steve Biddulph; Harper Collins. Nature or nurture. When it comes to trannies it is a deep mystery. However this book offers a new way - a celebration of the male child as a human with every possibility ahead of it. In the same way that a female child can now enjoy. No need to worry about gender. This book explains that male and female are different but equally important and that a full range of opportunities and emotions are the birthright of a male. If only parents would study this book a safer future full of choice would be promised for us all and maybe the forces of cross-dressing would eventually fade into obscurity a remnant of a socio divided past where clothes were used to divide and conquer .

SHOES
9-780761-101147 ; Linda O'Keefe; Workman publishing ; There is no more ridiculous piece of clothing than the shoe. It says more about our status our gender our role in life. It is sexy it is obsessional. Just from a purely artistic point of view the shoe is a work of art. This little book celebrates through 500 colour pictures and a well researched story of the shoe. Try to search out a copy and try not to dribble.

TAKE IT LIKE A MAN
ISBN 0283992174 ; Sidgewick & Jackson; Spencer Bright ; This is the autobiography of Boy George. If you wanted the whole story behind one of the most famous gender benders, this is the book.

THE TRANGENDER DEBATE
ISBN 1-902932-16-1 By Stephen Whittle. This bang up to date book is a slim volume for just £3.50. Stephen is a highly respected FTM transsexual who has a very well grounded view point. This book is a super little book to give you an overview of trans and gender defining theories, statistics, history, and a always terminology of the full transgender spectrum.

TRANSACTIONS
ISBN91-89443-01-2 By Erica Zander
Erica Zanda is a Swedish, Lesbian, male to female transsexual. She transitioned at age 48 and lives with her wife of 30 years and 2 adult sons. In this candid autobiography, Ms Zander discusses a wide range of topics related to gender and search for wholeness. Her text has an immediacy that is only possible because it was written throughout her transition , not years after through rose tinted memories.

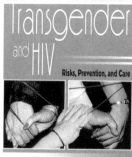

TRANSGENDER AND HIV
ISBN 0-7890-1268-5 By Walter Bockting PhD and Shiela Kirk MD
The writers have brought to health care workers and the transgender community a timely, relevant, and needed book on the potential relationship between Transgender and HIV. If you are delving into new areas and feel less than well informed this book really lays everything squarely down in the privacy of your own reading room.

TRANSVESTISM, TRANSSEXUALISM & THE LAW
Stephen Whittle, £10.95, available from The Beaumont Society and The Gender Trust. If the title makes you think this is a dry and uninteresting read, you are in for a pleasant surprise. The book is packed with useful and interesting information and written in a very accessible way. There is a lengthy introduction covering transvestism and transsexualism in a very clear and thorough manner, followed by a systematic and practical analysis of the law as it applies to us.

WHAT NOT TO WEAR 2
ISBN 0-297-84355-9 by Trinny Woodall & Susannah Constantine
Yes it's Trinny and Tranny back with a second book of do's and don'ts. They make many good observations as they prepare us for many situations, first date, first job, friends wedding etc. "We wish". Fun to read even more fun to look at the pictures. They are going to curl up in shame in 10 years time cos the fashions are going to be SO "00's" and there advice is going to look so daft. You have to put this on your shelf until 2013.

Articles

Eleventh Edition
36 Personal Profiles
Transfandango Ball
Andrea working as a shop girl
London Local Elections Ellen Sowle
Transsexual History Christine Burns
The Fox and Hounds Tranny Venue by Karen
Alternative Miss London
Lets Talk About Sex
Nikki - Pattaya - Revisited
Gay Parades in Europe

Tenth Edition
(Aniversary edition)
Vicky Lee - Ten years on
Frederike De Jong - Alexis Arquette drag celeb
Pandora - Eyebrow waxing
Jodie Lynn - Stepping out Girly tips
Vicky Lee - LGBT what is thatto do withme
Vicky Lee - Sept 11th keep it in perspective
Charis - Rock Lady
Viki - Her story from Budapest
Naomi - LA nights
Vicky Lee - Rocky Start
Vicky Lee - Meeting Richard O'Brien
Andy & Frederike De Jong - Gothic Trannies
Charles Fox - Make-up seminars
Andrea - Shopping and Photo shoot in London

Ninth Edition
Vicky - Introducing the WayOut Family
Vicky Lee - Life Style or Fetish Fantasy
Frederike de Jonge - Female Drag Queens
Various - Removing Facial Hair
Jodie Lyne - Trading Shapes
Jodie & pandora - Step by step make-up
Vicky Lee - Getting on line
Vicky Lee - Television exposure

Eighth Edition
Vicky - The first day of the rest of your life
Profile Photographer - Debbie Humphry
Alternative view - Raven I am a drag queen
Alternative view - Fraser Not a drag queen
Vicky - Laser Razor - a years diary
Vicky - 10 years of Repartee 20 of Roses
Girl Talk Magazine - new kid on the block
Profile Photographer - Frederike de Jonge
Profile Photographer - Mike Reid.

Seventh Edition
Vicky - Introducing Mr Frank Marino
Gina Lance - The Making of Calendar Girl
Nikki - A tribute to Stevie Nicks
Helen Webb - Singing with the drags
Tracie O'Keefe says NO to NO,
Gina Snowdoll - Chat on line how to,
Diana - So your man is a tranny
Vicky - Sabrina an exceptional service
Profile Photographer - Frederike de Jonge
Profile Photographer - Mike Reid.
Vicky - TVs on TV the gossip
Vicky - Choosing a name

Personal Reports

Eleventh Edition
Christie McNicol's - Australia
Eva Fels - Trans Women in Austria
Pamela A - Belgium
Rebeccas - Tranny Life in Copenhagen
Natasha - Cap D'Agde, France
Charis Berger - Germany update
Monica Dreamgirl - Amsterdam Holland
Mandy Romero - Dragging Down Italy
Francine Murray - Spanish Tranny Scene
Natalie & The Gemini Club - Gran Caneria
Marlayna Lacie - USA West Coast update
Gina Lance - Appearing on Television USA
Tranny Grange Goes West USA
Dale De Vere - New York New York
Nancy's New York - USA
Danielle - The Beaumont Society
Jenny Baker - Northern Concorde
Stacey & Kitty - Birmingham
Dani & Trans Yorks - Yorkshire
North East TG
Loraine from Hide & Sleek - Scotland
The Gemini Club - Ireland
Vicky Valentine - London Review

Tenth Edition
(Aniversary edition)
Nikki - Pattaya - The home of the ladyboys
Mandy Romero - World tour
Scarlet - Amsterdam, Edinburgh & London
Eva Fruitee - Egypt
Hannah Mannah - Sydney Australia
Eva Fels - trans women in Austria
Eva & Erica - Paris France
Nikki - Brittany France
Charis - Germany self support and trans shows
Monica - Holland
Eva & Joana - Rome Italy
Vicky Lee - Tokyo & Kyoto Japan
Frankie - Gran Caneria
Marlayna - USA West Coast
Nancy Boots New York USA
Simply Gorgous - New York Diary
Frederike - The final Wigstock NYC - USA
Danni - Trans York UK North
Barbara - Brighton UK South
Lacies - Alternative Miss Kent
Nikki & Debbie - Tranny Grange
Lorraine - Scotland
Jodie Lynn - London today
Vicky Lee - Alternative Miss London
Vicky Lee - Royal Ascot

Ninth Edition
Vicky - Europe breaks with Respect
Karen - Australia
Nessa - Austria update
Pamela - Belgium
Rebecca - Denmark update
Charis Berger - Germany + 3 Articles
Monica - Holland
Belinda - Prague
Frederike - Venice carnival
Steffan - Ibiza
Vicky & Marlayna - USA west coast update

Continued page 334

Tranny Guide Backissues ■ What did YOU miss

Articles

Sixth Edition -
Vicky - The Age of The Goddess
Vicky - The Legacy of Diana
Vicky - Brook Bond remembered
Vicky - Spice up your Trannying
Nikki - Women that made me what I am
Michelle Wilson - Civil Rights
Vicky - Introducing my partner Lesley
Lesley - Gender Images Bsc Research
Vicky - Lydya's an exceptional service
Lyn - CP is a disability, but Trannying isn't
Debbie - A view from the otherside
Vicky - Crossing Borders cross- dressed
Gina Snowdoll - The Internet "I love it"

Fourth Edition -
Drag Kings

Third Edition - 1995
Our one and only Fact or Fantasy Story.
Our first colour photo spread.

Second Edition - 94 -
Only a few available
already collectable.
First Edition - 93 -
I have one copy and I am
hanging on to it

THE TRANSVESTITE'S GUIDE TO LONDON
The Ultimate Insiders Guide to over 150 Friendly Shops, Services and Places to Go

SHOPS
HOTELS
TAXIS
PUBS
NIGHTCLUBS
DRAG SHOWS
DRAG BALLS
FETISH CLUBS
RESTAURANTS
SUPPORT GROUPS
HELPLINES
BEAUTICIANS

Way Out Publishing Company

Personal Reports

TG Forum - USA bars and clubs
Nikki - Las Vegas
Frederike Wigstock 2000
Stacey - UK Birmingham update
Donna - UK Manchester update
Gayle - UK South
Lorraine - Scotland update
Vicky Lee - UK London update
Andrea - UK London shoping trip
Fifth Edition -
Vicky - Gender Quake
Vicky - five years (How WayOut began)
Rev Horton - Faith and Cross Dressing
Vicky - What is an Inbetweeny
Maggie - Girls eye View
Vicky - Steffan "What is she like"
Dr Tracie O'Keefe - Trans-X-U-All "Why"
Sarah West - Trannies and the Net
Francis - London vs New York
Eighth Edition
Vicky- IGTA international affinity
Margaret's - Moscow
Deb Pike's - Ontario Canada
Rebeca's - Copenhagen Denmark
Steffan's - Paris, Nice, Cannes, Rome,
Ibiza, and Grande Caneria,
Frederike's Amsterdam Gay Pride
Frederike's Amsterdam update
Inma's - Barcelona Spain
Angela's - Switzerland
Nikki's - Thailand
Marlayna's - West coast USA
Marlayna's Reno - Nevada
Frererike in Las Vegas with Frank Marino
Miss Vera's New York USA
Frederike - Wigstock East USA 99
Stacey's - Birmingham UK
Donna's - Manchester UK
Tink's - Brighton UK
Tina's - South West UK
Lorraine's - Scotland UK
Vicky's - London update UK
Stacey's - Skin Two rubber ball UK
Seventh Edition
Vicky's - Sydney Mardi Gras
Nessa's - Austria
Eva's - Paris
Veronica's - Germany
Frederike's - Amsterdam
Zil's - Tokyo update
Marlayna's - LA (The Concrete catwalk) USA
Nikki's - Provincetown USA
Miss Vera's - New York USA
Frederike - Wigstock East USA 98
Diana - Chester finishing school
Sarah goes to Funny Girls in Blackpool
Michelle's - UK South
Kara & Kirsty's - Brighton UK
Stacey's - Birmingham update UK
Helen's - South West UK

"Who would have Adam and Eve'd it .. ..Not me for one"

© Copyright 2004
The WayOut Publishing
Company Ltd
ISBN: 0 9526880 9 3

"But I could not have done it without YOU"

Thank you very much to the following people that helped in the compilation of this section of the Guide:

Aleckssandra (report)
Andrea (article & report)
Anna (profile)
Alexis Divine (profile)
Asia SF (photos)
Bambi (profile)
Barbara (report)
Beth Boye (report)
Beth, Belgium (profile)
Cathy Kissmit (report)
Charis Berger (report)
Deena Gomersall (report)
Dignity Cruises (article)
DJ Titch (graphics)
Don Allen (photos)
Donna Gee (article)
Emma M (article)
Eva Fels (report)
Francis (photos)
Georgina (photos)
Gemini Academy (article)
Gina Lance (report)
Hannah Mannah (profile)
Hide & Sleek Loraine (article/photo)
Jamie (graphics)
James Stafford (photos)
Jennifer Simpson (profile)
Joanne (report)
Jodie Lynn (photos)
Karen Clark (profile)
Karen O'Connor (profile)
Kate (profile)
Katrina Collins (profile)
Kaya (profile)
Kirsty (article)
Kitty (article)

Lisa Bud (photo)
Mandy Romero (report & article)
Marie Tyler (profile)
Marlayna Lacie (report)
Mayflower Club (article)
Melanie Blush (profile))
Michaela (profile)
Monica Holland (report)
Ms Bob (report)
Natasha (profile)
Nessa Glen (profile)
Niamh Holding (profile)
Pandora De'Pledge (article & photo)
Pamela - Belgium (photos)
Phaedra Kelly (article)
Rachel Cox (letter)
Ramona (profile)
Rani (profile)
Rebecca (report)
Renee (photo)
Richard O'Brien (article)
Rob (photos)
Robert Harper (photos)
Rosy (profile)
Sacha (article)
Sarah Yorke (profile)
Stacey Christie (report)
Steffan (photos)
Sarah Lloyd (article)
Toni Vain (article)
Tony (photos)
Trans-action (report)
Tranny Grange (article)
Ulli Richter (photos)
Vicki Rene (report)
Vicky Valentine (photos)

"Thank you all SO much"
Vicky Lee

Finally ■ Advertisers Index

Dont forget that on the Shopping Mall more opportunities constantly appear throughout the year

www.wayout-publishing.com

The 'portal' to everything tranny on the Internet *(OK that's the last time I'll mention it - here)*